A-LEVEL
AND AS-LEVEL

BIOLOGY

Alison Redmore
Martin Griffin

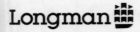

LONGMAN A AND AS-LEVEL REFERENCE GUIDES

Series editors: Geoff Black and Stuart Wall

TITLES AVAILABLE
Biology
Chemistry
English
Geography
Mathematics
Physics

Longman Group UK Limited,
Longman House, Burnt Mill, Harlow,
Essex CM20 2JE, England
and Associated Companies throughout the world.

© Longman Group UK Limited 1991

First published 1991
Fourth Impression 1992

British Library Cataloguing in Publication Data

Redmore, Alison
  Biology.
  1. Biology
  I. Title   II. Griffin, Martin
  574

  ISBN 0–582–06394–9

Designed and produced by
The Pen and Ink Book Company,
Huntingdon, Cambridgeshire.
Set in 10/12pt Century Old Style.

Produced by Longman Singapore Publishers (Pte) Ltd
Printed in Singapore

ACKNOWLEDGEMENTS

We would particularly like to thank Simon Redmore and Gillian Griffin for their support during the writing period and our title adviser, Eric Turner, for his expert advice.

Acknowledgements are also due to Kevin Porter, Andrea Hayers, Siân Davies, Pam Towns, Sue Martin, Jean Lea, Sue Ashby and Cilla Oates for their invaluable help in the research and gathering of material, and to Christine Queen and Linda Halls who typed sections of the manuscript. We would also like to thank the Examination Boards listed on the back cover for sending us copies of their syllabuses.

HOW TO USE THIS BOOK

Throughout your A-level and AS-level course you will be coming across terms, ideas and definitions that are unfamiliar to you. The Longman Reference Guides provide a quick, easy-to-use source of information, fact and opinion. Each main term is listed alphabetically and, where appropriate, cross-referenced to related terms.

- Where a term or phrase appears in **different type** you can look up a separate entry under that heading elsewhere in the book.
- Where a term or phrase appears in **different type** and is set between two arrowhead symbols ◄   ►, it is particularly recommended that you turn to the entry for that heading.

ABO BLOOD GROUPS

The ABO system is an example of **discontinuous variation** in man. Blood is grouped by the ABO system according to the **proteins** or **antigens** found on the red blood cells, giving four possible groups: A,B, AB and O. The synthesis of the proteins, called A and B, is determined genetically, and is an example of the interaction of **multiple alleles**.

If only antigen A is present, then anti-B antibodies will be in the plasma. If blood containing antigen B is added, agglutination or clumping of the blood will follow. During blood transfusions it is therefore important that the recipient's blood does not contain antibodies for the donor's antigens. Group O people have neither of the antigens so may donate their blood to all other groups. They are referred to as 'universal donors'. Similarly group AB are 'universal recipients', because they have neither antibody so may receive blood of any group.

◀ Multiple alleles, Rhesus blood groups ▶

ABSCISIC ACID, ABSCISSION

Abscisic acid is an inhibitor found in ageing leaves and is chemically identical to dormin, a growth-inhibiting substance found in buds. It is responsible for bringing about **leaf fall** in deciduous trees. A layer of cells called the abscission layer develops at the base of the **petiole**. Gradually the calcium pectate making up the middle lamella of the abscission cell walls dissolves so that the cells separate from each other and the leaf falls off. Abscisic acid stimulates this process, possibly by exceeding the amount of **auxin** (which inhibits leaf fall) found in the leaf and influencing the activity of the **enzyme** responsible for the formation of calcium pectate.

◀ Leaf fall ▶

ABSORPTION

Absorption is the uptake of **solutes** by cells, a process that may be active, requiring energy expenditure, or passive. It occurs across the wall of the ileum, through the epithelium of the kidney nephrons, across the root hairs from the soil solution, and in many other instances.

◄ Active transport, Diffusion, Facilitated uptake, Osmosis, Pinocytosis, Root systems ►

ABSORPTION SPECTRUM

An absorption spectrum is obtained by passing a beam of light through a substance such as chlorophyll and then through a prism, which separates it into its different wavelengths. The light is then projected on to a screen and any colours absent from the normal spectrum are those that have been absorbed. The results can be presented graphically to give an absorption spectrum. Chlorophyll absorbs mainly red and blue light. Green light is hardly absorbed at all and is reflected, which explains why chlorophyll appears green.

◄ Action spectrum ►

ACETO-ORCEIN STAIN

Aceto-orcein stain is used to study the stages of mitosis in a root tip squash. It selectively stains the dividing chromosomes, making them clearly visible.

ACETYL CHOLINE

Acetyl choline (Ach) is a chemical transmitter that allows the continuation of a nerve impulse from one neurone to the next. It is synthesised in the synaptic knob at the end of an axon and stored in synaptic vesicles until a nerve impulse arrives. The impulse triggers the vesicles to discharge small quantities of transmitter into the synaptic cleft. The Ach molecules then diffuse across the gap and attach to specific sites on the post-synaptic membrane to bring about depolarisation. The enzyme cholinesterase hydrolyses any excess Ach, rendering it inactive.

◄ Synapse, synaptic transmission ►

ACETYL CO-A

Acetyl co-enzyme A is an important compound that connects glycolysis and Krebs cycle. If oxygen is present, it is formed from pyruvate, produced at the end of glycolysis, but it will not be produced if conditions are anaerobic. The three-carbon pyruvate is decarboxylated and dehydrogenated, resulting in a molecule of carbon dioxide that will be excreted, two hydrogen atoms that are picked up by the co-enzyme NAD^+, and acetyl co-A. Acetyl co-A enters a mitochondrion and is hydrolysed. This causes the molecule to separate into the co-A portion, which is regenerated, and the acetate portion, which combines with the four-carbon oxaloacetate to form citrate in Krebs cycle.

Acetyl co-A can also be formed from fatty acids by beta oxidation, so enabling lipids to be oxidised for energy release.

ACHONDROPLASIA

Achondroplasia or chondrodystrophic dwarfism is caused by a **dominant gene mutation** so that whenever the abnormal **allele** is present, its effects are always expressed in the individual and the inheritance can be easily shown by examining the family tree.

Let D represent the defective allele, and d represent the normal allele. DD = genotype of homozygous dwarf; dd = genotype of normal individual; Dd = genotype of heterozygous dwarf.

The gene is inherited in a Mendelian fashion, and causes abnormal growth of the bones that are preformed in **cartilage**, leading to a stunted body, bow legs and a large dome-like head. 80 per cent of these dwarfs die within a year of birth but those that survive show normal mental development and can have children.

◄ Mendelian inheritance ►

ACID/BASE BALANCE

Acids are substances that will readily give up protons (a hydrogen atom after losing its single **electron**); a base is a substance which tends to accept a proton. Various acids and bases are found in mammalian body fluids; it is essential for most metabolic functions that a balance is maintained.

The concentration of carbonic acid in the blood is detected by the carotid bodies. Information is passed to the respiratory centre of the medulla oblongata, which controls **ventilation** rate, but the balance of proton/ hydrogencarbonate concentration in blood plasma is under renal control. Kidneys accomplish this function by the active secretion of ions into the renal tubule if the blood **pH** varies from the norm.

◄ Hydrogencarbonate ions ►

ACID RAIN

Acid rain is formed when acidic oxides in the atmosphere, such as sulphur dioxide, dissolve in rain water to form acids. The rain then causes damage to buildings as well as increasing the acidity of the soil, rivers and lakes that the rain falls on.

◄ SO_2 pollution ►

ACOELOMATE ORGANISATION

Acoelomate animals include platyhelminths and nematodes. The body of these organisms is organised in three layers (triploblastic) which develop as germ layers in the embryo. The ectoderm is outside, then there is the mesoderm and the endoderm is on the inside. From these develop the systems and organs of the mature animal. Unlike in coelomate animals, there is no separation of the organs from the body wall, so development of separate gut musculature, for example, cannot occur.

◀ Body cavity, Coelomate organisation, Triploblastic organisation ▶

ACQUIRED IMMUNO-DEFICIENCY SYNDROME (AIDS)

AIDS develops as a result of infection by HIV virus and leads to the depletion of the immune system of the body, leaving it open to attack from various infectious diseases. There is at present no known cure for AIDS, though massive amounts of money are being spent on research.

ACROSOME REACTION

The acrosome is a thin cap found at the tip of a sperm cell, covering the nucleus. It may be found on the sperm of various animals and plays a part in penetration of the egg cell during fertilisation. When the acrosome touches the vitelline membrane of the egg, it bursts open, releasing a lytic substance which softens this membrane at the point of contact. The membrane lining the acrosome then appears to turn inside out, forming a thin filament which penetrates the egg membranes, allowing the sperm nucleus to enter the egg. The whole process is called the acrosome reaction.

ACTIN

Actin is a protein that makes up the thin filaments in the I bands of a striated muscle.

◀ Sarcomere ▶

ACTION POTENTIAL

An action potential is the sudden and short-lived change of potential in an 'excitable' cell, such as a neurone, resulting in depolarisation of the membrane and the propagation of the nervous impulse.

◀ Nerve impulse, transmission ▶

ACTION SPECTRUM

An action spectrum (Fig. A.1) is obtained by exposing leaves to different wavelengths, or colours, of light and estimating the amount of carbohydrate produced in each case (i.e. the efficiency of photosynthesis at each wavelength).

If these results are plotted on a graph, it is clear that most photosynthesis takes place in red light and blue light, showing a close correlation to the absorption spectrum of chlorophyll. This indicates that most of the wavelengths of light absorbed by chlorophyll are used in photosynthesis.

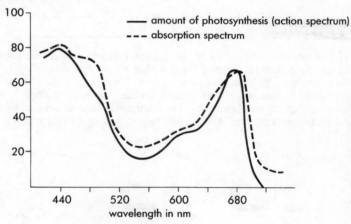

Fig. A.1 Action spectrum and absorption spectrum for chlorophyll

ACTIVATED DIFFUSION HYPOTHESIS

The activated diffusion hypothesis relates to the mechanism of solute translocation in the phloem. There are several ideas as to how this occurs, but the most widely supported hypothesis is that of **mass flow**, occurring from a 'source' to a 'sink'. The main drawback of this idea is that mass flow is essentially a passive process, but it has been demonstrated that translocation can be inhibited by metabolic poisons, so must require energy. It has been proposed, therefore, that the loading of phloem sieve tubes at the source and their unloading at the sink are both active processes, although the movement actually within the phloem is by diffusion, which is passive. This is known as the activated diffusion hypothesis.

◀ Mass flow ▶

ACTIVATION ENERGY

Most chemical reactions in **metabolism** require energy to activate or begin the reaction, even when the outcome of the process is that energy is released. This is because molecules need to be moving before they can collide and therefore react, and increased molecular movement needs an energy input. The energy required to overcome this barrier and get the process of breakdown or synthesis underway is called the activation energy. **Enzymes** speed up metabolic reactions that would otherwise be too slow, or might not occur at all, because they bring the reactants together and reduce the need for activation energy.

◀ Enzyme action ▶

ACTIVE SITE

The term active site refers to the precise part of an **enzyme** molecule to which the **substrate** attaches itself during an enzyme controlled reaction. Enzymes are globular proteins, and the active site has a particular configuration into which only certain specific substrate molecules will fit, hence the specificity of enzymes. The relationship between an enzyme and its substrate molecule can be explained by the lock and key hypothesis (Fig. A.2).

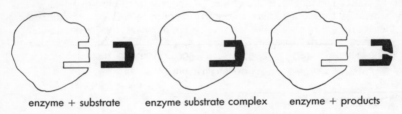

enzyme + substrate   enzyme substrate complex   enzyme + products

Fig. A.2 Lock and key hypothesis of enzyme action

When an enzyme is denatured by heating, it is this active site that is distorted so the substrate can no longer fit. The only other molecules that may fit an enzyme's active site are competitive inhibitors, because they closely resemble the substrate molecules in their structure.

◀ Competitive inhibition, Denaturation, Enzyme action ▶

ACTIVE TRANSPORT, ACTIVE UPTAKE

Much of the movement of molecules across membranes is passive (i.e. by diffusion or osmosis), but there are many instances when substances are moved across membranes against a concentration gradient. In this case the transport or movement is 'active', meaning that energy expenditure is required (Fig. A.3). This can be demonstrated by applying metabolic poisons such as cyanide (which prevents formation of ATP), or by depriving the tissue of oxygen. In both cases active transport ceases.

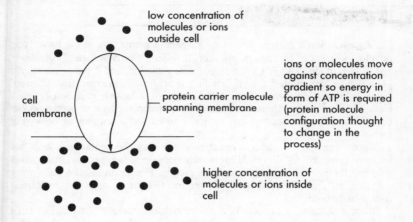

low concentration of molecules or ions outside cell

cell membrane

protein carrier molecule spanning membrane

higher concentration of molecules or ions inside cell

ions or molecules move against concentration gradient so energy in form of ATP is required (protein molecule configuration thought to change in the process)

Fig. A.3 Active transport

It is probable that there are carriers in the plasma membrane which attach themselves to the molecules or ions on the outside of the membrane, carry them to the interior of the cell and then return to outside. There are numerous examples of active transport in plants and animals. For example, the sodium pump in neurones, chloride secretory cells in fish gills, mineral uptake in plant roots.

ADAPTATION

The process of adaptation involves a change in structure or physiology to fit a new set of environmental circumstances. It can occur in sexually reproducing populations, since sexual reproduction results in variation (i.e. it produces a number of different phenotypes in the population). A change in climate, or the introduction of a new predator, or some other environmental factor, will then impose new selection pressures on these phenotypic variations. Those individuals that can exploit the situation best will reproduce more successfully, so a greater proportion of the next generation will have their particular phenotype. This phenotype will soon become the predominant characteristic, and the population is said to have adapted.

All living organisms are adapted to their particular niche − if they were not, they would not survive − and internally there is close correlation between structure and function, at both cellular and organ level. For example, mitochondria have a large surface area for the attachment of respiratory enzymes, leaves are adapted for photosynthesis, parasites are adapted to living in their host, insectivorous plants can digest insect protein and therefore grow in nitrogen deficient soil; there are many, many more.

◄ Selection pressure, Selective breeding ►

ADAPTIVE RADIATION

During **evolution** it may be seen that animals or plants of a single basic type develop differences through **adaptation** to different environmental conditions and modes of life. This is known as adaptive radiation, and it will occur only if gene-flow is interrupted (i.e. if **isolating mechanisms** prevent the 'adapted' types from breeding with 'non-adapted' types). Adaptive radiation is most likely to occur where there is reduced competition, or lack of predation, so that the radiating organisms can diversify to exploit a number of ecological niches.

A good example of adaptive radiation is the way the pentadactyl limb has become modified to serve different functions in different mammals, thus enabling them to fill a wider variety of niches. For example, the bat's wing adapts it for flight, whales have flippers for swimming, apes have grasping hands, and so on.

Other well-known examples of adaptive radiation include those of Darwin's finches in the Galapagos Islands, and the marsupial mammals of Australia, both groups being geographically isolated by water. Lack of competition and of predators allowed the finches to exploit many niches, becoming seed-eaters, insect-eaters, nectar-feeders and fruit-eaters, some nesting in trees and some on the ground. Similarly, the marsupial mammals had no competition from placental mammals, so diversified to fill all available niches.

◄ Adaptation, Darwin, Isolation ►

ADENINE

Adenine is a purine nitrogenous **base** that is found in **nucleotides** and in DNA and RNA.

◄ Genetic code ►

ADENOSINE DIPHOSPHATE (ADP)

Adenosine diphosphate is formed when **adenosine monophosphate** (AMP) is phosphorylated. It is converted into adenosine triphosphate (ATP) in cells when chemical energy needs to be stored, and is produced from ATP during energy expenditure.

ADENOSINE MONOPHOSPHATE (AMP)

Adenosine monophosphate is a nucleotide, formed from adenine, ribose and phosphate.

◄ Cyclic-AMP, Nucleotides ►

ADENOSINE TRIPHOSPHATE (ATP)

ATP is an organic compound which occurs in all living cells as a universal energy carrier. It is the form in which energy released in **respiration** is stored, and it provides the immediate source of energy for cell activities. Chemically it is a mononucleotide, containing ribose as its pentose sugar and adenine as its nitrogenous base. The three phosphate groups (hence triphosphate) are attached in a row to the fifth carbon atom of the ribose.

The bonds attaching the two end phosphate groups yield a large amount of energy when they are hydrolysed, about 30.6 kJ mol^{-1} each. This energy is a property of the whole ATP molecule and it is inaccurate to describe the bonds themselves as high-energy. The **hydrolysis** of ATP to ADP and phosphate is catalysed by a **hydrolase** enzyme, ATPase. ADP (adenosine diphosphate) can be phosphorylated back to ATP if enough energy is supplied.

$$ADP + Pi + 30.6 \text{ kJ} = ATP \qquad (Pi = \text{inorganic phosphate})$$

This energy may come from three different sources:

- **oxidative phosphorylation**, which uses chemical energy released from the redox reactions of the respiratory chain, occurring on the cristae in mitochondria.
- **photophosphorylation**, which occurs on lamellae in **chloroplasts**, using light energy harnessed by chlorophyll.
- **phosphate** transfer, which makes use of chemical energy stored in other 'energy-rich' compounds such as creatine phosphate in muscle cells. If ATP levels for muscle contraction are low, phosphate is transferred from creatine phosphate to ADP.

ADH

ADH is an anti-diuretic hormone released by the posterior lobe of the **pituitary gland**. Its effect is to increase the permeability to water of the cell membranes in the distal tubules and collecting ducts of the **kidney nephrons**. This means that more water is reabsorbed from the tubules into the blood, and a more concentrated urine is produced. When ADH is not being released, dilute urine is formed – a situation known as diuresis. Diabetes insipidus is an extreme instance of this which results if ADH is not produced at all. Large quantities of watery urine are excreted, and the body soon becomes dehydrated.

◀ Kidneys, Negative feedback, Osmoregulation ▶

ADHESION/COHESION THEORY

The adhesion/cohesion theory is used to account for the movement of water through the **xylem** vessels of a plant in a continuous stream. The main 'pull' for this stream is created by **transpiration**. As water evaporates through the stomata of leaves, more water is drawn up from the soil to take its place. In the case of trees, the distance involved is considerable and is only possible due to the adhesive and cohesive properties of water. Adhesion is a force of attraction between unlike molecules, here between the water and lignified vessel wall. In a narrow tube like a xylem vessel, a greater proportion of water molecules will be in contact with the walls, producing a greater adhesive force. Cohesion is a force of attraction between like molecules (e.g. between the water molecules themselves due to their polarity). The theory proposes that as water molecules are attracted to the next bit of the xylem wall above them by adhesion, they in turn attract other water molecules to join them by cohesion.

◀ Transpiration ▶

ADIPOSE TISSUE

Adipose tissue is derived from areolar **connective tissue**, and it contains large numbers of closely packed fat-filled cells. There are two types of adipose tissue, according to whether the fat stored is mainly saturated, and therefore more solid, or unsaturated, in the form of oil droplets in the cytoplasm. White adipose tissue contains saturated fat and has a low metabolic rate. Its functions are as follows.

- It acts as an energy store.
- In the dermis of the **skin**, it insulates the body against heat loss.
- Around the **kidneys**, it acts as a mechanical shock absorber.

Brown adipose tissue contains oil droplets and many mitochondria, and has a higher metabolic rate. On oxidation, it releases mainly heat energy. It is important for young mammals and in **hibernation**.

ADRENAL GLANDS

The adrenal glands are **endocrine glands** positioned just in front of the kidneys. They have two distinct regions. The central adrenal medulla secretes **adrenaline** and noradrenaline, and is controlled by the **sympathetic nervous system**.

The outer region is called the cortex and it is controlled by a tropic hormone from the anterior pituitary, adrenocorticotropic hormone (ACTH). The outer part of the cortex secretes **aldosterone**, which regulates sodium balance in the body. The inner part secretes hormones such as cortisol and corticosterone. These are steroid hormones concerned with resistance to stress, salt balance and carbohydrate metabolism.

ADRENALINE

Adrenaline is secreted by the adrenal medulla when stimulated by the **sympathetic nervous system**. It is sometimes termed the 'fight, fright or frolic' hormone, because it is secreted in times of danger and stress and it prepares the body to deal with the situation.

The hormone has many effects all over the body. Heart rate and cardiac output are increased, as is the ventilation rate. It stimulates glycogen breakdown in the liver, so the blood glucose level rises. Blood is also diverted to vital organs such as the brain and skeletal muscles by vasodilation of the arteries to these organs and vasoconstriction of arteries and arterioles serving the skin and the gut. It also stimulates the iris muscles to relax so that more light can enter the eye.

Adrenaline is chemically similar to noradrenaline, the chemical transmitter substance secreted across the synapses of neurones in the sympathetic nervous system.

AEROBIC RESPIRATION

Aerobic respiration can occur only in the presence of oxygen, but it is a far more efficient process than anaerobic respiration. The aerobic oxidation of glucose to carbon dioxide and water results in an energy yield of 2,880 kJ or 38 molecules of adenosine triphosphate (ATP), while the yield from anaerobic respiration is only 2 molecules of ATP.

Oxygen must be obtained from the respiratory medium, which may be air or water, and conveyed to the respiring tissues. The process of cellular respiration begins with glycolysis, which occurs in the cytoplasm and breaks down glucose to pyruvate. Provided oxygen is present, pyruvate is converted to acetyl co-A, which enters Krebs cycle in the mitochondria, where successive dehydrogenations feed hydrogen atoms into an electron transport chain, releasing energy for ATP formation. The gaseous waste product of aerobic respiration is carbon dioxide, and this must be removed from the respiring tissues and returned to the respiratory medium.

The summary equation of aerobic respiration is:

$$C_6H_{12}O_6 + 6O_2 \rightarrow 6H_2O + 6CO_2 + 2880 \text{ kJ}$$

Glucose is the most common respiratory substrate but fats and proteins can also be used.

AGARIC

Agarics are basidiomycete **fungi** that produce prominent fruiting bodies, commonly referred to as mushrooms and toadstools. The 'mushroom' in fact consists of masses of interwoven hyphae that grow up from the mycelium in the soil. Each 'gill' of the mushroom bears hundreds of sporangia called basidia and each basidium produces basidiospores.

AGGRESSION

Aggression is common in **territorial behaviour** and in **reproductive** behaviour. A male aggressor may seek to intimidate a rival who has entered his territory or may use aggressive behaviour to establish dominance over a herd of females or within a hierarchy. Female animals use aggression mainly to defend their young during the breeding season.

Aggression often involves a threat display rather than actual fighting. Mammals, fishes and birds may all adopt particular postures or reveal certain markings to warn off others. In many cases the display involves noise and making the body appear larger. For example, cichlid fish open their mouths and puff out their gill region, an aggressive cat will fluff up its fur, hiss and spit.

Sometimes aggressive behaviour can be modified to sexual behaviour, as in the courtship of certain spiders.

AIDS

◀ Acquired Immuno-Deficiency Syndrome ▶

ALCOHOLISM

Alcoholism is the dependence on alcohol caused by regular heavy drinking over a long period. It can be classed as a non-infectious disease. Irregular drinking of smaller amounts of alcohol can have unpleasant side-effects, but these are essentially short-term. Heavy drinking causes physical and physiological damage. This damage includes reduction in the amount of brain tissue, cirrhosis of the liver, irritation of the stomach mucosa, flushed skin and in men it can cause impotence. Babies born to alcoholic mothers have a one in three chance of reduced intelligence and facial deformities.

ALDOSE SUGARS

Aldose sugars are monosaccharides containing an aldehyde ($-CHO$) group in their molecule.
◀ Ketose sugars ▶

ALDOSTERONE

Aldosterone is a steroid hormone secreted by the adrenal cortex. It increases the active uptake of sodium ions from the glomerular filtrate into the blood capillaries surrounding the kidney nephrons. This raises the solute concentration in the plasma, which causes more water to be reabsorbed into the blood by osmosis.
◀ Kidneys, Osmoregulation ▶

ALGAE

Algae are autotrophic members of the kingdom Protoctista. Some algae are unicellular and others multicellular, though not differentiated into roots, stems and leaves. They are all either aquatic or restricted to very damp habitats, because they have no vascular tissue and are not resistant to desiccation. There are three phyla of algae: Chlorophyta (e.g. *Spirogyra* and *Chlamydomonas*), which are green; Rhodophyta (e.g. *Chondrus*), which are red; and Phaeophyta (e.g. *Fucus*), which are brown.

Algae are important producers in aquatic habitats. They make up much of the phytoplankton and are also represented by the large seaweeds on rocky shores. Their growth can become a problem, however, if the water is too rich in nutrients such as nitrates and phosphates. This is eutrophication and results eventually in the death of fish because of a lack of oxygen in the water.

◀ Brown algae, Filamentous algae, Nitrate pollution ▶

ALIMENTARY CANAL

An alimentary canal, or gut, is a tube in which digestion and absorption of food materials take place. In cnidarians and platyhelminths there is only one opening to the gut, but in other animal groups there is a mouth for ingestion and an anus for egestion. This allows differentiation of the canal to occur, into specific digestive and absorptive areas, and into regions of different pH so that optimum enzyme activity can be achieved. Digestive juices containing enzymes are secreted into the alimentary canal by associated ducted glands, which also secrete acids or bases to alter the gut pH.

◀ Gastric juice, Ileum, Pancreas, Villus ▶

ALLELE

An allele is an alternative form of a gene, and consists of a particular sequence of nucleotides that occupies the gene locus, or position on a chromosome. In diploid organisms, there are two alleles present for each gene, occupying the same gene loci on homologous chromosomes. These alleles may code for the same or different versions of the characteristic controlled by the gene, resulting in homozygous or heterozygous genotypes, and may be dominant or recessive in the way they are expressed.

◀ Dominant alleles, Gene expression, Homologous chromosomes, Recessive alleles ▶

ALLERGY

An allergy is caused by an immune response to an antigen called an allergen. Common allergens are found on pollen grains, fungal spores, house dust, feathers and fur, as well as in certain foods. Non-allergic people are not sensitive to these substances, but allergic people react to them as if they were pathogenic. Histamine is released into the tissues, causing localised inflammation, mucus secretions are increased to 'flush out' the allergen, and antibodies are synthesised by the lymphocytes. Most of the unpleasant symptoms of allergies such as hayfever and asthma are due to the inflammation and increased mucus in the respiratory system.

Food allergies are not as clearly understood, partly because they are so difficult to detect and diagnose. Allergens that are implicated most often include eggs, lactose in cows' milk, gluten in wheat flour and food additives such as the yellow colouring, tartrazine.

◀ Immunity ▶

ALLOPOLYPLOIDY

◀ Polyploidy ▶

'ALL-OR-NOTHING' LAW

◀ Nerve impulse transmission, Synapse, synaptic transmission ▶

ALPHA CELLS, ISLETS OF LANGERHANS

The alpha cells in the islets of Langerhans in the pancreas secrete the hormone glucagon. This is antagonistic to insulin and stimulates the breakdown of glycogen to glucose.

◀ Blood glucose level ▶

ALTERNATION OF GENERATIONS

Alternation of generations involves a life cycle in which a diploid spore-producing generation alternates in strict sequence with a haploid gamete-producing generation. The life cycles of cnidarians such as *Obelia* do not show true alternation of generations because both the polyp and medusa forms are diploid.

Alternation of generations is shown most clearly in bryophytes and ferns, which have alternating diploid sporophytes and haploid gametophytes. In mosses and liverworts, the gametophyte is the dominant form, while in ferns and clubmosses, the sporophyte is dominant.

◀ Fern, Haploidy, Liverwort, Moss ▶

ALTRUISM

◀ Reciprocal altruism ▶

AMINO ACIDS

Amino acids are colourless, crystalline solids that are generally soluble in water but insoluble in organic solvents. The majority of amino acids contain an acidic carboxyl group ($-COOH$) and a basic amino group ($-NH_2$), arranged as shown in Fig. A.4. Condensation reactions between these groups allow amino acids to combine together to form dipeptides and polypeptides. It is the sequence of amino acids in the polypeptide chains that gives a protein its primary structure. This is determined by the triplet code on DNA in the nucleus.

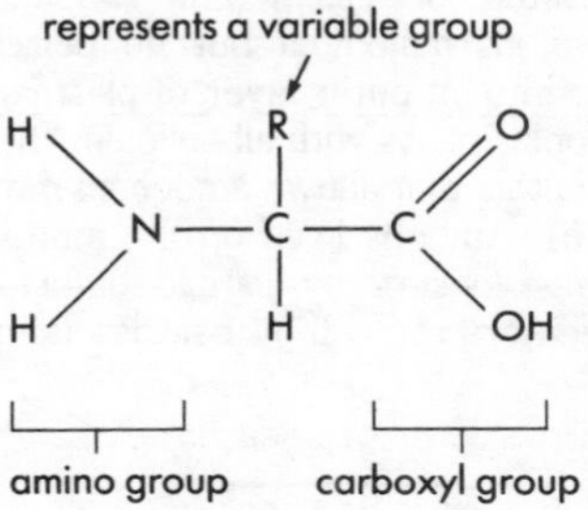

Fig. A.4 Structure of an amino acid

The R group varies for each amino acid. For example, in glycine R = H, in alanine, R = CH_3, and in cysteine, R = CH_2SH. Over 170 amino acids have been identified in cells and tissues, but only about twenty of these form proteins. Plants synthesise the amino acids they require, using carbohydrate residues from photosynthesis and nitrate ions obtained from the soil. Animals must ingest most of their amino acids in dietary protein, though some so-called 'non-essential' amino acids can be synthesised by transamination.
◀ Peptide linkage, Proteins ▶

AMMONIA

The body is unable to store proteins or amino acids, so any surplus nitrogenous waste must be excreted. These unwanted amino acids are deaminated, and ammonia (NH_3) is formed from the amino group ($-NH_2$) that is removed. Ammonia must not be allowed to accumulate because it is highly toxic even in small quantities, but if it is to be excreted as it is, then a large volume of water must also pass out to dilute its toxicity. Ammonia excretion occurs, therefore, only in freshwater animals such as teleosts (bony fish), where osmotic influx means that excess water is present. A majority of animals have a problem conserving water, so they change the ammonia into less toxic forms such as **urea** or **uric acid** for excretion.
◀ Ornithine cycle, Osmoregulation ▶

AMNION

The amnion is the innermost fetal membrane. It encloses a fluid-filled amniotic cavity in which the fetus is suspended.
◀ Fetal membranes ▶

AMOEBA, AMOEBOID MOVEMENT

Amoeba is a unicellular free-living protoctistan, belonging to the phylum Rhizopoda. Its protoplasmic organisation is simple, with few organelles present, and there is a plasmalemma but no pellicle. The cytoplasm is differentiated, however, into an outer layer of plasmagel, or ectoplasm, and inner plasmasol, or endoplasm. As with all colloids, the gel and sol forms are interconvertible, and it is this that allows amoeboid movement and feeding to take place (see Fig. A.5). Amoeba lives on the mud layer at the bottom of ponds, and gas exchange occurs by simple diffusion across the plasma membrane. Water that enters the cell by osmosis is expelled periodically by contractile vacuoles.

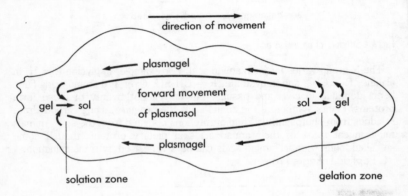

Fig. A.5 Amoeboid movement according to the fountain-zone theory

Amoeboid movement is shown by rhizopods such as Amoeba, and also by vertebrate white blood cells. It involves the formation of a pseudopodium by the cytoplasmic streaming of fluid plasmasol, which is then converted into the firmer plasmagel. It is not yet known whether this movement results from a 'push' from behind or a 'pull' from in front, though the latter fountain-zone theory is held more widely. When Amoeba is feeding, or when neutrophil white blood cells encounter bacteria, pseudopodia are projected either side of the food particle or bacterium. They enclose, or engulf, the 'food' vacuole, into which hydrolytic enzymes are then secreted for intracellular digestion.

AMPHIBIA

Amphibia are a class of the phylum Chordata, and although essentially land animals, they must go back to **aquatic habitats** to breed. The larval forms are tadpoles, which breathe by gills, whilst the adult forms have **lungs**. The transition from tadpole **larva** to adult is an example of **metamorphosis**. The group includes **frogs**, toads, newts and salamanders.

◀ Chordates, Toad ▶

AMPHOTERIC NATURE OF PROTEINS

A protein consists of many **amino acids** joined together by peptide bonds. Since the peptide bonds involve all the carboxyl and amine groups of the amino acids, these groups are not available for ionisation. Many of the 'R sidechains of the amino acids do carry ionisable groups, however, examples being: $-OH$ (in serine), $-COOH$ (in glutamic acid) and $-NH_2$ (in lysine). The pH of the medium will influence the ionisation of these groupings. For example,

$$R.COOH \rightleftharpoons R.COO^- + H^+ \qquad \text{reaction 1}$$
$$R.OH \rightleftharpoons R.O^- + H^+ \qquad \text{reaction 2}$$
$$R.NH_2 + H^+ \rightleftharpoons R.NH_3^+ \qquad \text{reaction 3}$$

In a low pH, hydrogen ion concentration is high, so reactions 1 and 2 will be pushed to the left, while reaction 3 will be pushed to the right. This means that only the $-NH_2$ groups will ionise, and the protein molecule will act as a cation, or positively charged ion.

In a high pH, hydrogen ion concentration is low, so the above situation is reversed. The $-COOH$ and $-OH$ groups will ionise, and the protein will act as an anion.

There will be an intermediate pH, when the number of negative charges on the protein equals the number of positive charges, and at this point it is described as a zwitterion (an ion of two types) and is amphoteric (can act as an acid or a base).

The pH at which the protein is a zwitterion, carrying no net charge, is called the iso-electric point (IEP), and is a physical constant for a particular protein. For example, haemoglobin IEP = pH 6.8.

◀ Peptide linkage, Proteins ▶

AMYLASE

Amylases are enzymes which hydrolyse starch to maltose. Pancreatic amylase and salivary amylase are important in mammalian digestive systems; germinating seeds produce amylase to mobilise **starch** food stores for growth; saprophytes secrete amylases to digest starch in their substratum, so hastening decay.

◀ Digestion, Enzyme, Saprophyte ▶

ANABOLISM

Anabolism is the synthesis of complex molecules from simple molecules by living organisms. The process requires energy from respiration or sunlight, and is catalysed by enzymes. For example, photosynthesis, protein synthesis, nucleic acid synthesis.

ANAEROBIC RESPIRATION

Anaerobic respiration does not require the presence of oxygen, and is basically glycolysis being carried on in fermentation by yeast, or under oxygen debt conditions in skeletal muscle. In fermentation, the pyruvic acid produced in glycolysis is decarboxylated and reduced to ethanol. In oxygen debt conditions, the pyruvic acid is reduced to lactic acid. Anaerobic respiration is very inefficient in terms of energy yield, producing a net total of only 2 ATP for each molecule of glucose used.

◀ Decarboxylation ▶

ANEMOHILOUS FLOWERS

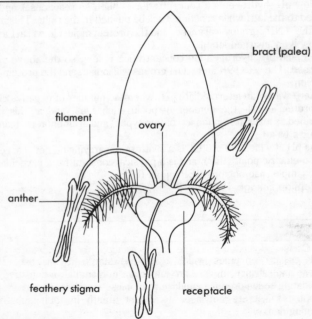

Fig. A.6 Wind-pollinated flower

Anemophilous flowers are pollinated by wind. Such flowers usually have reduced sepals and petals to allow efficient wind access and unhindered pollen dispersal, and the sepals and petals are green, since it is not necessary to attract insects. The stamen and stigmas are exposed and hanging (pendulous), and can thus easily release pollen into the air currents or receive it. The stigmas have an increased surface area by being feathery. Profuse amounts of small, dusty pollen grains are produced, since cross-pollination by wind is a rather wasteful process. Examples of anemophilous flowers are poplar, hazel, grasses (Fig. A.6). Flowers are usually unisexual, with the male flowers being more numerous.

◄ Floral morphology, Pollination ►

ANGIOSPERMS

The flowering plants or angiosperms comprise the phylum Angiospermophyta of the plant kingdom. They are seed-bearing plants with true flowers, the seeds being enclosed in a fruit formed from the ovary. There are two classes, class Monocotyledoneae and class Dicotyledoneae.

◄ Dicotyledon, Monocotyledon, Seed ►

ANILINE SULPHATE

Aniline sulphate stains lignin yellow and can be used as a stain for temporary preparations of plant tissue sections. The section can be observed mounted in aniline sulphate, or can be stained and mounted in glycerine.

◄ Phloroglucinol ►

ANNELIDA

Annelids are worms which belong to the phylum Annelida. They are triploblastic coelomates and show well-developed organs. Metameric segmentation occurs, in which the body is divided into many basically similar segments, each containing similar nerve and muscle units. This enables more refinement of body control to be achieved. There are three classes of Annelids:

- Class Polychaeta. These are confined to sea water and show cephalisation, since they have a clearly defined head, distinct from the remainder of the body. They have many chaetae, borne on parapodia. For example, *Nereis* (ragworm).
- Class Oligochaeta. These are soil or freshwater organisms, without a distinct head, and with few chaetae and no parapodia. For example *Lumbricus* (earthworm).

- Class Hirudinea. These are predators or ectoparasites, and have no clear head, no chaetae and no parapodia. For example, *Hirudo* (medicinal leech).

◀ Coelomate organisation, Oligochaete, Parasitism, Polychaete, Predation, Segmentation, Triploblastic organisation ▶

ANTAGONISTIC MUSCLES

With respect to particular joints, muscles always occur in antagonistic pairs, or paired groups. The muscle that initially moves the joint is called the 'prime mover' and the muscle that reverses the action of the prime mover is the 'antagonist'. When the joint is at rest, the tone or tension in the prime mover is balanced by the antagonist tone, otherwise the joint would move. This balancing of tone in sets of muscles is made possible by the sensory **proprioceptors** within the muscles. For example, when the **elbow joint** is flexed, the biceps act as the prime mover (and also brachialis) and the triceps act as antagonist. When the elbow joint is extended, the triceps are the prime mover and the biceps (plus brachialis) are the antagonists. The circular and longitudinal muscles of the gut wall and of the body wall of an earthworm are also antagonistic, and contract alternately to produce movement.

◀ Forelimb of mammals, Hydrostatic skeleton, Peristalsis ▶

ANTHERS

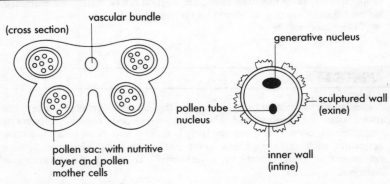

Fig. A.7 a) Anther (cross section)   b) Pollen grain

Anthers (Fig. A.7a) are the swollen sacs on the end of the filament in a stamen. When ripe, they contain pollen grains, (Fig. A.7b), and dehisce or split open to shed them for insect or wind **pollination**. Most anthers contain four pollen sacs or microsporangia. Within a pollen sac a number of pollen mother cells (microspore mother cells) each divide meiotically to produce four pollen grains. These have a resistant outer coat, called the exine, which is often characteristically sculptured with spines and ridges. The cells lining the pollen sac have a nutritive function, and are termed the tapetum. Outside this is a thickened fibrous layer, which dries out unevenly, setting up tensions which eventually cause dehiscence.

◀ Fertilisation, Meiosis, Sporangia ▶

ANTIBODY

An antibody is a substance produced by lymphocytes, in the presence of a specific antigen, that can combine with that antigen to neutralise, inhibit or destroy it. Antibodies belong to a group of **proteins** called globulins (immunoglobulins) and five different classes exist in humans: IgG, IgA, IgM, IgD and IgE. Each has a distinct chemical structure and a specific biological role. IgG antibodies enhance **phagocytosis**, neutralise toxins (i.e. are antitoxins) and particularly protect the fetus and newborn. IgA antibodies occur on mucous membranes providing local protection. IgM causes agglutination and lysis of microbes. IgD antibodies stimulate antibody-producing cells to produce more antibodies. IgE antibodies are involved in allergic responses.

Various other chemical systems in the body support the action of antibodies but are not themselves antibodies, since they lack specificity. For example, complement is a system of eleven proteins in the plasma, which include opsonin. This coats bacteria enabling the phagocytes to engulf them more readily. Cells infected with virus produce a protein called **interferon**, which interferes with the viral replication.

◀ Allergy, Antigens, B-lymphocytes, Immunity, Opsonins, T-lymphocytes, Virus, Viral replication ▶

ANTICODON

The anticodon is a triplet of three adjacent **nucleotides** on the looped end of the **transfer RNA** molecule, and it determines the specific amino acid that the particular t-RNA molecule can attach to. When the t-RNA carries this amino acid to the **ribosome**, the anticodon will attach to the complementary **codon** on the **messenger RNA**, and the amino acid can become assembled into the **polypeptide**.

◀ Protein synthesis ▶

ANTI-DIURETIC HORMONE

◀ ADH ▶

ANTIGENS

An antigen is any substance that when introduced into the blood or tissues induces the formation of antibodies, or reacts with them if they are already present.

◄ Antibody, Immunity ►

AORTA

◄ Arteries, arterioles ►

APHIDS

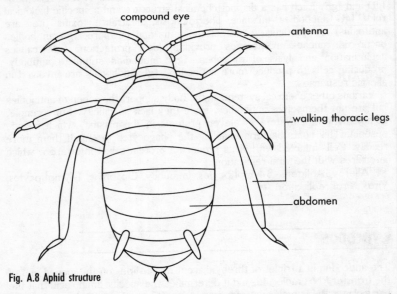

compound eye

antenna

walking thoracic legs

abdomen

Fig. A.8 Aphid structure

Aphids (Fig. A.8) are plant bugs belonging to the insect order Hemiptera and are commonly known as green fly, black fly and white fly. They suck plant juices and, since they can occur in huge infestations, they cause a lot of damage to flowering plants (flowers, fruits, vegetables). They are preyed upon by ladybird insects, and this gives a measure of **biological control**. They also act as vectors of plant **virus** diseases, transferring the virions from infected plants to healthy plants as they suck the sap. Aphids show incomplete metamorphosis with wingless nymphs and winged adults. Over much of the year they will reproduce in huge numbers by parthenogenesis (i.e. the egg develops without being fertilised by a male).

◄ Vectors ►

APICAL DOMINANCE

Auxin or IAA has many effects on plant growth and one of these is to inhibit the growth of side branches from lateral buds. If the apical bud is removed from a plant, side branches will arise from several lateral buds, indicating that the apex suppresses the growth of lower parts of the plant. This is known as apical dominance and is the principle behind pruning, where lateral growth will take place only if the apex is removed. IAA painted on the cut end of the main stem will inhibit lateral growth in the same way that the apex does.

APICAL MERISTEM

◀ Primary growth ▶

APOPLAST, APOPLASTIC PATHWAY

◀ Water uptake in roots ▶

AQUATIC HABITATS

Animals and plants may inhabit a variety of aquatic habitats and will have adaptations which make them successful in these particular environments. Plants may show features such as bladders or air spaces in their stems to keep them afloat, a water-resistant cuticle, light waterproof fruits or seeds, and physiological processes that maintain the turgidity of their cells despite being bathed in dilute or concentrated solutions. Higher animals will have moist skins or gills for gaseous exchange, fins, flippers or webbed feet for locomotion and very often a streamlined shape. They have water-resistant surfaces and homoeostatic osmoregulatory devices to maintain the correct salt/water balance in their bodies.

Aquatic habitats may be subdivided into two main types: fresh-water or marine.

◀ Fresh-water ecosystems, Marine environment ▶

ARACHNIDS

Arachnida is a class of the phylum Arthropoda, and contains the **spiders**, mites, ticks and scorpions. Their bodies are divided into two distinct regions: a cephalothorax, which bears the four pairs of jointed legs, and an abdomen. They have no antennae or compound eyes, but their bodies are covered in sensory hairs, and they possess six to eight simple eyes. The mouth is located between the third and fourth segment of the cephalothorax; chelicerae are present on the third segment and are used for the capture of prey.

On the abdomen, spiders have specialised silk glands and spinnerets for construction of their web and scorpions have a stinging process.

ARTERIES, ARTERIOLES

Arteries and arterioles carry blood away from the heart. The main artery is the aorta, which subdivides to form arteries, which subdivide in turn to form arterioles. With the exception of the pulmonary artery to the lungs and umbilical arteries to the placenta, all arteries carry oxygenated blood.

Arterial blood is under high pressure, having just been pumped from the heart, so the walls of arteries contain smooth muscle and elastic tissue to accommodate the pulsed flow.

◄ Blood vessels ►

ARTHRITIS

Arthritis is a degenerative disease that causes inflammation of synovial joints. The bones of the joint consolidate and mobility is reduced.

ARTHROPODS

Arthropoda is a major phylum of the animal kingdom comprising approximately 80 per cent of all known animal species, grouped into five classes: Crustacea, Insecta, Chilopoda, Diplopoda and Arachnida. Members range in size from microscopic aquatic crustaceans to huge land crabs, and inhabit sea and fresh water as well as the land and the air; some are even parasites. The arthropod body shows coelomate organisation and metameric segmentation, but these are not as complete as they are in the annelids. Cephalisation is obvious, with six fused segments constituting the head.

All animals in this phylum have a hard exoskeleton or cuticle made of chitin, which is commonly impregnated and hardened to form a protective armour. It provides internal anchorage for muscles, protects the animal from excessive water loss, and portions have been adapted to provide jointed mouthparts, lenses of eyes, pincers, legs, paddles for swimming, sense organs, appendages for copulation, and wings. In fact, the success of this phylum is largely due to the possession of such a skeleton. The exoskeleton does, however, limit the maximum size to which they grow and prevents size increase occurring at all except during a period of moulting or ecdysis.

◄ Cuticle, Ecdysis, Exoskeleton, Insects, Myriapoda, Spiders ►

ARTIFICIAL CLASSIFICATION

Artificial classification is used in the production of dichotomous keys, which are constructed for the purpose of identifying a limited number of specimens. Features may be used that are not based on how closely the animals or plants are related, and which give no indication of their taxonomy. For example, a key to separate and identify meadow flowers might be based on petal colour and shape; or a key to separate and identify soil invertebrates might ask questions such as 'Legs or no legs?'.

ARTIFICIAL INSEMINATION (AI)

In animal breeding it is not always suitable or practical to bring together male and female of the particular species and expect immediate successful copulation and subsequent insemination. This can be because of the temperament of the male animal (e.g. bull) or because the stud male may be some distance away, and it would be too expensive in terms of time and money. Semen is therefore collected from the male animal, in sterile conditions, and kept frozen until required.

When the female animal is 'in season', or receptive to the sperm, the semen is injected to the top of the vagina using a suitable syringe. Insemination can thus occur without the actual act of copulation.

ARTIFICIAL SELECTION

Artificial selection forms the basis of animal and plant breeding. Man imposes his own selection pressures and in so doing alters the phenotypes and gene frequencies of certain species. Males and females (or plants) with the desired characteristics (e.g. good milk production in Jersey cattle) are selected and allowed to interbreed. Offspring that do not show the desired qualities are prevented from mating by extermination, segregation or sterilisation. In this way, over several generations the quality of crops and livestock can be improved. Animals subjected to artificial selection include cattle, pigs, sheep, horses, pigeons, poultry and dogs – all for particular purposes of food production or other requirements. Plants such as wheat, barley and potatoes have been bred for higher yield and greater resistance to disease or adverse weather conditions. In artificial selection, Man plays the role normally performed by nature.

ASCORBIC ACID

Ascorbic acid is vitamin C.
◄ Vitamins ►

ASEPTIC TECHNIQUES, ASEPSIS

Asepsis is the exclusion of germs or micro-organisms from the environment of a laboratory or operating theatre. The foundations of these principles were laid by Louis Pasteur over a century ago, when he showed that pathogenic organisms could be destroyed by heat treatment or sterilisation. Since then other ways have been found, such as the use of antiseptics. Nowadays aseptic techniques involve sterile procedures to ensure minimum risk of introducing infection.

◀ Sterilisation ▶

ASEXUAL REPRODUCTION

In asexual reproduction, only one parent is required and there is no joining of gametes. The new individuals are produced by mitotic cell division, so are identical, and large numbers can be formed relatively quickly. Asexual reproduction may involve the whole organism splitting in two, as in binary fission in bacteria and in unicellular protoctistans, or an identical miniature may form as an outgrowth from the parent, as in budding in Hydra. Spore production in fungi, mosses, ferns and bacteria is asexual and results in rapid population increases.

Vegetative propagation is a type of asexual reproduction. It occurs in flowering plants and may involve perennating organs such as bulbs, corms and rhizomes, or other structures such as strawberry runners. It can also occur artificially by taking cuttings.

◀ Mitosis, Spore, Sporulation ▶

ASSIMILATION

Assimilation in animals refers to the utilisation of the absorbed products of digestion, either as respiratory substrates or as raw materials for anabolism, or synthesis. All body cells require glucose and amino acids for respiration and protein synthesis, and their levels in the blood are regulated mainly by the action of hormones on the liver. The liver also monitors the amount of fat circulating in the blood, and excess is diverted to fat depots, such as those in the adipose tissue in the dermis.

◀ Net assimilation rate ▶

ASTHMA

Asthma is a common condition in children from families where there is a history of allergic reactions. The circular muscles in the walls of the bronchi contract, so that breathing and particularly expiration become difficult and the patient 'wheezes'. An asthma attack may occur due to an allergic response to inhaled dust or pollen, or to an infection such as bronchitis, or as a result of psychological or emotional upset.

◀ Allergy, Disease ▶

AUTECOLOGY

Autecology is the study of a population of a given species in an environment. In particular it involves measurement of population size and growth, and investigation of the factors affecting the birth and death rates and distribution of the population.

◀ Population growth, Sampling techniques ▶

AUTONOMIC NERVOUS CONTROL

The autonomic nervous system is responsible for the many involuntary activities of the body, such as the rate of heart beat, peristalsis, erection and ejaculation, secretion of saliva and sweat. Organs that are not under voluntary control are connected to the central nervous system via ganglia, and these peripheral ganglia and their associated nerves make up the autonomic nervous system.

The autonomic nervous system can be divided both structurally and functionally into two sections:

- the sympathetic system, which has ganglia close to the spinal cord, so the post-ganglionic fibres are longer than those leading to the ganglia. The synaptic transmitter substance is noradrenaline, which resembles the endocrine hormone adrenaline. The overall effects of the sympathetic system are to stimulate the body (in a similar way to adrenaline).

- the parasympathetic system, which has ganglia that lie within the effector (e.g. the bladder or genitalia), so in this case the preganglionic fibres are the longest. The system uses the synaptic transmitter acetycholine, and it consists of the vagus nerve and its branches plus certain other cranial and spinal nerves. The overall effects of the parasympathetic system are the reverse of the sympathetic – that is, it 'pacifies' while the sympathetic stimulates

◀ Sympathetic nervous system ▶

AUTOPOLYPLOIDY

◀ Polyploidy ▶

AUTOSOME

An autosome is a chromosome that is not a sex chromosome. Within a diploid nucleus there will be a set number of pairs of autosomes and one pair of sex chromosomes. The genes present on each pair of autosomes form an autosomal linkage group.

AUTOTROPHIC NUTRITION

Autotrophic nutrition involves the synthesis of organic compounds from carbon dioxide and other simple inorganic raw materials. Autotrophic organisms occupy the producer trophic level in food webs, and all the consumers ultimately depend on their activities. Energy is required for autotrophic nutrition and this may be obtained from light or from chemical reactions.

- Light energy is used by green plants in **photosynthesis.**
- Chemical energy is used by certain prokaryotes in chemosynthesis (e.g. nitrifying bacteria in soil).

◀ Nitrogen cycle, Producers ▶

AUXIN

Auxins, such as indoleacetic acid or IAA, are the most abundant plant-growth hormones. They are concerned with growth due to cell elongation and differentiation, and they cause tropic responses to external stimuli. They also promote the growth of adventitious roots from stems, maintain apical dominance by suppressing the development of lateral buds, initiate fruit formation even if pollination has not occurred, inhibit leaf fall and, with other hormones, promote secondary growth and wound healing.

Auxin is produced in the tip of stems and coleoptiles, and diffuses down the stem to the zone of cell elongation. Here it exerts its effect by breaking some

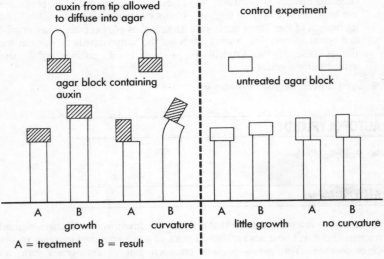

Fig. A.9 Effects of auxin on decapitated coleoptiles

of the polar crosslinks that hold the microfibrils of cellulose together. This makes the cellulose wall elastic so that, as water fills the vacuole by osmosis, the wall can stretch and the cell gets longer.

The action of auxin can be demonstrated by removing the tips of oat coleoptiles and allowing the auxin produced by the tips to diffuse into agar blocks. These blocks are then placed either symmetrically or asymmetrically on the decapitated coleoptiles, resulting in either vertical or curved growth (Fig. A.9).

Synthetic auxins have many commercial applications. They are used as hormone rooting powder on cuttings by fruit growers to produce seedless fruits and as selective weedkillers in certain herbicides.

◀ Geotropism, Phototropism ▶

AVES

The class Aves contains the birds. They are endothermic, lung-breathing chordates with pentadactyl limbs, of which the front pair is modified into wings for flight. Some birds, such as ostriches, penguins and domestic fowl, have lost the ability to fly, but the group as a whole shows many adaptations for this purpose. These include the wings with their flight feathers, and also various ways of reducing body mass, such as hollow bones, a beak instead of teeth, the excretion of semisolid 'urine', and so on. As well as the flight feathers, the skin is covered in downy feathers to provide insulation.

Many birds show elaborate reproductive behaviour, involving courtship displays, pair-bonding and parental care. Fertilisation is internal and large yolky eggs are laid in calcareous shells.

◀ Endothermy, Migration ▶

AXILLARY BUDS

Axillary buds lie in the axil of the leaf of a plant, although they do not always originate there precisely. Most commonly they originate on the stem, just below the preceding leaf, and reach their final position only by the elongation of the stem into an internode, together with some downward displacement of the bud into the leaf axil below.

Like other buds, the axillary bud is initiated from cells in the tunica of the stem apex, and therefore its origin is described as exogenous. These buds have meristematic cells at their tips that are potentially capable of forming side branches, but only when the inhibiting effect of auxin from the stem tip is removed.

◀ Apical dominance, Stem structure. ▶

AXON

◀ Neurone ▶

B

BACILLUS

Bacterial cells have characteristic shapes and the earliest descriptions and classifications were based on this. All 'rod-like' **bacteria** are referred to as bacilli (singular: bacillus), although they vary considerably in shape, size and motility, and the rods may occur singly or in chains. Examples of bacillus bacteria in the soil include nitrifying bacteria, such as *Nitrobacter* and *Nitrosomonas*, which are small, motile, single rods, and nitrogen-fixing bacteria, such as *Azotobacter*, which are motile chains. Other well-known bacilli are the human gut symbiont *Escherichia coli* and the pathogenic *Salmonella typhi*, which cause typhoid.

◀ Nitrogen cycle, Typhoid ▶

BACTERIA

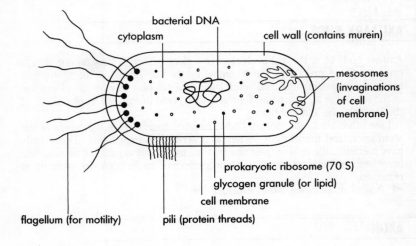

Fig. B.1 Structure of a typical bacterial cell

Bacteria are now classified together with cyanobacteria in the phylum **Prokaryotae**. They are nearly all unicellular and extremely small, the smallest being only 0.1μm across. Some are pigmented but most are colourless, and many are motile due to the presence of one or more flagella. Bacterial flagella are smaller and simpler than eukaryotic flagella, consisting of just one microtubule.

The bacterium, or bacterial cell (Fig. B.1), has a rigid cell wall made mainly of a peptide-polysaccharide called murein. Lipids, proteins and other polysaccharides are often present, and there may be a slime capsule around it to protect against desiccation. Within the cytoplasm are ribosomes, glycogen granules and bacterial DNA, which is in the form of a large circular chromosome and smaller plasmids. Bacteria mainly reproduce asexually by binary fission, though a type of sexual reproduction called conjugation may also occur.

Bacteria are classified according to shape: cocci are spherical, bacilli are rod-shaped, spirochaetes or spirilla are spiral forms and vibrios are comma-shaped.

The majority of bacteria are saprophytes, though some are parasites and cause disease. Saprophytic bacteria play an important role in decomposition and nutrient recycling in the soil, and are used commercially in **biotechnology** and industries such as cheese making, vinegar production and tanning.

◄ Disease transmission, Nitrogen cycle ►

BACTERIOPHAGE

◄ Virus, viral replication ►

BALANCE

The sense of balance is at its most highly developed in humans. Walking upright means that our centre of gravity is a long way off the ground, and our body surface in contact with the ground is extremely small. All the skeletal muscles of the body are involved in maintaining balance and the process is coordinated by the **cerebellum** in the hindbrain. The cerebellum receives information from receptors in the skin, from proprioceptors in muscles and joints, and most importantly from sensory receptors in the inner ear.

The inner ear contains two types of receptor concerned with balance. The ampullae of the **semicircular canals** contain crista that detect head movements, while the utriculus and sacculus contain otoliths that detect head position.

◄ Utricle ►

BALANCED DIET

◄ Diet ►

BANDING IN CEPAEA NEMORALIS

Cepaea nemoralis is a common land snail that provides a good illustration of balanced **polymorphism**. Many different forms coexist in the same population, with each type conferring a selective advantage when on a different background or at a different time of the year. The forms vary in their shell colour and banding, and hence in the amount of camouflage provided against their predators, which are thrushes.

Shell colour and banding are determined genetically by closely linked genes. The gene for colour has six to eight alleles, the main ones coding for brown, pink and yellow, of which brown is dominant to pink, and pink to yellow. Because the selection pressures are variable, all phenotypes are selected for at some time, so all are maintained in the population.

◀ Linkage ▶

BASE

A base is a proton or hydrogen ion acceptor, while an acid is a proton donor. Ammonia is an example of an inorganic base.

$$NH_3 + H^+ \rightarrow NH_4^+$$

Inorganic bases may dissolve to form alkalis, increasing the **pH** or alkalinity of the medium where they are. It is therefore important that the **acid/base balance** in body fluids is kept constant.

The amine group of amino acids is an example of an organic base.

$$R-NH_2 + H^+ \rightarrow R-NH_3^+$$

Organic bases include the purines and pyrimidines, which are components of **nucleotides** and form the **genetic code** on DNA.

BASIDIOMYCETE

Basidiomycetes belong to the kingdom **Fungi**, class Basidiomycota. The mycelial hyphae are septate, and the spores are produced externally on special structures called basidia. For example, *Agaricus* (mushroom).

◀ Agaric ▶

BEE

The honey bee, *Apis mellifera*, is a member of the order Hymenoptera of the class Insecta, and is related to the wasps and ants. Honey bees live in large colonies which have a highly precise and organised social structure, containing three levels or castes: queens, drones and workers. The colony centres on the queen, who is larger than the other bees and the only egg-laying individual in the hive. Her eggs are fertilised by the drones, which are males, this being their only function in the colony. At the end of the summer, drones are ejected from the hive by the workers and left to die, so that they don't use up scarce winter resources. The queen lays her eggs in hexagonal cells one egg per cell on a wax honeycomb. Unfertilised eggs give rise to drones by parthenogenesis, while fertilised eggs develop into workers or into queens, depending on the diet the larvae are given. Queen larvae receive 'royal jelly', which is a special nutritive food produced by the workers, while larvae destined to become workers are fed on honey (sugar) and pollen (protein). After their last moult, the larvae of both types pupate in silken cocoons within the comb cells and after a few days the adults emerge. Normally the queen will kill any new queen larvae with her sting, but occasionally the workers prevent this and a new queen matures. The old queen then leaves the hive with a swarm of workers and drones, to establish a new colony elsewhere. The workers perform various jobs throughout their life, which may be as short as five weeks in the active period of summer. They feed and groom the queen, clean and ventilate the hive, build wax honeycomb using the wax-secreting glands on their bodies, and forage for pollen and nectar, which are stored in the comb. It is while they are foraging for pollen that the bees act as agents of insect **pollination**. Their legs are modified to carry pollen (pollen baskets). Worker bees can communicate by certain dances, which impart information about food sources. Pheromones also play an important role in maintaining the integrity of the colony.

◀ Insects, Social behaviour ▶

BEER MANUFACTURE

◀ Brewing, Fermentation ▶

BEHAVIOUR

Behaviour is the pattern of reactions shown by an organism to its environment, including its reactions towards other animals. Some behaviour patterns are determined genetically and are present from the birth/hatching, while other patterns are acquired by learning from the environment. Behaviour patterns range from simple reflex responses to extremely complex and elaborate rituals, as seen in some **reproductive behaviour** for instance.

◀ Aggression, Altruism, Courtship behaviour, Innate behaviour, Instinct, Learned behaviour, Reflex action, Social behaviour ▶

BENEDICTS SOLUTION

Benedicts solution is used in testing for **reducing sugars**.

◀ Food tests ▶

BETA CELLS

The beta cells in the islets of Langerhans in the **pancreas** secrete the hormone insulin, which regulates blood glucose concentration.
◄ Blood glucose level ►

BILATERAL SYMMETRY

Bilateral symmetry is when an organism can be divided in only one plane to give halves that are more or less mirror images of each other. This plane is usually the median plane, running from anterior to posterior and from dorsal to ventral, and it cuts the animal into left and right halves. In the animal kingdom, only **Cnidaria** and **Echinodermata** do not show bilateral symmetry.
◄ Radial symmetry ►

BILE

Bile is produced by the hepatic cells of the liver, stored in the gall bladder and released into the duodenum under the influence of a **hormone** called cholecystokinin. This is secreted by cells in the duodenal wall when acid from the stomach enters the duodenum, and it causes contraction of the **smooth muscle** cells in the gall bladder wall. Bile is a watery solution and contains bile pigments and salts. The bile pigments, such as bilirubin, are byproducts of the breakdown of **haemoglobin** and are excreted via this route, in the **faeces**. The bile salts are sodium taurocholate and sodium glycocholate, which have an important digestive function. They emulsify lipids in the duodenum, breaking them down into numerous smaller droplets, so increasing their surface area for **lipase** to act on. Bile also contains sodium hydrogencarbonate, which neutralises the acid chyme from the stomach, and provides the optimum **pH** for the pancreatic enzymes (pH 7–8).
◄ Digestion, Emulsification, emulsions, Excretion, Hydrogencarbonate ions, Pancreas ►

BINOMIAL NOMENCLATURE

◄ Linnaeus ►

BIOCHEMICAL OXYGEN DEMAND

◄ BOD ►

BIODEGRADATION

Biodegradation is the breakdown of material by **microorganisms**.
◄ Decomposers ►

BIOLOGICAL CONTROL

Biological control is the control of parasites and pests by the use of other organisms, and is an alternative to chemical control, which might leave harmful residues. For example, mosquito larvae and pupae can be destroyed by stocking the ponds where they live with fish that eat them; the prickly pear in Australia has been controlled by using insects that parasitise it; **aphids** are controlled by ladybird beetles.
◄ Insecticides, Malaria, Parasitism ►

BIOMASS

Biomass is the mass of all organisms forming a given population or trophic level, or inhabiting a particular region.
◄ Pyramids of biomass, Trophic levels ►

BIORHYTHMS

Biorhythms are patterns of regular repeating biological events that organisms undergo. They may be annual, seasonal or daily, with the latter being referred to as circadian rhythms. Most biorhythms are under **negative feedback** control, and may be linked to light.
◄ Menstrual cycle, Photoperiodism, Temperature regulation ►

BIOSPHERE

The biosphere are the parts of the earth and its atmosphere which are inhabited by living organisms.

BIOSYNTHESIS

Biosynthesis is the manufacture of biological substances and is an anabolic process, requiring energy input.
◄ Anabolism, Photosynthesis, Protein synthesis ►

BIOTECHNOLOGY

Biotechnology is the use of organisms, especially **bacteria**, to make useful products and provide useful services. It can be used to manufacture enzymes, drugs, antibodies, alcohol, **single cell protein** and fuels, and to help clean up the environment, as in the treatment of industrial effluents and oil spillages, and in sewage treatment.

◄ Brewing, Enzyme, Fermentation, Genetic engineering, Monoclonal antibodies, Recombinant DNA, Recombination, Wine production ►

BIOTIC FACTORS

The distribution of organisms depends on many different factors. Biotic factors are those which arise from the activities of organisms, rather than from the soil or climate, and particularly relate to food supply and **predation** and to **competition** with other organisms. Intraspecific competition occurs between members of the same species, and could be for space and pasture among grazing animals, for instance, or for light and water among seeds germinating too close together. Interspecific competition occurs between individuals of different species, such as the competition for water, space, light and nutrients that takes place between a crop plant and weeds.

◄ Climatic factors, Edaphic factors, Food chains, Food webs, Trophic levels ►

BIRDS

◄ Aves ►

BIRTH

Birth occurs when the **fetus, placenta** and **fetal membranes** are expelled through the birth canal, and it involves the process of labour. The gestation period of humans is forty weeks, and birth should occur with a few days of this time. Initiation of birth is partly controlled by **hormone** levels, there being a decrease in **progesterone**, due to the ageing of the placenta, and an increase in **oestrogens**, secreted by the fetus itself. The ageing placenta also becomes less efficient as an exchange surface area, so the fetus suffers discomfort and possibly struggles more. This mechanically stimulates the **uterus**, which may cause **oxytocin** release by neurosecretion from the posterior pituitary. Oxytocin then stimulates uterine contractions.

True labour starts when the women experiences uterine contractions, and the cervix, or exit from the uterus, dilates. The first stage of labour is from when the cervix commences dilation and the contractions start, until the cervix is fully dilated The second stage of labour ends when the fetus is expelled – that is, the baby is born. The third stage of labour is the separation and expulsion of the placenta and fetal membranes, and the control of bleeding.

◄ Pituitary gland ►

BISTON BETULARIA

◄ Industrial melanism ►

BIURET TEST FOR PROTEINS

The biuret test can be used qualitatively to show the presence of protein in a food sample, or can be used quantitatively to measure the concentration of a protein in a solution or biological fluid.

◄ Food tests ►

BIVALENTS

Bivalents are formed when **homologous chromosomes** pair together in synapsis during **meiosis**.

BIVALVES

Bivalves are members of the phylum **Mollusca**, class Pelycopoda. They have reduced heads, are filter feeders and have a shell hinged in two halves. For example, mussels, oysters and scallops.

◄ Filter feeding ►

BLOOD

Blood in humans consists of about 55 per cent by volume of plasma and 45 per cent by volume of cells. The plasma is a straw-coloured solution of various proteins, such as plasma albumin, plasma globulins and fibrinogen. Together with the salts dissolved in the plasma, albumin helps to maintain the osmotic pressure of blood, and thus the blood volume and blood pressure. Many globulins are antibodies produced by the plasma cells. Fibrinogen is one of the blood clotting proteins. The plasma also carries cells, heat, hormones, nutrients such as glucose, amino acids and vitamins, and excretory products such as urea, uric acid and hydrogen carbonate, from source to destination. The cells consist of red blood cells and white blood cells, and also small cytoplasmic fragments called platelets, which are concerned with blood clotting.

◄ B-lymphocytes, Phagocytosis, T-lymphocytes ►

BLOOD CIRCULATION

Mammals have a double circulation (Fig. B.2) this means that blood must pass

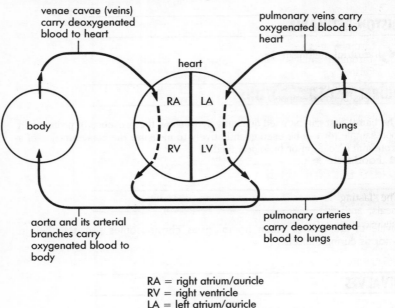

RA = right atrium/auricle
RV = right ventricle
LA = left atrium/auricle
LV = left ventricle

Fig. B.2 Double blood circulation in mammals

through the **heart** twice on its way round the body. The blood circulates through the pulmonary circulation to the **lungs** to be oxygenated. It then returns to the left side of the heart, and is pumped to the body organs and tissues via the systemic circulation. Deoxygenated blood returns to the right side of the heart, and is pumped again to the lungs.

The heart is the muscular pump which causes the blood to circulate.

◀ Blood vessels, Pulmonary blood circulation ▶

BLOOD CLOTTING

Blood clotting has three important functions. It prevents excessive bleeding when blood vessels are damaged, prevents or reduces the entry of pathogenic organisms into the body via wounds and forms a scab which provides a 'scaffold' for new replacement tissue to be regenerated during healing.

When a blood vessel wall is ruptured, it exposes underlying collagen fibres, to which blood platelets start to stick. This is an active process and expends

ATP. The wound surface is thus covered by a plug of blood platelets, which liberate chemicals to initiate the clotting process. A succession of various chemical reactions now occurs:

- blood platelets release thromboplastin;
- thromboplastin, together with calcium ions and other factors in the plasma, helps to convert prothrombin (inactive precursor in plasma) to thrombin (active clotting enzyme);
- thrombin catalyses the conversion of soluble fibrinogen to insoluble fibrin;
- fibrin forms a meshwork of threads over the wound, in which red blood cells become trapped and a clot is formed.

After formation the clot hardens and shrinks to form a scab, under which the tissues can heal.

◀ Blood, Defence ▶

BLOOD GLUCOSE LEVEL

The 'fasting' level of glucose in the blood is the amount present between meals, and gives a measure of the respiratory level (i.e. that amount of glucose being carried to the tissues for metabolic needs). In humans this level is in the range 3.4 to 5.6 millimoles per litre (old units 60 to 100 mgs per decilitre). Total blood sugar levels include such sugars as fructose and ribose and are about 20 per cent higher. After a meal the blood glucose concentration may rise to about 9.0 millimoles per litre; if it should exceed the renal

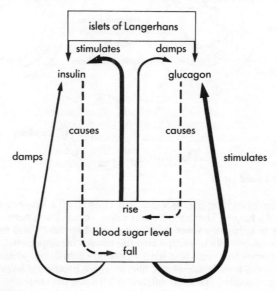

Fig. B.3 Blood glucose level

threshold of 10.0 millimoles per litre, then some will leak into the urine. The blood glucose level is regulated by **negative feedback** control. Insulin from the **beta cells** of the pancreatic islets of Langerhans stimulates the reduction of blood glucose, by accelerating its uptake by cells, and by accelerating its polymerisation to **glycogen** in the liver. **Glucagon** from the **alpha cells** of the islets, together with **adrenalin** and **thyroxine**, all counteract the effects of insulin, and tend to raise blood glucose concentration (Fig. B.3)

BLOOD GROUPS

◀ ABO groups, Multiple alleles, Rhesus blood groups ▶

BLOOD VESSELS

Blood vessels are arteries, veins and capillaries (Fig. B.4). Arteries carry blood away from the heart, under high pressure, and divide into smaller vessels called arterioles. These eventually become capillaries at tissue level, where exchange occurs with the body cells. The capillaries rejoin to form venules and then veins, which convey blood under lower pressure back to the heart.

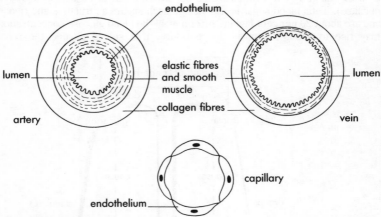

Fig. B.4 Blood vessels

Capillaries are microscopic, and consist of a one-cell-thick endothelium round a lumen. There are fenestrations, or windows, between the endothelial cells to enhance exchange of oxygen and nutrients and to allow phagocytic white blood cells to escape into the tissues by diapedesis.

Arteries and veins also have an endothelium lining, around which is a layer of smooth muscle and elastic fibres, with a protective layer of collagen fibres on the outside. The main difference between the structure of an artery and a vein is in the thickness of the middle layer. Arteries need more smooth muscle so that they can maintain the pulse derived from the heart beat, and they need elastic tissue so they can stretch slightly with each pulse. Another difference between arteries and veins is that veins have semilunar valves in them to prevent the backflow of blood.

◄ Blood circulation, Lymph ►

BLUE-GREEN ALGAE

◄ Cyanobacteria ►

B-LYMPHOCYTES

B-lymphocytes are also known as B-cells. They are white blood cells that synthesise antibodies when stimulated to do so by the presence of a specific antigen. There are thousands of different B-cells since each one produces only one type of **antibody**. The antibodies are secreted into the blood plasma and tissue fluid, where they neutralise toxins or speed up the phagocytosis of bacteria. This is known as the humoral immune response.

◄ Antigens, Humoral response, Immunity ►

BOD

BOD, or the biochemical oxygen demand, is the most widely used measure of aquatic pollution. There is a close relationship between organic matter, such as sewage or dead algae from algal blooms, and the dissolved oxygen available for fish. This is because oxygen is required by the bacteria that break down the organic matter. A litre sample is taken from the water to be tested, and the amount of oxygen needed for bacteria to completely oxidise the organic matter over a period of five days is recorded. A typical BOD value for water close to a sewage outflow might be 200 ppm (parts per million) oxygen, while human water supplies should have a BOD of less than 1 ppm.

◄ Nitrate pollution ►

BODY CAVITY

In the Cnidaria (*Hydra, Obelia*, jelly fish, sea anemone) the body cavity is a simple sac called the enteron. It has a single opening which serves as a mouth and anus, and it functions as the gut. It is lined by the endoderm, since these organisms are diploblastic. In most triploblastic groups of animals, a spacious body cavity develops within the mesoderm. This is the coelom, and in **annelida, echinodermata** and **chordates**, it surrounds the organs, isolating their muscular movements from those of the body wall. In **arthropoda** and **molluscs** the coelom is reduced to small cavities in the gonads and excretory organs, and the main body cavity is an enlarged cavity of the blood system. This is called the haemocoele, and the tissues are directly bathed with blood.

◄ Coelomate organisation, Triploblastic organisation ►

BOHR EFFECT

The amount of oxygen carried or released from **haemoglobin** is determined by several factors besides oxygen tension, one of which is **pH**. In an acid environment hydrogen ions bind to haemoglobin and it unloads oxygen more efficiently. This happens in the vicinity of respiring cells and muscles, due to **lactic acid** build-up and to high CO_2 concentration. In a less acid environment, hydrogen ions leave the haemoglobin and its oxygen-carrying capacity is increased. This happens in the alveolar capillaries, where oxygen uptake is enhanced. This shift in the oxygen-carrying capacity of haemoglobin due to pH change is the Bohr shift.

BONE

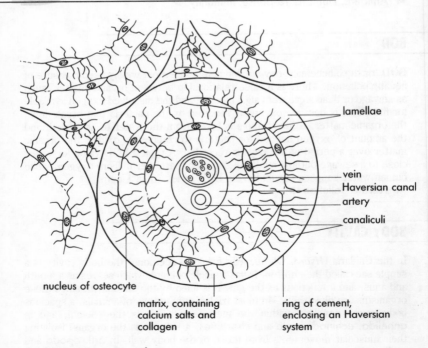

lamellae

vein
Haversian canal
artery
canaliculi

nucleus of osteocyte

matrix, containing calcium salts and collagen

ring of cement, enclosing an Haversian system

Fig. B.5 Haversian systems in bone

Bone is a hard supporting connective tissue that makes up the **endoskeleton** in most **chordates**. It consists mainly of a matrix containing small spaces, called lacunae, which house the bone cells or osteoblasts. The osteoblasts secrete the matrix, which consists of inorganic crystals deposited on a network of collagen fibres (Sharpey fibres). These crystals contain calcium phosphate and calcium carbonate, forming a complex molecule called hydroxyapatite. Since the bone matrix is impermeable, canaliculi or small channels occur between the lacunae to enable transfer of **tissue fluid** and metabolites. An aged osteoblast which no longer secretes matrix is called an osteocyte. The oesteoblasts are arranged in specific patterns and will therefore secrete the matrix in distinct patterns. The most common pattern is found as the Haversian systems of compact bone (Fig. B.5). The matrix is produced in concentric cylinders, one around the other, around a central duct called the Haversian canal. This carries **arteries, veins, capillaries, lymphatic vessels** and nerves. Haversian canals of adjacent systems join via Volkmann's canals. Spongy bone consists of thin plates of bone, called trabeculae, which follow the lines of compression force to give strength to the bone. In between the trabeculae are spaces which contain bone marrow. The outside of a bone is covered by a tough white collagen fibre layer called the periosteum.

◀ Connective tissues, Nervous system, Skeleton, Support systems ▶

BONY FISH

Bony fish are classed in phylum Chordata, class **Osteichthyes**. Examples are cod, haddock, plaice, whiting and halibut, all found in the sea, and trout, pike, roach and tench, in fresh water. Salmon and eels migrate between the sea and fresh water.

◀ Chordates, Fish, Teleost ▶

BRAIN

The brain (Fig. B.6) is the part of the **central nervous system**, protected by the skull in **chordates**. In the **embryo** the brain originates as three lobes, the forebrain, the linking midbrain, and the hindbrain. The forebrain differentiates into several structures, the largest of which are the **cerebral hemispheres**. These are concerned with conscious thoughts and activities, intelligence and memory. Other structures of the forebrain are the thalamus, **hypothalamus** and **pituitary gland**, all situated in the between brain region. The hindbrain consists of the **cerebellum**, concerned with posture, movement and balance, and the **medulla oblongata**, which contains centres controlling **heart** beat, **ventilation**, swallowing and vomiting. The midbrain and hindbrain make up the brain stem, from which the cranial nerves emerge.

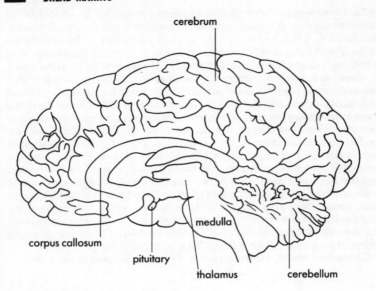

Fig. B.6 Sagittal section of a human brain

◀ Nervous system ▶

BREAD MAKING

Bread is made from flour blended with some fat and salt, to which is added an active **yeast** suspension containing a little sugar. The flour, fat and yeast are kneaded to thoroughly blend them together, and the dough is left in a bowl covered by a cloth, until it has doubled in size. The increase in volume is due to the CO_2 forming in the dough as the yeast ferments the sugar. The risen or 'proved' dough can then be baked in a hot oven. The bread that is formed will have an open texture due to the yeast activity.

◀ Fermentation ▶

BREATHING

Breathing is the way in which the **respiratory surfaces** are ventilated so that **gaseous exchange** can occur between air and blood in a land animal, or water and blood in an aquatic animal.

◀ Ventilation, Ventilation mechanisms ▶

BREWING

Brewing is the production of alcoholic beverages, such as beer and wine, using **yeast** to ferment sugars into alcohol and carbon dioxide. The production of beer involves a controlled **fermentation** of an infusion made from grains, usually barley. The barley grains are germinated under controlled conditions, so that amylases and peptidases in the seeds convert the **starch** to **maltose** and the **proteins** to **amino acids**, respectively. This 'malting' is stopped by raising the temperature to denature the enzymes. Warm water and dried hops are added to the malt, forming a liquor known as 'wort', which is boiled for several hours, and then cooled and filtered. The dried hops are added to give flavour, but they also contain antimicrobial chemicals. The wort is then inoculated with brewer's yeast, *Saccharomyces cerevisiae* or *S. carlsbergensis*, and allowed to ferment for two to five days. The thick yeast head that forms on the surface is periodically skimmed off. When the beer has reached an alcohol content of 4–8 per cent, it is racked off into casks or storage tanks, where secondary fermentation may continue at a slow rate. The beer is clarified, often enriched with CO_2, and can then be sold.

◄ Amylase, Beer manufacture, Denaturation, Wine production ►

BROWN ADIPOSE TISSUE

Brown adipose tissue contains cells with many mitochondria and hence a high metabolic rate. Here lipid is mostly unsaturated, stored as droplets rather than in solid form, and brown fat is an important generator of body heat. Thin people often have a considerable amount of brown fat, which is thought to produce heat to keep them warm, while those with little brown fat may become overweight, with excessive reserves of white fat. This is possibly to give them better insulation, to compensate for the lack of heat production from brown fat. Hibernating mammals lay down extensive stores of brown fat before going into hibernation. These are used up slowly during the winter, but on 'waking', the tissue becomes very active, producing much heat quickly. This rapidly warms the body to normal temperature, so that full activity can be resumed as soon as possible.

◄ Hibernation, Lipids, Mitochondrion ►

BROWN ALGAE

Brown algae belong to the phylum **Phaeophyta**. Many species reach a considerable size and are fairly complex. They form the bulk of algal material attached to the seashore in the littoral **zone**, and are zoned according to the ability of the species to withstand desiccation when exposed to air. *Fucus* species (Fig. B.7) and *Ascophyllum* tend to occur in mid-tide regions, whilst *Laminaria* species occur at low-tide level.

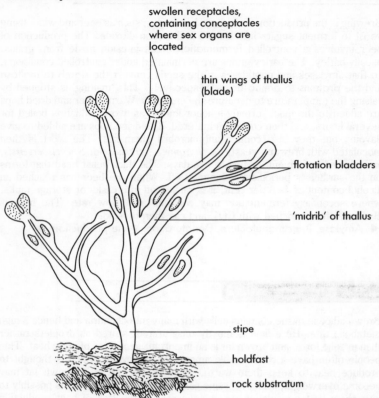

swollen receptacles, containing conceptacles where sex organs are located

thin wings of thallus (blade)

flotation bladders

'midrib' of thallus

stipe

holdfast

rock substratum

Fig. B.7 The structure of *Fucus vesiculosus*

BRYOPHYTA

Bryophyta are the mosses and the liverworts. They show **alternation of generations**, with the **gametophyte** being dominant, and they require a moist habitat for survival and reproduction.
◄ Life cycles, Liverwort, Moss ►

BUDDING (IN HYDRA)

Hydra reproduces asexually by budding (Fig. B.8) and the buds break free to become independent individuals. In many cnidarians the buds remain attached

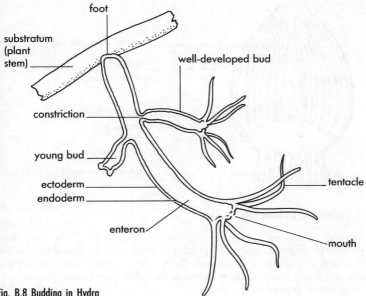

Fig. B.8 Budding in Hydra

to the parent polyp and so a colonial organism is produced (e.g. *Obelia*). Budding occurs when food is plentiful. Both ectoderm and endoderm divide, forming a protuberance which grows out from the body wall, containing a branch of the enteron. It enlarges, and tentacles and a mouth form at the free end. When development is complete, the base of the bud constricts and the new individual is formed. These float near the water surface for about three days to allow **dispersal**, before attaching to a suitable **substratum**.

◀ Asexual reproduction ▶

BUFFERS

Buffers are associations of certain chemicals which resist change in **pH** when acids or bases are added. They are important in controlling the pH of blood and other biological fluids, and thus have a role in **homeostasis**. Buffer systems that are important in the body are the carbonic acid–hydrogen carbonate system, the phosphate buffer system, the protein buffer system and the oxyhaemoglobin–**haemoglobin** buffer system.

◀ Acid/base balance, Bohr effect ▶

BULBS

Bulbs are organs for **perennation** (survival over adverse periods) produced

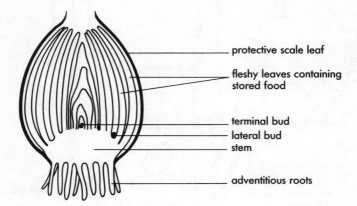

protective scale leaf

fleshy leaves containing stored food

terminal bud
lateral bud
stem

adventitious roots

Fig. B.9 Structure of an onion bulb

by certain plants, such as tulips and onions (Fig. B.9). They also allow vegetative propagation, since new plants can grow from the lateral buds in the bulb as well as from the terminal bud. Bulbs contain stored food in fleshy leaf bases, this being starch in bulbs although the onion bulb stores glucose.

◀ Vegetative reproduction ▶

BUOYANCY

Buoyancy is important to organisms in **aquatic habitats**. In plants it helps to keep them in the surface waters where the greatest intensity of light exists for **photosynthesis**. *Fucus vesiculosus* (bladder wrack) and *Ascophyllum nodosum* (knotted wrack) both have air-filled bladders as flotation organs while stems of hydrophytic spermatophytes contain aerenchyma with many air spaces between the cells.

Teleost fish have swim bladders containing gas, the density of which can be regulated. This enables them to maintain their position at a certain depth without having to expend energy. Cartilaginous fish, on the other hand, have no swim bladders and must keep swimming if they are to maintain their position. Aquatic mammals (e.g. seals, whales) have a thick covering of insulating blubber. Since fat has a lower density than water, this also gives them buoyancy.

◀ Brown algae, Swimming in bony fish ▶

BUTTERFLY

Butterflies belong to the order Lepidoptera of the class Insecta. They have complete metamorphosis of egg to caterpillar to pupa to adult. Many butterfly species are important economically. The adults are useful as pollinators of flowers, while the caterpillars can cause extensive damage to foliage crops such as cabbages.

◄ Life cycles, Metamorphosis, Moth ►

C₃ PLANTS

C_3 plants are those in which the first product of photosynthesis is a three-carbon sugar. In the **Calvin cycle**, carbon dioxide is accepted by 5C ribulose bisphosphate, which then splits into two molecules of glycerate 3-phosphate. Most plants outside the tropics are C_3 plants.

C₄ PLANTS

C_4 plants are those in which the first product of photosynthesis is a four-carbon compound. The carbon dioxide acceptor is the three-carbon **PEP**, or phosphoenolpyruvate, which forms 4C oxaloacetate. This in turn forms malate, which is stored in special bundle sheath cells. The process is named the C_4 or Hatch–Slack pathway and is an adaptation for conditions where carbon dioxide concentration may be limiting.

In the tropics, for example, the high light intensity will tend to speed up the rate of photosynthesis, but the lush vegetation is using up more carbon dioxide than is being released by respiration. The Calvin cycle does not itself require light, but can operate only if hydrogen atoms carried by reduced NADP from the light stage are present. The C_4 pathway, on the other hand, can operate all through the night, fixing carbon dioxide for later use. When more CO_2 is needed during the day, the malate is decarboxylated to recycle PEP and release carbon dioxide, which is taken up by RuBP into the Calvin cycle.

Examples of C_4 plants include the monocotyledons, maize, sugarcane and millet, and the dicotyledons, *Amaranthus* and some euphorbias. The polyploid hybrid *Spartina townsendii* is also a C_4 plant, although it grows outside the tropics. It flourishes on mud flats, however, where it may be submerged for part of the day, so CO_2 concentration may become limiting. All C_4 plants possess the so-called Kranz anatomy, consisting of the special bundle sheath cells where malate is stored.

14C LABELLING

14C is a radioactive isotope of carbon which is constantly being produced, as cosmic rays react with nitrogen in the upper atmosphere forming 14C. The half-life of 14C is 5,800 years (i.e. 1 g of 14C decays to 0.5 g 14C in that time).

Any organic molecule can be formed using 14C carbon dioxide, rather than 12C, so the pathway of that chemical can be traced through its metabolism. Such compounds are said to be 'labelled', and can be separated by chromatography and analysed by autoradiography. This technique has been a useful tool in the comparative analysis of the C_3, C_4 and CAM pathways.

◄ Radioactive tracers ►

CALCIFEROL

Calciferol is vitamin D.
◄ Vitamins ►

CALCIUM

Calcium is an essential mineral nutrient for both plants and animals. It affects the permeability of cell membranes and is necessary as an enzyme activator.

In plants calcium pectate forms the middle lamella between plant **cell walls** so if calcium is lacking, the apical meristems cannot function. Cell division cannot be completed, so growth will be stunted. In animals, calcium is an essential constituent of **bones** and teeth, and calcium deficiency may lead to osteomalacia, where the bones become softened. Calcium ions are also required for the processes of **muscle contraction** and **blood clotting**. Good sources of dietary calcium include dairy products such as milk and cheese, though calcium is notoriously difficult to absorb.

CALVIN CYCLE

◄ Photosynthesis ►

CAMBIUM

Cambium is the main lateral meristem involved in secondary growth in plants.
◄ Growth ►

CAPILLARIES

◀ Blood vessels ▶

CARBOHYDRATE

Carbohydrates are organic compounds consisting of carbon, hydrogen and oxygen, with an approximate general formula, $(CH_2O)_n$. Green plants synthesise carbohydrates by **photosynthesis**, but animals must ingest them in their diet. They are sources of immediate and stored energy in all organisms, and several carbohydrates have important structural roles in plants.

The simplest carbohydrates are **monosaccharides**, or simple sugars. Their general formula is $C_n . (H_2O)_n$, where n is 3 for a triose sugar, 5 for a pentose sugar and 6 for a hexose sugar. The most common monosaccharide is the hexose glucose.

Disaccharides are formed from a condensation reaction between two hexose sugars. Their formula is therefore $C_{12} . H_{22} . O_{11}$. The main translocated sugar in plants is the disaccharide sucrose, formed from a molecule of glucose and a molecule of fructose.

Polysaccharides consist of many hexose units linked by condensation reactions. Their general formula is therefore $C_n(H_2O)_{n-1}$. Starch and glycogen are the main energy storage compounds in plant cells and animal cells respectively, and cellulose is an essential compound in plant cell walls.

CARBON CYCLE

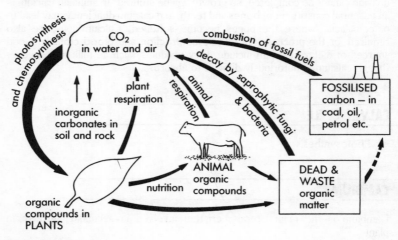

Fig. C.1 The carbon cycle

The carbon cycle (Fig. C.1) is the route taken by carbon from the atmosphere (as CO_2) after fixation in **photosynthesis** in green plants. The production of carbohydrates, proteins and fats contributes to plant growth and subsequently to animal growth through complex food webs. The dead remains of both plants and animals are then acted upon by saprophytes in the soil which ultimately release gaseous CO_2 back to the atmosphere. During life, CO_2 is also returned to the atmosphere through **respiration**, and indirectly through nitrogenous excretion.

◀ Food chains, food webs ▶

CARBON DIOXIDE (CO_2)

Carbon dioxide is the acidic oxide of carbon and is slightly soluble in water to form carbonic acid. It is the source of inorganic carbon for photosynthesis, and is released as a waste product of respiration.

CARBON DIOXIDE FIXATION

Carbon dioxide fixation is the conversion of gaseous carbon dioxide into organic compounds. This takes place in the dark stage of **photosynthesis**.

CARDIAC CYCLE

The cardiac cycle is the sequence of events taking place in a single heartbeat. A single cycle consists of atrial systole, when the atria contract, ventricular systole, when the ventricles contract, and diastole, when both pairs of chambers relax. The process takes about 0.8 seconds and is cyclical, maintained by the heart's own pacemaker acting on the cardiac muscle. The cardiac cycles can be counted by listening for the characteristic 'lub-dup' sounds caused by the sudden closing of first the mitral and tricuspid valves, and then the semilunar valves.

◀ Heart ▶

CARDIAC MUSCLE

Cardiac muscle fibres are found only in the **heart**. They show longitudinal and transverse striations, possess large mitochondria and are divided up into uninucleate cells.

Other types of muscle can contract only when stimulated to do so by nerve impulses of sufficient intensity. Cardiac muscle is myogenic, however, meaning that it needs no external stimulation before it contracts. Contractions are initiated by the sino-atrial node, or SAN, which is a region of specialised cardiac fibres in the wall of the right atrium.

CARDIAC OUTPUT

The cardiac output is the amount of blood flowing from the **heart** in a given period of time. It depends upon the volume of blood expelled at each beat and on the number of beats per unit time, and it can be expressed using the following formula.

Cardiac output = stroke volume × heart rate

(The stroke volume in man is measured indirectly by assessing the blood gases passing into the blood through the lungs). Hormones such as **adrenaline** can increase the cardiac output, as can stimulation by the sympathetic nervous system.

CARNIVORE

The term carnivore may apply generally to any animal that eats other animals (i.e. to any secondary consumer). It may also apply specifically to a member of the order of mammals Carnivora (e.g. cats, dogs and seals). Carnivores require adaptations to help them to catch their prey, so many are fast-moving and possess claws, stings, sharp teeth and other devices for this purpose.

◀ Dentition, Trophic levels ▶

CARRYING CAPACITY

The carrying capacity of a habitat for a particular population is the point at which the birth rate is equal to the death rate (i.e. when environmental resistance limits the increase in growth of the population). If the carrying capacity is exceeded, gross overcrowding and competition will eventually cause a decline.

◀ Population growth ▶

CARTILAGE

◀ Connective tissues ▶

CATABOLISM

Catabolism is the phase of metabolism that consists of breaking down complex compounds into simpler ones. Catabolic reactions are usually accompanied by a release of energy and are therefore exergonic (though some breakdown reactions when eliminating waste may be endergonic).

$$AB \rightarrow A + B \quad [-G]$$

◀ Metabolism ▶

CATALASE

Catalase is an enzyme that occurs in both plants and animals. It is a conjugated protein with an iron-containing prosthetic group. It greatly speeds up the breakdown of hydrogen peroxide, which is toxic, to water and oxygen, which are harmless.

CATALYSIS, CATALYST

Catalysts are compounds which change the rate of a chemical reaction. Positive catalysts accelerate reactions, while negative catalysts slow down the rate. A catalyst is a participant in the reaction and may undergo physical change during the reaction, but it reverts to its original state when the reaction has been completed.

Enzymes are protein catalysts for reactions which occur in biological systems. These will catalyse only a small number of reactions, unlike non-protein catalysts such as H^+, OH^- and transition metals. Enzymes are thus highly specific.

◄ Enzyme action ►

CELL

A cell is a unit of structure of living matter, a mass of protoplasm bounded by a membrane and usually containing a nucleus. The nucleus contains genetic material in the form of DNA, which controls cell development and activity. From a functional point of view, a cell can be considered as a self-regulating chemical system, the sum of its chemical reactions being termed metabolism.

The contents and shapes of cells vary according to their function and to the type of organism in which they occur.

◄ Cell differentiation, Eukaryotic cells, Prokaryotae, Prokaryotic cells ►

CELL CULTURES

◄ Tissue culture ►

CELL CYCLE

The cell cycle describes the cyclical sequence of events which occur in actively dividing cells.

During **interphase** there is first a period of growth, called 'G1', then there is a period of synthesis, 'S', when DNA is replicated in preparation for the next division. This is followed by a second growth phase, 'G2', then by mitotic nuclear and cytoplasmic division. The cycle is then repeated. The duration of the cycle will depend on the type of cell, its age and on the availability of nutrients for biosynthesis.

◀ Mitosis ▶

CELL DIFFERENTIATION

Cell differentiation is the process of specialisation of cells. In plants differentiation depends on the deposition of cellulose in the secondary cell wall. If it is evenly deposited, then a spherical cell develops, but if it is uneven, a long narrow cell may be formed.

In animals, cell differentiation into tissue types depends partly on the position of the cells in the early embryo and partly on the various influences of adjacent tissue cells.

CELL DIVISION

Cell division is an increase in cell number which occurs as a result of mitotic or meiotic division of the nucleus. Cell division in plants is promoted by cytokinins in the presence of auxins, while in animals cell division is mainly under genetic control.

◀ Meiosis, Mitosis ▶

CELL FRACTIONATION

Cell fractionation is the separation of the different components of the cell. It involves the maceration or breakdown of cells, followed by ultracentrifugation to separate out the organelles.

CELL MEMBRANES

All cells are bounded by a membrane called the plasma membrane, and in eukaryotic cells the cell organelles are also membrane-bound. Organelles such as the nucleus, mitochondria and chloroplasts have double membranes, or envelopes, while others have just one membrane (e.g. lysosomes). The endoplasmic reticulum of a cell forms a network of interconnecting membrane-bound channels throughout the cytoplasm. Cell membranes are partially permeable, and are made of phospholipids.

◀ Bacteria, Cellulose, Fluid mosaic model, Membrane permeability ▶

CELLULAR RESPIRATION

The term 'cellular respiration' refers to the reactions of glycolysis, Krebs cycle and electron transfer in cells.

◀ respiration ▶

CELLULOSE

Cellulose is a structural polysaccharide, in which the glucose residues are arranged in such a way as to give both H and OH groups on each side of the chain. Cross-linkages by means of hydrogen bonds can therefore be made at very frequent intervals between the chains, resulting in microfibrils with a high tensile strength. Cellulose (Fig. C.2) is the chief consituent of plant cell walls, and is an important ingredient in the diet of herbivores.

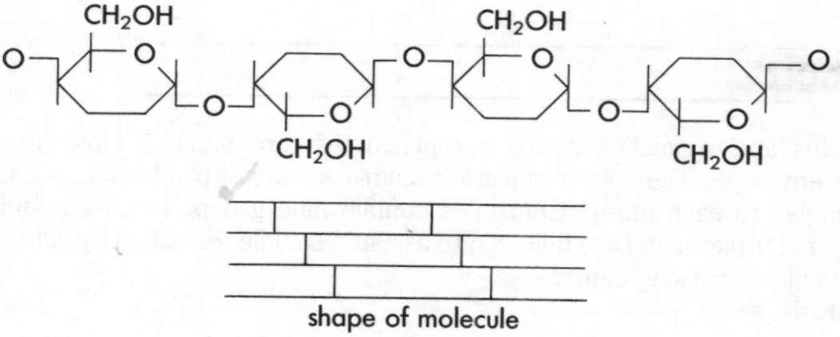

shape of molecule

Fig. C.2 Cellulose molecule structure

◀ Polysaccharides, Ruminants ▶

CELL WALL

Cell walls are found in prokaryotes and in plants. They delimit the cells and maintain their shape, though the possession of a cell wall also restricts the possible movements of a cell. In prokaryotes, the cell wall is composed mainly of murein, while in plant cells, the main material is cellulose.

In plants a primary cell wall is laid down on the middle lamella during cell division, and is later thickened to give the secondary cell wall. The primary cell wall consists of cellulose microfibrils running through a matrix of other polysaccharides, such as pectins or hemicelluloses. Water molecules are also present, a fact that is important in establishing the apoplastic pathway for water movement through plants. Once the cell has reached its maximum size, extra layers of cellulose may be laid down on the inside surfaces of the cell, outside the plasma membrane, resulting in the formation of the secondary cell wall. In some tissues, such as xylem, lignin may then be deposited in all the layers of cellulose. This is termed lignification.

The basic functions of the cell wall are to provide mechanical strength for individual cells and for the plant as a whole, and to allow turgidity and the maintenance of a hydrostatic skeleton in the plant.

CENTRAL NERVOUS SYSTEM (CNS)

The central nervous system of vertebrates consists of the brain and spinal cord.

CENTRIFUGATION

Centrifugation is the rapid spinning of materials which separates lighter from heavier fractions in a system. The method is used to separate and identify fractions in a fluid medium (e.g. blood).

CENTRIOLES

Centrioles are organelles in the cytoplasm that are situated close to the nuclear envelope. They occur in pairs in animal and lower plant cells, and lie at right angles to each other. Centrioles contain nine groups of microtubules, arranged in triplets, and are believed to assist in spindle formation by acting as microtubule-organising centres.
◀ Mitosis ▶

CEPAEA NEMORALIS

◀ Banding in Cepaea nemoralis ▶

CEREBELLUM

The cerebellum is located in the dorsal region of the hindbrain, and is concerned with the control of muscular co-ordination. If the cerebellum is damaged in any way, all movements become jerky and imprecise.
◀ Balance, Brain ▶

CEREBRAL HEMISPHERES, CEREBRUM

The cerebrum is the main part of the forebrain, and is partially divided into two hemispheres. Internally, there are two distinct layers – the outer cerebral cortex of densely packed nerve cell bodies and, beneath, the white matter consisting of nerve fibres.

Areas on the surface of the **brain** correspond to specific functions, which may be sensory (receiving information from receptors), or motor (initiating impulses to effectors), or associative (concerned with interpretation, memory, reasoning and so on).

CFCs

◀ Chlorofluorocarbons ▶

CHEESE MANUFACTURE

The manufacture of cheese is a biotechnological process, making use of *Lactobacillus* bacteria, and *Penicillium* fungi.

The bacteria are first introduced into sterilised milk, where they convert lactose milk sugar into lactic acid. The resulting drop in pH denatures milk protein, or casein, causing it to curdle. The solid curds are separated from the liquid whey, compacted into shape and left in a dry atmosphere to mature. Wires covered in fungal spores may be passed through cheese in order to produce blue cheese, such as Stilton.

◀ Biotechnology ▶

CHEMORECEPTORS

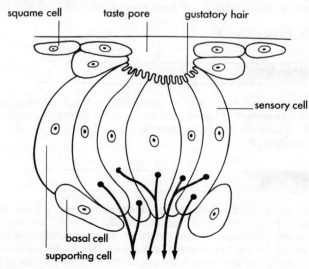

Fig. C.3 Taste bud

Chemoreceptors are sensory receptor cells that generate nerve impulses in response to different types of chemical. Examples include cells in the taste buds on the tongue that are sensitive to either sweet, saline, acidic or phenolic chemicals (Fig. C.3), and cells in the nasal mucosa that are concerned with smell.

CHEMOTHERAPY

Chemotherapy is the use of chemical drugs to treat disease, either by killing the pathogenic micro-organisms or by selectively inhibiting the growth of specific cells, such as carcinomas.

CHIASMA

A chiasma is formed where the chromatids of homologous chromosomes cross over each other during prophase I of **meiosis**. At these sites there is an exchange of genetic material between the chromatids, leading to new gene combinations.
◀ Gene mapping ▶

CHITIN

Chitin is an amino-polysaccharide that has a structural function in the shells of crustaceans, in the exoskeleton of most insects and in the cell wall of some fungi.
◀ Cuticle, Exoskeleton ▶

CHLORENCHYMA

Photosynthetic **parenchyma** may be called chlorenchyma. Chlorenchyma is found in the mesophyll of leaves, and in the outer cortex of green stems, where light is available for **photosynthesis**.
◀ Leaf structure ▶

CHLORIDE IONS

Chloride ions, Cl^-, are required by both plants and animals for the maintenance of water and solute potentials in cells. In plants they may also be involved in the light stage of photosynthesis. In animals, chloride ions are present within resting nerve axons and muscle fibres, giving them their negative charge, chloride ions in blood plasma assist in the carriage of carbon dioxide, via the chloride shift.

CHLOROFLUOROCARBONS (CFCs)

CFCs are chemicals developed as propellants in aerosols and as refrigerants. They are serious pollutants, because they contribute to the degradation of the ozone layer in the stratosphere. An increased amount of ultra-violet light will therefore pass through to the earth's surface.
◀ Stratosphere ▶

CHLOROPHYLL

Chlorophyll is a porphyrin molecule with a central magnesium ion. It consists mainly of chlorophyll a, which is a bluish-green pigment, and chlorophyll b, which is a yellowish-green pigment. Both these absorb red and blue light, and use it to drive the reactions of photosynthesis.
◀ Action spectrum, Chloroplast, Photoactivation of chlorophyll ▶

CHLOROPHYTA

Chlorophyta is a phylum of the kingdom Protoctista, and contains the green algae. Green algae may be unicellular (e.g. Chlamydomonas – Fig. C.4), filamentous (e.g. *Spirogyra*), or colonial, (e.g. Volvox). They are all aquatic, and their dominant photosynthetic pigments are chlorophyll a and b.

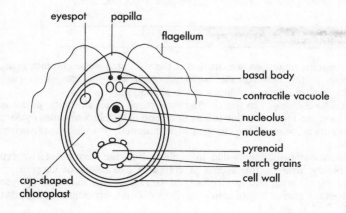

Fig. C.4 Chlamydomonas

CHLOROPLAST

◀ Plastids ▶

CHORDATES

Chordates are members of the phylum Chordata in the animal kingdom and are subdivided into six main classes: cartilaginous fish, bony fish, amphibians, reptiles, birds and mammals.

The main characteristics of the phylum are the presence of a notochord at some stage of the life history, visceral clefts, a dorsal hollow nerve cord, segmental muscle blocks and a post-anal tail. They also possess closed blood systems, in which blood flows forwards ventrally and backwards dorsally.

◄ Amphibia, Birds, Fish, Mammals, Reptilia ►

CHROMATIN

Chromatin is a complex arrangement of DNA and protein (histone). It is the form adopted by chromosomes in non-dividing cells.

CHROMATOGRAPHY

Chromatography is the process of separating the components of a mixed solution by slow passage through a tube or over adsorbing material. The technique depends on the differential movement of each component under the influence of a moving solvent, due to their different solubilities or ionisation states. Gas chromatography employs the same principle but with a carrier gas as the moving phase to carry a gaseous or vaporised sample.

CHROMOSOME MUTATION

Chromosome mutations are changes in the structure of the chromosomes, or changes in the chromosome number, which lead to changes in enzyme production, and thus to changes in the phenotype.

Structural changes to the chromosome result in an alteration in the gene positions, and may occur due to fragmentation of the chromosomes by X-rays. If it occurs in gametes, the change can be inherited, provided the offspring are viable.

Chromosome mutations due to numerical change may be of two types. **polyploidy** involves the adding of complete extra sets of chromosomes, producing offspring that are triploid, 3n, tetraploid, 4n, and so on. Polysomy involves the gain or loss of individual chromosomes, producing individuals that are $2n - 1$ or $2n + 1$.

◄ Down's syndrome ►

CHROMOSOME NUMBER

The chromosome number is the normal complement of chromosomes in the

nucleus of a cell of a particular species (e.g. forty-six – twenty-three pairs – in humans). It may also refer to the number within the complement of chromosomes arbitrarily given to a particular chromosome pair.
◀ Diploid, diploidy ▶

CHROMOSOMES

Chromosomes are single units of DNA plus protein found in cells. Each chromosome consists of a number of genes which control the synthesis of proteins and hence enzymes. In diploid organisms, the chromosomes exist in homologous pairs, the number of which is characteristic of the species.
◀ Diploid, Diploidy, DNA, Gene, ▶

CILIA

Cilia are locomotory organelles in ciliate protoctistans such as *Paramecium*, and are also widespread in higher organisms, forming ciliated epithelia in mammalian respiratory tubes, for instance.

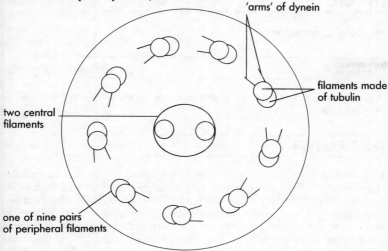

Fig. C.5a Structure of a cilium

They have the same internal structure as flagella (Fig. C.5a), with a characteristic '9 + 2' arrangement of microtubules. They are shorter than flagella, however, being only approximately 5–10 μm long, and they usually occur in groups or covering the cell. The activity of cilia is co-ordinated so that they beat in a wave, or metachronal rhythm (Fig. C.5b). This movement requires ATP, and involves a fast down-stroke with the cilium straight, followed by a slower recovery stroke with the cilium bent. The bending process is initiated at the base and transmitted to the tip.

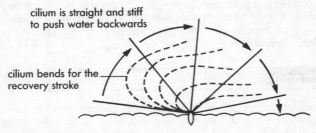

cilium is straight and stiff
to push water backwards

cilium bends for the
recovery stroke

Fig. C.5b Action of a cilium

CILIATES

Ciliates are members of the phylum Ciliophora, in the kingdom Protoctista, all of which move by means of cilia (e.g. *Paramecium*).

CISTERNAE

◀ Golgi complex ▶

CISTRON

A cistron is that portion of a chromosome that codes for one polypeptide.
◀ Gene ▶

CLASSIFICATION

Classification is the arrangement of living organisms into groups with similar characteristics. This arrangement may be based on superficial similarities such as colour and length, in which case it is an artificial classification. Alternatively, it may be based on how closely the organisms are related, in which case it is a natural classification. In a natural classification, organisms are grouped into a heirarchy of taxa, from kingdom, to phylum, to class, and so on, with each division of a group containing organisms of more similar characteristics.
◀ Taxonomy ▶

CLIMATIC FACTORS

The distribution of organisms depends on several factors. Those factors that are related to the climate of an environment are known as climatic factors. These include light intensity, temperature, salinity and so on.

CLIMAX COMMUNITY

The climax community is the final steady state community that exists at the end of a successional sequence for a given set of environmental conditions. Over much of Britain, the climax community would be oak woodland if the succession was allowed to proceed that far. In practice, grazing, trampling and land clearance prevent this happening.

CLOTTING

◀ Blood clotting ▶

CNIDARIA

Cnidaria is a phylum of animals with two cell layers (diploblastic) separated by a jelly-like mesogloea. They are radially symmetrical, with tentacles that bear nematoblast cells. The group includes hydroids, jellyfishes, sea anemones and corals.

◀ Hydra ▶

CNS

◀ Central nervous system ▶

COCHLEA

The cochlea is the coiled part of inner ear concerned with reception of sound. It divides longitudinally into three parallel canals:

- vestibular canal (connecting with oval window);
- middle canal;
- tympanic canal (connecting with the round window).

The three canals are separated by two membranes, Reissner's membrane, between the first and second canals, and the basilar membrane between the second and third.

◀ Ear ▶

CODOMINANCE

Codominant alleles at a given gene locus will both be expressed in the phenotype of a heterozygote (e.g. red/white alleles for coat colour in cattle).

Let R represent the allele for red hairs and W represent the allele for white hairs. The following genotypes and phenotypes may be produced:

- RR = red hairs,
- RW = roan (red and white hairs),
- WW = white hairs.

CODON

A codon comprises three adjacent bases in a molecule of DNA or messenger RNA that code for a particular amino acid or 'stop'.
◀ Genetic code ▶

COELENTERATES

◀ Cnidaria ▶

COELOMATE ORGANISATION

Coelomate organisation occurs in **tripoblastic** animals, where the mesoderm divides to produce a fluid-filled cavity called a coelom, lined with epithelium. The importance of coelomate organisation is that it separates gut muscle from locomotory muscle, and therefore allows the development of specialised organs for both locomotion and digestion. In addition, the coelomic fluid may act as a hydrostatic skeleton and/or a circulatory system, and it provides space for the enlargement of internal organs.
◀ Earthworm ▶

CO-ENZYME

Co-enzymes are small non-protein organic molecules that are required for the active sites of enzymes to function (e.g. nicotinamide adenine dinucleotide, NAD^+, which is a co-enzyme for dehydrogenase enzymes in cellular respiration).

COFACTOR

Cofactors are any non-protein substances that are needed for the functioning of an **enzyme**. These are often inorganic ions, such as Fe^{2+}, needed for the functioning of catalase, and Cl^- needed for the functioning of amylase. They may be prosthetic groups or coenzymes.

COHESION

◀ Adhesion/cohesion theory ▶

COLLENCHYMA

Collenchyma is a type of plant tissue consisting of living cells, in which the cell wall has extra cellulose deposited at the corners. The main function of the tissue is mechanical support, particularly in the outer regions of the cortex of unthickened stems, and in the midrib of leaves.

COLLOID

A colloid is a substance whose particles (macromolecules or aggregates of smaller molecules) range from 1 mμ to 100 mμ in size. These particles do not separate out under the influence of gravity, but intersperse with the liquid medium they are in. When the solid particles are suspended in liquid, the colloidal solution is called a 'sol', but when the liquid particles are interspersed between the solid ones, a gel is formed. Colloids can transform from sols to gels according to environmental factors such as temperature, pH and pressure. Cytoplasm is colloidal, and many of its properties, such as cytoplasmic streaming, depend on sol to gel transformations.

COLONISATION

Colonisation means the dispersal of an organism from its place of origin to a novel environment or position, where it can either exploit an empty niche or compete successfully with the existing occupant. If the colonising organism survives and reproduces, it will then occupy territory in this new area.

COMMUNITIES

All the organisms making up the biotic component of a habitat form the community of that habitat. A community contains several populations which all interact together, resulting in a dynamic unit, with trophic levels, a flow of energy and recycling of nutrients.

COMPANION CELLS

◄ Sieve tubes ►

COMPENSATION POINT

The compensation point occurs when the carbon dioxide being used up in photosynthesis just balances the carbon dioxide released from respiration. This means that there is no net gas exchange with the environment.

COMPETITION

◀ Interspecific competition, Intraspecific competition ▶

COMPETITIVE INHIBITION

Competitive inhibition takes place at the active site of an enzyme. It occurs where the inhibitor closely resembles the structure and shape of the substrate, so the two molecules compete for the active site. The extent of the inhibition will depend on the relative concentrations of the substrate, the inhibitor and the enzyme. Competitive inhibition is reversible.

◀ Non-competitive inhibition ▶

CONDENSATION REACTIONS

Condensation reactions occur in anabolic processes, and involve the joining together of two components by the elimination of a molecule of water. They are very common in biological systems, and occur in the synthesis of compounds such as peptides and polypeptides, disaccharides and polysaccharides, triglycerides, nucleotides and nucleic acids. The opposite reaction to condensation is hydrolysis.

◀ Hydrolase, hydrolysis ▶

CONDITIONING

◀ Learned behaviour ▶

CONIFER

Coniferophyta is a phylum of plants which bear cones without flowers or fruits (e.g. *Pinus*, Scots pine).

CONJUGATION

◀ Gene transfer in bacteria ▶

CONNECTIVE TISSUE

Connective tissue is the major supporting and binding tissue in animals, and its functions also include insulation, blood production and protection against bacterial invasion. It develops from the mesenchyme of embryonic mesoderm, and essentially consists of widely spaced cells separated by an organic matrix. The cells have low metabolic rates, and secrete non-living products into the matrix that become components of the tissue, such as protein fibres and salts. There are several types of connective tissue, and the main ones are as follows:

- Areolar, or loose connective tissue, which is the least specialised type. It contains loosely woven fibres, randomly arranged, and is found in the mesenteries and around all the organs of the body.
- White fibrous connective tissue, which contains abundant white collagen fibres arranged in parallel bundles. Collagen is flexible but will not stretch, so the tissue is ideally suited for resisting pulling strains and it particularly occurs in tendons.
- Yellow fibrous connective tissue, which contains abundant yellow elastin fibres in an irregular network, with a few collagen fibres for added strength. The tissue has elasticity (i.e. will stretch without breaking when pulled and then return to its original position when the force is removed) and occurs in ligaments, in artery walls and in the lungs and air passages.
- Adipose tissue, which contains large numbers of fat cells and is found in the dermis ('subcutaneous fat layer') and around organs. Its functions include thermal insulation, energy storage and absorbing mechanical shocks.
- **Cartilage**, which has a firmer matrix than the connective tissues so far described, the matrix consisting of a substance called chondrin. Cartilage is flexible and has a measure of elasticity but is also extremely hard-wearing. It occurs at the ends of bones in synovial joints and in many other locations, such as the pinna of the ear.

Bone also has a firm matrix, consisting of about one third collagen fibres and two thirds inorganic salts such as calcium hydroxyapatite. There are two main types of bone, spongy and compact, spongy containing spaces for marrow tissue.

◄ Tendon, Ventilation ►

CONSERVATION

The term conservation means 'to keep entire' or retain, and it may be applied in different ways. It is generally taken to refer to the conservation of nature, but **water conservation**, heat conservation in thermoregulation, energy conservation and conservation of non-renewable resources such as coal, oil and minerals are all valid uses of the term.

Nature conservation is an active and dynamic process. It is concerned with maintaining ecosystem stability and species diversity, and with retaining a wide range of habitats. In many cases it involves positive interference by man, to interrupt successions or to cull predators, for example. Special conservation areas with restricted access may be established in which all communities and environmental factors are closely managed.

Conservation has become necessary largely because of the effects that human activities have had on the environment in the past. The increasing human population has imposed increased pressures on the land; more houses for more people, more wide roads for more cars, more factories for jobs and commodities, and so on, such that most remaining fertile land has been taken over by agriculture. People and their cars, factories and farms are also the source of pollutants, many of which cause great harm to natural habitats. There are numerous examples of pollution on a local scale, such as car exhaust emissions or eutrophication due to detergents or nitrate pollution, and there are also problems on a global scale, such as the greenhouse effect, damage to the ozone layer, acid rain and ionising radiation due to nuclear fallout.

Conservationists have been pointing out their concerns for many years, but it is only relatively recently that the issues have become more widely accepted by the public and the media, and that 'green' politics have begun to have an influence. Attitudes are beginning to change, particularly among the younger generation. For example, more people are now prepared to pay a bit extra to buy recycled paper goods and aerosols that do not contain CFCs.

◄ 'Green revolution', Pollution, RSPB ▶

CONSUMERS

Consumers are heterotrophic organisms in a food web. Herbivores are primary consumers and carnivores may be secondary, tertiary or even quaternary consumers, depending on what animal they are feeding on.

◄ Trophic levels ▶

CONTINUOUS VARIATION

Continuous variation occurs where characteristics are controlled by many alleles at different loci. There is an 'additive' effect of expression resulting in a graded effect in the phenotype (e.g. height, hair colour in humans).

◄ Discontinuous variation, Polygenes, Polygenic inheritance ▶

COPULATION

Copulation is the act of inserting a male sperm depositor into a female receptacle in order to deliver sperm for the fertilisation of ova. The process is best developed in the terrestrial insects and in mammals. It increases the efficiency of internal fertilisation since it minimises the wastage of gametes and removes the risk of damage due to dehydration.

◄ Fertilisation, Sexual reproduction, Sperm ▶

CORK, CORK CAMBIUM

Cork cambium is a lateral meristem, together with vascular cambium. The activity of vascular cambium in secondary thickening results in an increase in girth due to the production of secondary xylem and phloem. As these new tissues are formed, the epidermis is stretched and eventually ruptures, being replaced by the periderm or cork layer developing below it. The meristematic cells of the cork cambium or phellogen divide radially and tangentially to give secondary cortex to the inside and phellem or cork to the outside. The walls of older cork cells become suberised and the cell contents die, resulting in a protective layer for the woody stem that is impervious to both gases and liquids. In some trees, bark is formed as a result of new cork cambia forming internally to the previous layers and effectively cutting them off from nutrients so that they die.

◀ Secondary thickening, Vascular cambium ▶

CORTEX

A cortex is an outer layer of tissue in an organ.

In the primary growth of plant stems and roots, cortex is a parenchymatous layer that occurs just under the epidermis. In secondary growth, secondary cortex is formed just beneath the cork layer or bark. In animals, the outer layer of the cerebrum of the brain is termed the cortex, as is the outer region of the kidneys, and the outer region of the adrenal glands.

◀ Root systems, stem structure ▶

COUNTER-CURRENT MECHANISMS

A counter-current mechanism is a system that makes maximum use of diffusion in the exchange of substances between one medium and another. Diffusion of molecules occurs down a concentration gradient until the concentrations are in equilibrium, and a counter-current system aims to maintain that gradient so that the equilibrium point is delayed. The flow of the two media is in opposite directions (Fig. C.6).

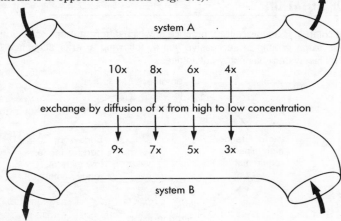

Fig. C.6 Counter-current flow

There are many examples of counter-current exchange systems in biology. These include: water/blood flow in the gills of bony fish, where respiratory gases are exchanged; glomerular filtrate in renal tubule/blood in peritubular capillaries in the kidney, where glucose and other nutrients are reabsorbed; and blood circulation in arteries/blood circulation in veins in the flipper of a seal, where heat is exchanged.

◄ Gills of fish, Kidney ►

COURTSHIP BEHAVIOUR

Courtship behaviour is a type of instinctive behaviour that is an essential prelude to successful mating in many animals.

◄ Reproductive behaviour ►

CRAMP

Cramp is muscular pain caused by reduced sodium ion concentration in the tissues. It also results from an accumulation of lactate in the muscle due to anaerobic respiration. If the affected muscle is rubbed to improve blood circulation, then lactate is transported out of the muscle to the liver and the pain subsides.

◄ Lactic acid, Oxygen debt ►

CRISTAE

◄ Mitochondrion ►

CROP ROTATION

Crop rotation is an agricultural practice in which different crops are cultivated on the same ground in successive years, following a strict sequence (Fig. C.7). This system has many advantages.

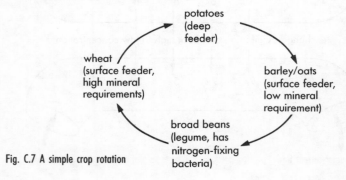

Fig. C.7 A simple crop rotation

- Different plants have different mineral requirements, so there will not be the same demand for essential nutrients each year. Fertilisers will not have to be added annually.
- The root systems of plants vary considerably. Some plants will extract minerals from the surface soil layers and others from deeper down.
- Varying the crops reduces the accumulation of weeds, pests and diseases that thrive on only one crop of the sequence.
- Including a legume crop in the sequence means that when the roots are ploughed in after harvesting, the nitrogen content of the soil will be increased (nitrogen fixation in the root nodules forms ammonia from gaseous nitrogen).
- In a well-planned rotation, the new crop is planted as soon as the old has been harvested, so the soil is left bare for the minimum amount of time. This reduces the risk of leaching.

◀ Rhizobium ▶

CROSSING OVER

Crossing over occurs in meiosis when chiasmata form between chromatids. The DNA breaks and rejoins, resulting in exchange of genetic material between the maternal and paternal homologues. This causes new combinations of characteristics in the phenotype and is an important contributor to variation.

◀ Chiasma ▶

CROSS-OVER VALUES/FREQUENCIES

◀ Gene mapping ▶

CROSS-POLLINATION

◀ Pollination ▶

CRUSTACEA

Crustacea is a superclass of arthropods and contains several classes. They are mainly aquatic animals (e.g. crab, crayfish), with only a few terrestrial representatives (e.g. woodlouse). The head is not clearly defined but there are two pairs of antennae and in most crustaceans a pair of compound eyes on stalks.

CULTIVATION

Crop production in fields depends to a great extent on climate, soil quality, water availability and altitude. Increased production can be achieved if artificial environments such as glasshouses are used, but there are also cultivation methods available that can improve productivity or economic yield.

- Crop rotation requires the least chemical intervention. Pests and diseases are kept to a minimum and fertiliser is required only every few years, if at all. The soil structure is maintained.
- Intensive monoculture requires the use of fertilisers and pest control chemicals. Since the fertilisers used are usually inorganic, they may leach into water systems and cause eutrophication. The soil structure may be damaged and subject to erosion. This system does, however, produce high yields and harvesting is economical since large machines can be used.
- Mixed farming involves alternating crop cultivation and livestock pasture on the same land. The animal manure enriches the soil and gives it an excellent crumb structure, though fields must be fairly small so crop harvesting may be more expensive.

◄ Crop rotation, Insecticides, Nitrate pollution, Productivity ►

CUTICLE

A cuticle is a non-living waterproof outer covering that is secreted by the exposed epidermal cells of plants and by the ectodermal epithelium of arthropods.

In plants the cuticle is made of a waxy substance called cutin and its function is to prevent the delicate leaf tissues from desiccation. In

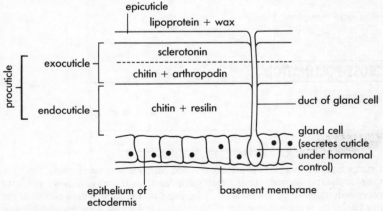

Fig. C.8 Structure of the arthropod cuticle

dicotyledonous leaves it is therefore thicker on the upper epidermis, which receives direct light, than it is on the lower.

In arthropods the term cuticle may be applied to the whole **exoskeleton** since it is all secreted by the ectodermal epithelium, but it particularly refers to the outermost layer or epicuticle. This is composed of lipoprotein and wax, and is the main waterproofing layer for the anthropod. The rest of the exoskeleton, or procuticle, can be distinguished chemically into two layers, an endocuticle and an exocuticle (Fig. C.8).

The endocuticle is made of the aminopolysaccharide chitin, together with resilin, an elastic protein which makes it flexible. In the exocuticle, chitin combines with arthropodin, which becomes hardened and cross-linked by phenols to form sclerotonin. The result is a rigid and extremely tough skeletal material.

The exoskeleton of an arthropod imposes limits to its growth and must be shed periodically in **ecdysis**. This, and the secretion of a new cuticle/exoskeleton, is under hormonal control.

◄ Waterproofing ►

CUTTINGS

One method of vegetative propagation is by cuttings, which may be of the stem or leaf. Plants such as tradescantias, fuschias and roses are propagated by stem cuttings, while leaf cuttings are commonly used for African violets and begonias.

Stem cuttings can be made of woody or non-woody stems, and can consist of the apical region or a section of the stem lower down without too many leaves. The stem is cut just below a node and the leaves near the base (and any others in excess) are removed. The base of the cutting is then dipped in fungicide and placed in soil, sharp sand or vermiculite. The potted cutting is enclosed in a humid atmosphere until adventitious roots have grown from the base and the cutting has 'taken'. For some cuttings, particularly of non-woody stems, 'rooting hormone' powder may be applied to the cut end – this is synthetic **auxin** which stimulates the growth of adventitious roots.

Leaf cuttings are usually taken of plants with fleshy leaves growing in a rosette habit. The leaf stalk is cut off at the leaf base, dipped; in fungicide, then placed in soil or some other culture medium. As for stem cuttings, auxin powder may speed up root growth.

◄ Vegetative reproduction ►

CYANOBACTERIA (BLUE-GREEN BACTERIA)

Cyanobacteria were formerly referred to as blue-green algae, but are now classified with other bacteria in the kingdom Prokaryotae. They may be unicellular or filamentous and are all photosynthetic. They contain chlorophyll and also phycocyanin, which is a blue pigment, and sometimes also phycoerythrin, a red pigment. The pigments are located on membranes at the periphery of the cell.

Cyanobacteria are of economic importance because of their ability to fix nitrogen (e.g. *Anabaena, Nostoc*).

◄ Nitrogen fixation ►

CYCLIC-AMP

Cyclic adenosine monophosphate (cyclic-AMP) is a mononucleotide in which the single phosphate group is attached to both the carbon 3' and the carbon 5' of the ribose sugar, thus forming a ring. ATP in the cytoplasm can be converted to cyclic-AMP by the action of an enzyme in the cell membrane, adenyl cyclase. Increased levels of cyclic-AMP in the cell will then either inhibit or stimulate metabolic reactions by inhibiting or activating enzymes. It is believed to act as a 'second messenger' in hormonal control. When a hormone binds to its receptor site on the membrane of a target cell, it activates adenyl cyclase, which in turn catalyses ATP to cyclic-AMP. Cyclic-AMP is known to stimulate the thyroid cells to release thyroxin, for example, so this is probably the way the thyroid-stimulating hormone (TSH) from the anterior pituitary exerts its effect.

◄ Pituitary gland ►

CYCLIC PHOTOPHOSPHORYLATION

◄ Photophosphorylation ►

CYSTIC FIBROSIS

Cystic fibrosis is a hereditary disease caused by a recessive gene mutation. It cannot yet be detected while the fetus is in the uterus and it affects one out of every 1,600 live births in Britain. One in twenty people is believed to be a carrier of the abnormal allele.

The mutation affects the production of mucus by goblet cells, resulting in mucus that is too viscous and hence blocks the ducts or tubes into which it passes. Blockage particularly occurs in the salivary duct and pancreatic duct so that food is difficult to swallow and the duodenum and ileum enzymes are not secreted. Sufferers must therefore take in enzymes with their food.

Another serious consequence of the mutation is that the mucus produced in the respiratory passages cannot be moved by cilia and is therefore likely to become infected. Physiotherapy is required to help clear the lungs.

◄ Gene mutation ►

CYTOCHROMES

Cytochromes are protein pigments which contain an iron prosthetic group within a porphyrin ring structure (similar to haemoglobin and chlorophyll). They form part of the electron transfer chain of cellular respiration in mitochondria and also the electron carrier system of photophosphorylation in chloroplasts.

Cytochromes are co-enzymes, and can easily be reduced and oxidised. The last carrier in the respiratory chain is cytochrome oxidase, which is an enzyme and therefore remains unchanged by the reaction.

◀ Oxidative phosphorylation, Photophosphorylation ▶

CYTOKININS

Cytokinins are plant growth substances that will stimulate mitosis if auxin is present. They promote cell division in the apical meristem and cambium of stems, though in roots they are inactive or inhibitory. They also promote the growth of lateral buds and leaves in stems, and in this respect they are antagonistic to auxin, which maintains apical dominance. They delay senescence, or the normal ageing process in leaves, keeping them green and fresh even when detached from the plant. Synthetic cytokinins such as kinetin can therefore be used commercially to prolong the shelf life of leafy vegetables such as cabbage and lettuce.

CYTOPLASM

Cytoplasm is a general term for the cell contents outside the nucleus and within the cell membrane, it consists of organelles and other inclusions suspended in an aqueous solution known as the cytosol. Dissolved in the cytosol are numerous small molecules, such as nucleotides, amino acids, sugars, vitamins and salts, and there are many enzymes in colloidal suspension. Although the majority of intracellular reactions occur within organelles, the cytoplasm is also metabolically active and is the site of such processes as glycolysis and fatty acid synthesis.

The cytosol has recently been shown to contain a complex network of protein microtubules called the cytoskeleton that maintains the shape of the cell. Microfilaments made of actin are also present and may have a role in the cytoplasmic streaming that occurs in the cytoplasm of all living cells.

◀ Organelle ▶

DAIRYING

Dairying is a type of farming involving milk production from cows whose milk has a high fat content. Milk production is the largest enterprise in UK agriculture.

There is a strong relationship between the distribution of dairy farms and environmental factors, and the most important regions are in the west, where the combination of heavy rainfall and mild winters favours the development of lush pastures.

Although dairy farms are numerous outside this region, their development can often be attributed to other environmental conditions, such as the soil. For example, in Kent and Sussex the most important dairying districts are on heavy clay soils, which retain their moisture and are difficult to cultivate.

DARK REACTION

The dark reaction is the second stage of **photosynthesis** when carbohydrate units are synthesised from carbon dioxide, which is reduced by the hydrogen obtained from water in the first stage. This stage of photosynthesis can take place in the dark as long as sufficient hydrogen has been provided by the light stage.

DARWIN

Charles Darwin was a keen naturalist who developed theories on **evolution** occurring by the **natural selection** of chance variations. He suggested that animals and plants had arisen by a process of gradual slow change over successive generations. Through his studies he obtained powerful evidence to support the existence of an evolutionary process, and put forward a hypothesis to explain the mechanism of this process.

His theory depends on the existence of chance variations within a species. These may be:

- continuous **variation**, due to the reshuffling of genes;
- discontinuous variation, due to mutations of genes or chromosomes.

◀ 'Fitness', Speciation ▶

DAY LENGTH

Day length is the period of light in a twenty-four-hour time span which results in photoperiodic responses in an organism.

◄ Photoperiodism ►

DEAMINATION

Excess or unwanted amino acids are too toxic to be stored in animals. Those molecules not used to build up proteins for growth and replacement are therefore converted into carbohydrate molecules by the removal of an amino group (NH_2) from each amino acid molecule. This removal is termed deanimation and it occurs in the liver.

The removal of NH_2 from an amino acid molecule results in the formation of ammonia (NH_3) as well as a carbon compound which can be used as a source of energy. The ammonia passes into the **ornithine cycle** to be converted into urea.

◄ Liver functions in homeostasis ►

DECAPOD

The decapods are a sub-group of the arthropodan super-class **Crustacea**. Members of this sub-group have ten appendages (jointed legs). The crab (Fig. D.1) is an example.

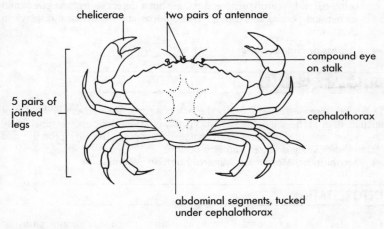

Fig. D.1 Structure of a crab

DECARBOXYLATION

Decarboxylation is the removal of the carboxyl group (COOH) from a molecule. It occurs at important stages in the release of energy, involving the production of CO_2, and it is catalysed by decarboxylase enzymes.
◀ Oxidative decarboxylation ▶

DECOMPOSERS

Saprophytic bacteria and fungi are referred to as decomposers, because the dissolving of solid organic matter by these organisms is the first step in the decay of dead plants and animals. The elements present in organic matter must be recycled, so decomposers are required at the end of **food chains** for the recycling of those elements incorporated in the bodies of plants and animals. Decomposition by saprophytes is also referred to as biodegradation. Non-biodegradable waste (e.g. plastics) cannot be decomposed and will therefore cause pollution of the environment.

DEFENCE

Defence has two important meanings in biology:

- First, it concerns mechanisms involved in the prevention of foreign bodies (antigens) entering and staying in an organism. The majority of such mechanisms are associated with the invasion of micro-organisms which bring about disease and infection (pathogens).
- Second, it concerns defences shown by plants to prevent them being eaten by herbivores, and defences shown by herbivores to prevent them being eaten by carnivores, and so on. Such defences include poisons in leaves and petals, and claws, stings, horns and behavioural displays in animals.

◀ Aggression, Immunity ▶

DEFICIENCY DISEASES

Deficiency diseases are caused by the lack of a particular nutrient in the diet of an animal, or in the soil in the case of a plant. Nutrient deficiency is most likely to occur in the mineral and vitamin supply, though protein and 'calorie'-deficiency diseases can also occur.
◀ Kwashiorkor, Marasmus, Mineral nutrition, Vitamins ▶

DEFORESTATION

Deforestation is the removal of trees, whether to make way for agriculture or to obtain the timber or timber products. If carried out in the right areas, to the correct extent, a balanced community can be maintained, and this is the aim of forestry programmes. On sloping ground, however, where soil is often thin, the removal of trees results in unprotected top soil being eroded by wind and rain. This makes land infertile and may cause floods due to the silting up of rivers and lakes.

DEGENERATE CODE

A triplet of bases on DNA, and by transcription, on messenger-RNA, codes for a single amino acid. When more than one triplet of bases codes for a single amino acid the code is called degenerate.
◄ Genetic code ►

DEHYDROGENASE ENZYMES

Dehydrogenase enzymes catalyse the removal of hydrogen atoms from a substrate molecule, usually passing them on to a co-enzyme such as NAD^+. This removal of H atoms is an important source of energy, so dehydrogenase enzymes are essential in cellular respiration.
◄ Oxidative phosphorylation ►

DENATURATION

All enzymes are globular proteins, and their functioning depends on the precise three-dimensional shape of their molecules. Any factor that alters the secondary and tertiary linkages in the protein can cause denaturation. Such factors include extremes of pH and also high temperature.

Above 40°C, the hydrogen and other bonds that maintain the tertiary structure start to break and the shape of the protein molecule is altered, although the peptide bonds remain intact. Enzymes are therefore irreversibly inactivated, or denatured, by excessive heat.

Other globular proteins such as haemoglobin and immunoglobulin also depend on their shape for functioning, so are also denatured by excessive heat.
◄ Enzyme action, Enzyme inhibition ►

DENTITION

The dentition of a mammal refers to its complete set of teeth – that is, the incisors, canines, premolars and molars, their structure and their arrangement. Dentition is closely related to the diet and feeding habits of the mammal, and varies considerably between herbivores and carnivores.

Herbivores need to pull up grass and then grind it to extract the cell contents from within the tough cellulose cell walls. They have no canine teeth,

DENTITION

and in sheep the upper incisors are also missing (Fig. D.2). Instead, the lower incisors bite off the grass against a horny pad on the upper jaw and the grass blades are drawn in to the cheek teeth through the diastema, the gap left by the absent canines. The grass blades are then ground by the side to side chewing action of the premolars and molars. These teeth are worn down to give ridges of harder enamel and troughs of dentine, with the teeth of the upper and lower jaw fitting closely together.

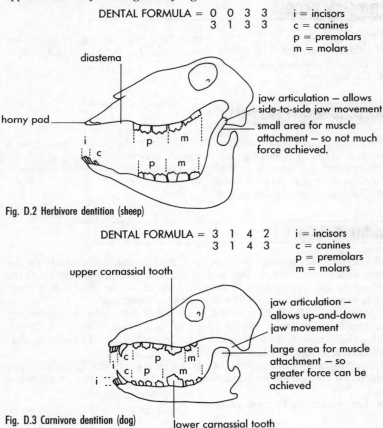

DENTAL FORMULA = 0 0 3 3   i = incisors
                  3 1 3 3   c = canines
                                 p = premolars
                                 m = molars

diastema

jaw articulation — allows side-to-side jaw movement

horny pad

small area for muscle attachment — so not much force achieved.

i   p   m
c
p   m

Fig. D.2 Herbivore dentition (sheep)

DENTAL FORMULA = 3 1 4 2   i = incisors
                  3 1 4 3   c = canines
                                 p = premolars
                                 m = molars

upper cornassial tooth

jaw articulation — allows up-and-down jaw movement

large area for muscle attachment — so greater force can be achieved

c   p   m
i
c   p   m
i

Fig. D.3 Carnivore dentition (dog)

lower carnassial tooth

Carnivores, such as dogs and cats, eat meat, often of prey animals that must first be caught. They therefore require sharp pointed canines to seize and kill the prey, and chisel-shaped incisors to help grip the animal and nibble off meat close to the bones (Fig. D.3). The cheek teeth are cusped for cracking and crushing bones, and the third upper premolar and first lower molar on each side, the carnassial teeth, are modified to slice flesh from the carcase like a pair of scissors.

◄ Carnivore ►

DEOXYRIBONUCLEIC ACID (DNA)

DNA is a polynucleotide that occurs in the nucleus of all eukaryotic cells and in the cytoplasm of prokaryotic cells. It is even present in many viruses. A segment of DNA is termed a gene and DNA molecules together with histones form chromosomes. The chromosomes of an organism control its whole development and functioning, since all **protein synthesis** is directed by DNA.

The DNA molecule consists of two chains of nucleotides with each nucleotide consisting of deoxyribose, a phosphate group and one of four organic bases: adenine (A), guanine(G), cytosine (C) or thymine (T). The **nucleotides** join up by condensation, catalysed by DNA polymerase enzyme.

The two chains of nucleotides then coil to form a double helix of alternating phosphate and sugar groups, with the sugar groups of the two chains being linked by their bases, which pair up in a specific way: A with T and C with G (Fig. D.4). The sequence of bases on DNA is termed the **genetic code** and it is this that controls heredity and protein synthesis, a triplet of three bases being responsible for each amino acid in the protein.

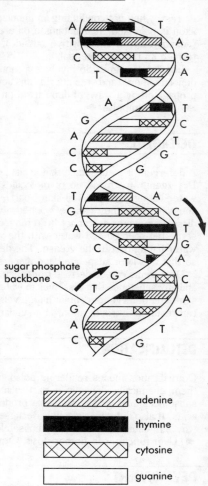

Fig. D.4 Structure of DNA

DEOXYRIBOSE

Deoxyribose is ribose sugar with one less atom of oxygen. There is an H atom attached to the second carbon atom instead of an OH.

◄ Deoxyribonucleic acid (DNA) ►

DEPOLARISATION

At rest, when not conducting an impulse, the membrane surrounding a nerve axon is polarised. It maintains a different electrical charge on its two sides (negative inside and positive outside), with the difference in charge being termed its resting potential.

Impulse transmission involves a momentary reversal of polarity, which is depolarisation, and results in an action potential. An impulse is then propagated by a wave of depolarisation passing along the axon.

◀ Nerve impulse ▶

DETERGENTS

A detergent is a substance that assists cleaning by removing dirt and grease. Detergents are made up of molecules that have a water-liking part and a water-hating part (i.e. oil-liking part), and they work by mixing with oily substances so they can be washed away in water. Oil and grease do not dissolve in water so cannot be removed by water alone. Detergent particles settle between oil and water with the water-liking part in the water and the water-hating part in the grease. The detergent thus emulsifies the oil/grease so that it is kept suspended and dispersed in the water.

Detergents can be derived from soap, or they can be soapless or synthetic, and any substance that dissolves in water and oil can act as a detergent. Many synthetic detergents contain high levels of phosphate, so detergent pollution can result in eutrophication, in a similar way to nitrate pollution.

DETOXIFICATION

Detoxification means rendering poisonous substances harmless by changing them chemically. This is a particular role of the liver, which detoxifies substances such as the ammonia produced during the deamination of amino acids. It also detoxifies alcohol. Because men's livers are bigger, this explains why, in general, they can metabolise alcohol faster than women can.

◀ Liver functions in homeostasis, Ornithine cycle ▶

DEVELOPMENT

Development encompasses growth and the changes that occur throughout the life of an organism from the time it is a fertilised gamete. As well as size increase, it includes increase in complexity and the production of specialised cells, and also the positioning of cells.

Embryo development is triggered by fertilisation and starts with division of the fertilised cell into daughter cells. This is followed by the arrangement of cells into distinct layers, and cell specialisation, resulting in organs and systems being formed. At a later stage, development may also mean learning and the acquisition of behaviour patterns; learning to walk, for example, requires the development of muscle co-ordination and balance.

◄ Learned behaviour, Ovule development, Pregnancy ►

DICOTYLEDON

A dicotyledonous plant is one that grows from a seed which contains two cotyledons or seed leaves. Dicotyledons are recognisable externally by the net-like pattern of veins on their leaves (reticulate venation) and by their floral parts, which are in fours or fives. They possess one main tap root with smaller lateral roots, and internally their vascular bundles are arranged in a ring.

◄ Lamina of leaf, Vascular bundles ►

DIET

The diet of an animal is the food it ingests. It should include all the necessary nutrients in the required relative amounts to ensure good health and proper growth. Such a diet is called 'balanced'. In man, a balanced diet should contain proteins, carbohydrates, lipids, vitamins, minerals, water and dietary fibre or roughage. The relative amounts will depend partly on the age, sex and occupation of the individual concerned.

◄ Carbohydrate, Fibre in human diet, Mineral nutrition ►

DIFFERENTIATION

Differentiation is a stage of development and a special feature of growth. Cell and tissue differentiation has been a major process in evolution, from the undifferentiated unicells to the complex multicellular chordates. It is the formation of different specialised cells from unspecialised ones, and involves modifications for particular functions. The differentiated cells then form the tissues, organs and systems of the body.

DIFFUSION

Diffusion is the net movement of molecules (or ions) from a region of comparatively high concentration to a region of lower concentration, down the concentration gradient. This movement continues until the molecules (or ions) are uniformly distributed in a state of equilibrium, and it is a passive process because no energy expenditure is involved. The rate of diffusion increases if the concentration gradient is steep and if the diffusion distance is small.

Diffusion is one of the processes involved in the exchange of materials into and out of cells. In particular, it accounts for the movement of oxygen into cells for respiration, the movement of carbon dioxide out of cells as a waste product and the distribution of food materials.

◄ Active transport, Facilitated diffusion, Osmosis ►

DIGESTION

Digestion is the breaking down of molecules in food material into an absorbable form. It takes place by physical means, including teeth, gut muscles, and by chemical means, involving hydrolytic digestive enzymes and solutions like bile.

Digestion that occurs outside cells such as by the alimentary canal, is extracellular, while digestion inside cells, such as by lysosomes, is intracellular.

◄ Amylase, Bile, Gastric juice, Ileum, Lipase, Lysosomes, Pancreas, Pepsin ►

DIHYBRID INHERITANCE

Dihybrid inheritance of two pairs of contrasting characteristics is determined by unlinked genes (e.g. size of plant and flower colour in pea plants). When heterozygous individuals are crossed, the offspring produced have genes for the two contrasting characteristics, and their phenotypes are in the ratio of 9:3:3:1.

◄ Independent assortment of two pairs of alleles, Mendelian inheritance, Mendelian ratios ►

DIPEPTIDE

When two amino acids combine, a **condensation reaction** occurs between the amino group (NH_2) of one acid and the carboxyl group (COOH) of another. A molecule of water is removed and the two **amino acids** become joined by a peptide bond to form a dipeptide.

◄ Peptide linkage ►

DIPLOID, DIPLOIDY

Diploidy is the state in which cells contain two of each type of **chromosome**, the maternal and the paternal, with the nucleus containing a full set of chromosomes for the species (diploid number). This state is maintained by mitotic cell division. Most **life cycles** include diploid stages, when the cells contain the diploid number of chromosomes.

◄ Haploidy, Mitosis ►

DIRECTIONAL SELECTION

Directional selection operates in response to a gradual change in the environment. This change exerts a **selection pressure** which clearly favours those phenotypes in the population that are best adapted to the changed environment, resulting in the emergence of new forms. This type of selection is called progressive or directional selection and it is the most common cause of evolutionary change. A good example is the selection of **industrial melanism** that occurred in peppered moths in response to a sootier environment.

◀ Disruptive selection, Evolution, Stabilising selection ▶

DISACCHARIDES

A disaccharide is formed when two single hexose sugars (**monosaccharides**) combine to form a double sugar. The process involves the removal of water or condensation with the formation of a glycosidic link. Disaccharides are sweet, soluble and form crystals. Examples are sucrose (cane sugar) = glucose + fructose; lactose (milk sugar) = glucose + galactose; maltose (found in germinating seeds) = 2 × alpha glucose (Fig. D.5).

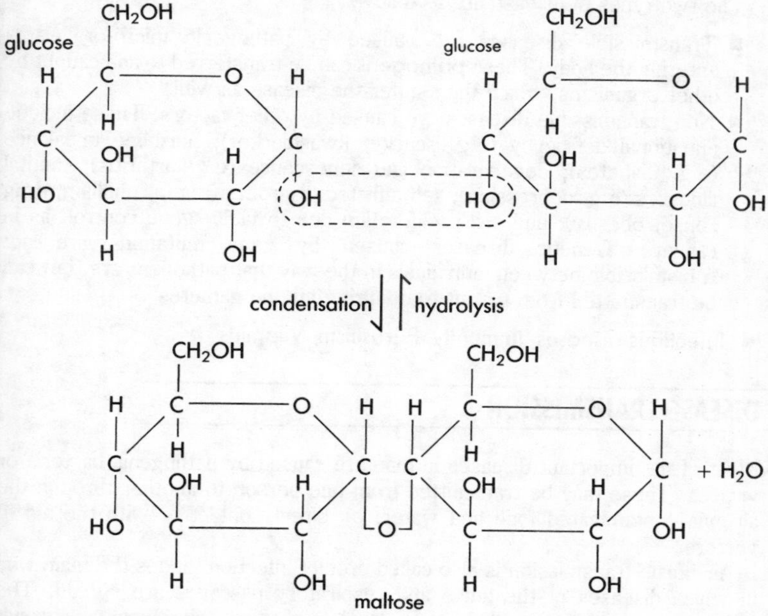

Fig. D.5 Formation of maltose

◀ Carbohydrate ▶

DISCONTINUOUS VARIATION

Discontinuous variation may arise as a result of favourable gene mutations that are retained within the population. This type of variation produces relatively large clear-cut differences between members of the same species with no intermediates. The characteristics that show discontinuous variation are clearly genetically determined and cannot be altered by environmental influences during the lifetime of an individual. They are likely to be controlled by just one or two genes, since polygenic control would produce intermediates.

◀ Continuous variation, Gene (point) mutation, Polygenes, Polygenic inheritance ▶

DISEASE

Disease occurs when a part or parts of the body are not functioning normally or efficiently. The parts of the body affected, and how they are affected, are symptomatic of the disease.

The two types of disease are as follows.

- Transmissible diseases are caused by pathogenic micro-organisms entering the body. These **pathogens** can be transferred to and caught by other organisms, which then suffer the disease as well.
- Non-transmissible diseases are caused by other factors. These include nutritional deficiency (e.g. scurvy; kwashiorkor); hormone imbalance (e.g. diabetes); degeneration and senescence (e.g. arthritis); mental illnesses (e.g. depression); self-afflicted disorders (e.g. alcoholism, drug abuse, obesity); and cell proliferation due to faulty gene control, as in cancers. Genetic diseases caused by gene mutations are not transmissible between individuals in the way that pathogens are, but can be transmitted from parent to offspring via the gametes.

◀ Infectious diseases, Immunity, Parasitism, Vitamins ▶

DISEASE TRANSMISSION

Most of the important diseases in man are caused by pathogenic bacteria or viruses. These may be transmitted from one person to another through the air, via contaminated food and water, by direct contact or with the aid of vectors.

Air-borne transmission is also called droplet infection, and is the main way in which diseases of the lungs and respiratory passages are spread. The micro-organisms are expelled in tiny droplets of saliva and mucus, as a result of sneezing, coughing or even just breathing. Bacterial diseases spread this way include whooping cough and tuberculosis, while viral infections include influenza and measles.

Food and water can become contaminated with bacteria if sanitation and hygiene are poor. Salmonella food poisoning is spread in or from the undercooked meat of infected animals, while diseases such as cholera and typhoid are mainly spread through the contamination of water supplied by the untreated faeces of infected individuals.

Diseases spread by direct contact are described as contagious. Bacterial infections in this category include the sexually transmitted diseases gonorrhoea and syphilis, and contagious viruses include the cold sore virus, herpes simplex and the AIDS virus, HIV.

Vectors are organisms that carry pathogens from one organism to another and for human diseases these are mainly blood-sucking insects. Typhus is caused by bacteria spread by lice, and yellow fever is caused by viruses carried by *Aedes* mosquitoes. *Anopheles* mosquitoes act as vectors for the protozoan *Plasmodium*, which causes malaria.

◀ Acquired Immuno-Deficiency Syndrome (AIDS), Disease, Poisoning, Virus, Viral replication ▶

DISPERSAL

Dispersal is the spreading of organisms away from the parent plant or animal in the form of spores, seeds, fruits or larvae, according to the species in question. This distribution away from the parent helps to reduce overcrowding and intraspecific competition for nutrients, and results in the colonisation of new areas. Agents of dispersal include animals, wind and water.

◀ Intraspecific competition, Larva, Seed dispersal ▶

DISRUPTIVE SELECTION

Disruptive selection operates when environmental conditions favour two or more contrasting phenotypes within the population. Increased competition within the population may push the phenotypes further apart and split the population. If gene flow is prevented, then speciation may occur.

◀ Directional selection, Speciation, Stabilising selection ▶

DISSOCIATION

Dissociation occurs when the ions of ionic compounds separate, or dissociate, when dissolving in water. This occurs because of the polarity of the water molecules, which tend to interpose between the component ions of the ionic compound. Most biochemical reactions take place in aqueous solution because the dissociated ions move freely and react more easily. Dissociation influences the properties of solutions, making them electrically conductive, for example. Covalently bonded molecules do not normally dissociate, though some side groups of covalent biological molecules may ionise, or become charged, when in solution.

◀ Hydrogen bond ▶

DISSOCIATION CURVE

◄ Haemoglobin ►

DNA

◄ Deoxyribonucleic acid ►

DNA PROBES

A DNA probe is a radioactively labelled copy of a specific gene, and it is used in the diagnosis of genetic disorders. DNA is isolated from the white blood cells of the patient and is then fragmented, using restriction endonuclease enzymes. The fragments are separated by **electrophoresis** and incubated with the DNA probe. This will combine only with its complementary sequence on the patient's DNA, allowing the labelled fragments to be identified by autoradiography.

◄ Genetic engineering and manipulation, Genetic screening ►

DOMINANT ALLELES

The characteristic determined by a dominant **allele** is always expressed in the **phenotype**, even in the presence of an alternative allele. For example, in the monohybrid inheritance of height in pea plants, the dominant allele T is expressed as tallness, whether the genotype is homozygous TT or heterozygous Tt.

◄ Recessive alleles ►

DOWN'S SYNDROME

Down's syndrome, or mongolism, is a genetic disorder that results from non-disjunction of autosomal chromosomes. The twenty-first pair of homologous chromosomes fails to separate in meiosis during gametogenesis, with the result that a trisomal gamete is produced. This is more likely to happen in egg formation than in sperm formation, particularly in women over thirty-five or forty years of age, possibly because of the age of the egg cells themselves.

If the trisomal gamete is fertilised, forty-seven chromosomes will be present in the zygote, and it is this that gives rise to Down's syndrome. Symptoms of the disorder include severe mental retardation, heart defects and an increased susceptibility to leukaemia. Down's syndrome children have small, round heads and thick necks and their eyes appear mongoloid.

The foetus of an older mother can be screened for Down's syndrome by amniocentesis.

◀ Genetic screening ▶

DOUBLE CIRCULATION

◀ Blood circulation ▶

DRY MASS

The dry mass of an organism, soil sample, leaf, etc. is its mass after all water has been excluded. The sample structure is dried in an oven at 100°C and weighed at intervals until two identical readings have been taken. This is then recorded as its dry mass. Dry mass gives a better indication of growth due to biosynthesis, and fluctuates less than fresh mass, but all life is killed by the drying process.

DYNAMIC EQUILIBRIUM

A dynamic equilibrium is a steady state in which opposing reactions or mechanisms are proceeding at the same rate. In population numbers, for example, if the combined birth rate and immigration rate is the same as the combined death rate and emigration rate, then the population numbers will be stable

birth rate   death rate
+   +
immigration rate   emigration rate

The situation is active and dynamic, yet the outcome is a constant steady state.

EAR

The mammalian ear is concerned with the senses of hearing and balance. Structurally it may be divided into three parts: an outer ear in contact with the atmosphere, an air-filled middle ear, and a fluid-filled inner ear (Fig. E.1).

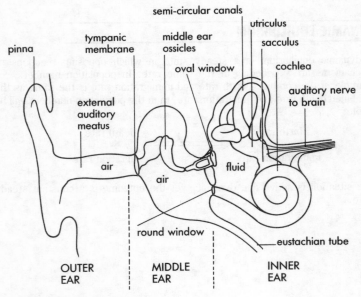

Fig. E.1 Structure of the human ear

Sound waves are collected by the pinna, and directed down the external auditory meatus to the tympanic membrane, causing it to vibrate. These vibrations are conveyed to the inner ear, and also amplified, by the tiny bones or ossicles in the middle ear – known as the hammer, anvil and stirrup because of their shapes. Vibration of the oval window displaces fluid (perilymph) in the vestibular canal of the cochlea (Fig. E.2) and this moves the

Reissner's membrane. This, in turn, displaces fluid (endolymph) in the median canal, which moves the basilar membrane. As the basilar membrane moves, sensory hair cells of the organ of Corti become distorted, setting up action potentials that are transmitted along the auditory nerve to the brain.

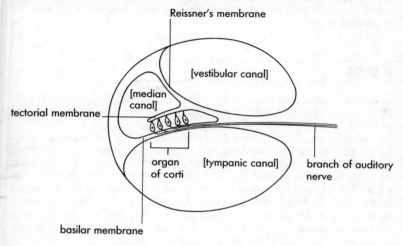

Fig. E.2 Structure of the cochlea (side view)

The pitch of sounds (i.e. high notes or low notes), is determined by which region of the basilar membrane is stimulated. The membrane towards the apex of the cochlea vibrates more with low-frequency sounds (low notes), while the membrane at the base vibrates more with high-frequency sounds. Sound intensity is determined by the degree of displacement of the basilar membrane. Loud sounds cause a greater displacement, creating a higher frequency of impulses in the auditory nerve.

EARTHWORM

Earthworms are classified as oligochaete annelids. They have a soft cylindrical body which is metamerically segmented, each segment bearing two pairs of chaetae or bristles. The chaetae can be protracted or retracted and this is important in locomotion, which occurs by contraction of the body wall muscles against a hydrostatic skeleton. Earthworms are hermaphrodite, and contain both male and female gonads. Self-fertilisation is prevented, however, by elaborate behaviour patterns when pairing to exchange sperm, and by the relative positions of the genital openings. The clitellum is a specialised area which secretes the cocoon in which fertilised eggs are laid. Gaseous exchange occurs by diffusion across the moist body surface, so earthworms are susceptible to desiccation. They burrow through soil, ingesting soil particles and extracting organic matter from them as they pass through the gut. The gut runs the entire length of the body from mouth to anus, and soil is moved along by peristalsis, made posible because of the earthworm's **coelomate organisation**. Earthworms are therefore of great economic importance. Their burrowing activities aerate the soil and improve drainage, and by ingesting and egesting soil particles they contribute to the crumb structure of the soil.

◀ Annelida ▶

ECDYSIS

Arthropods possess an **exoskeleton**, or **cuticle**, that completely encloses the body tissues and so limits **growth**. Ecdysis is the periodic shedding, or moulting, of this cuticle to permit further increase in size.

In insects, ecdysis is initiated by a steroid hormone called ecdysone, which causes the secretion of a moulting fluid containing enzymes. These enzymes dissolve away the soft inner part of the old cuticle, leaving the hard outer layer. Beneath this, a new cuticle of chitin is secreted by the epidermis. The remains of the old cuticle then split along a line of weakness and the insect draws itself out. Before the new cuticle hardens, there is a rapid increase in volume, as the insect swallows water or air. After this, the insect cannot increase its physical dimensions until it moults again, but growth actually continues all the time, with a steady increase in biomass.

ECHINODERMATA

Echinodermata is a phylum in the animal kingdom, containing radially symmetrical marine animals such as starfishes and sea urchins. The larvae of the group are free-swimming and bilaterally symmetrical, so the pentaradial symmetry of the adults is a regressive evolutionary step.

Echinoderms have an external skeleton consisting of calcareous rods and plates just under the skin surface, usually covered with tubercles or spines. There is a spacious coelom and a water vascular system of canals used in respiration, and also in locomotion via the tube feet attached to the canals.

◀ Starfish ▶

ECOLOGY

Ecology is the study of the interactions of organisms in relation to each other and to their physical and biotic environment. It has given rise to the detailed analysis of such themes as **population**, **succession**, feeding relationships, **energy flow**, **conservation** and the effects of human activites on ecosystems.

◀ Autecology, Energy, energy flow in ecosystem, Trophic levels ▶

ECOSYSTEM

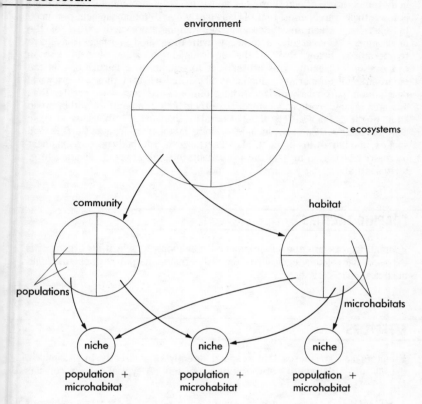

Fig. E.3 Ecosystem

An ecosystem is a natural unit made up of biotic (living) and abiotic (non-living) components whose interactions give rise to a stable, self-perpetuating system. It is made up of one or more **communities** of organisms, containing populations that fall into one of three nutritional groups. These are the producers, consumers and decomposers. The system is fuelled by **energy** from the sun which is trapped by the producers, and then flows through the other **trophic levels**.

◀ Biotic factors, Climatic factors, Edaphic factors, Population ▶

ECOTHERMY

Ectothermy is a means of **temperature regulation** which depends on heat obtained from outside the body, by radiation or conduction from the environment. All animals other than birds and mammals are ectothermic. The body temperature of ectotherms is similar to the environmental temperature but is actually rarely equal to it. This is partly due to metabolic heat produced by exercise, which may increase body temperature above that of the environment. Conversely, ectotherms with moist body surfaces may have temperatures below that of the environment because of heat lost in evaporation. All ectotherms are subject to temperature fluctuations as the environmental temperature fluctuates. This may restrict their geographical distribution, particularly on land, where temperature ranges are greater than in water. Many ecotherms can regulate their body temperature within broad limits by the use of a variety of behavioural mechanisms. Methods used to gain heat or restrict heat loss include basking in the sun, like butterflies and snakes, and burrowing at night, like desert lizards. Methods used to lose heat or restrict heat gain include thermal gaping (e.g. alligators); salivating (e.g. tortoises); and being nocturnal (e.g. moths).

EDAPHIC FACTORS

Edaphic factors are the environmental conditions to which an organism is exposed that relate specifically to the soil – that is, its physical, chemical and biological characteristics.

EFFECTORS

Effectors are structures that respond directly or indirectly to a stimulus, usually under the control of the nervous system. A typical pattern consists of:

STIMULUS → receptor → sensory nerve → Central Nervous System → motor nerve → effector → RESPONSE.

Most commonly the effector would be a muscle or a gland, though other effectors could be cilia and flagella, pigment cells and light-producing organs, An example of effectors that have a direct response to a stimulus, independent of nervous control, are the stinging cells of cnidarians (coelenterates).

EGESTION

Egestion is the elimination of waste from the digestive tract. The waste is in the form of semi-solid **faeces** and it is stored temporarily in the rectum before passing out through the anus, a process known as defaecation. This differs from **excretion** since, with the exception of bile pigments, the material that makes up faeces is not produced by metabolism.

ELBOW JOINT

The elbow is a hinge joint in the forelimb, formed between the humerus and the ulna and radius. The joint allows the limb to be flexed and extended through an angle of 180° in one plane only.
◄ Forelimb of mammal, Hinge, Joint ►

ELECTRON

Electrons are negatively charged particles of negligible mass that orbit the nucleus of an atom. In a neutral atom the number of electrons around the nucleus is the same as the number of positively charged protons in the nucleus, so their charges cancel each other out. Electrons are arranged in up to seven shells at different energy levels, with a fixed maximum number of electrons in each shell. The electrons closest to the nucleus have the least energy. If energy in the form of heat or light, is added to the system, an electron may be 'excited', or promoted to a higher energy level. Such electrons return almost immediately to their original level, releasing the newly absorbed energy as they do so. This electron movement is of vital importance in processes such as photosynthesis.

ELECTRON CARRIER

◄ Hydrogen acceptors, Hydrogen carriers ►

ELECTRON MICROSCOPE

An electron microscope uses an electron beam instead of light and powerful electro-magnets instead of lenses. The electron microscope can give clear pictures of objects that are magnified by over 5,000,000 times (a good light microscope can magnify up to 1,500 times). With this power of magnification, the electron microscope has vastly increased our knowledge and understanding of the structure and function of the cell and many other microscopic organisms and structures. The powerful, clear pictures provided by the electron microscope are made possible because the electron beam has a much shorter wavelength than light, consequently its resolving power is far greater (it can resolve objects 1 μm apart, compared with 200 μm in the light microscope). The electron beam is directed on to a screen from which black-and-white photographs (photoelectronmicrographs) are taken.

Two types of electron microscope are used: the transmission electron microscope and the scanning electron microscope. The former passes beams of electrons through very thin sections of specially prepared material, producing a flat image of the specimen. The scanning electron microscope, however, passes a fine beam of electrons to and fro across the specimen. The emission of electrons from the specimen creates an image which shows the natural contours of the specimen surface.

The electron microscope is, however, very expensive to purchase and operate and can be used only in specialised rooms. Living material cannot be viewed and the preparation of material is very complex and may result in the distortion of the material.

ELECTRON TRANSFER, ET SYSTEMS

◄ Oxidative phosphorylation ►

ELECTROPHORESIS

Electrophoresis is a method used to separate a mixture of **proteins** (e.g. blood). The proteins are applied to a strip of absorptive paper, and dishes containing conducting solution are placed at either end of the strip. Large, charged molecules, such as proteins, migrate in an electric field, so when a current is run through the paper, the proteins will migrate towards cathode if negatively charged (−ve); if positively charged, they will migrate to anode (+ve). The rate of migration varies from one protein to another, depending on the size, shape and charge of the molecules, and so the proteins separate.

Gel may be used as an alternative to paper. The current will flow through the gel, taking the proteins with it.

EMBRYO

An embryo is a young animal or plant produced after the fusion of the male and female gametes (or, uncommonly, by parthenogenetic development of the ovum). In flowering plants, the embryo is contained within the seed and consists of the embryonic shoot (plumule) and root (radicle) and either one or two seed leaves (cotyledons). In animals, the embryo is contained in egg membranes. These may be secreted by the ovum itself (e.g. the vitelline membrane); secreted by cells in the ovary (e.g. chorion of insect eggs); or secreted by the oviduct (e.g. the white and shell of bird eggs, jelly of frog's spawn). In the viviparous mammals, the embryo becomes enclosed by the foetal membranes in the maternal body. The embryonic period is generally considered to finish with hatching from membranes or birth.

EMULSIFICATION, EMULSIONS

Emulsification is the process whereby large fat droplets are broken up into many tiny droplets suspended in water (an emulsion) e.g. action of bile salts. This causes an exposure of a greater surface area of the fat droplets to the digestive action of lipase.

◄ Bile, Digestion ►

END-BULB OF SYNAPSE

◀ Synapse, synaptic transmission ▶

ENDOCRINE GLANDS

Endocrine glands (Fig. E.4) are ductless glands, their secretions being transported directly by the blood. They produce hormones, most of which act on specific target organs, although some have diffuse effects on all body cells. All hormones are effective in small quantities and can act as inhibitors or promoters. Most endocrine glands are controlled by the anterior **pituitary gland** and the **hypothalamus**, enabling the co-ordination and interaction of **hormone** secretions.

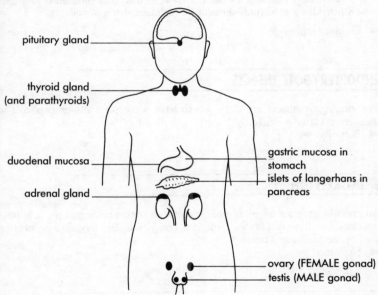

pituitary gland

thyroid gland
(and parathyroids)

duodenal mucosa

adrenal gland

gastric mucosa in stomach
islets of langerhans in pancreas

ovary (FEMALE gonad)
testis (MALE gonad)

Fig. E.4 Position of the major endocrine glands

◀ Homoeostasis ▶

ENDODERMIS

The endodermis occurs in a layer of cells surrounding the vascular tissue core, or stele.

◀ Apoplast, apoplastic pathway, Root systems, Suberin ▶

ENDOPLASMIC RETICULUM (ER)

Endoplasmic reticulum consists of a system of membranes found throughout the cytoplasm and connected to the nuclear envelope. They form a series of parallel, tubular or flattened cavities called cisternae, the outer surface of which may be lined with ribosomes, making it rough ER. **Rough endoplasmic reticulum** is particularly concerned with protein synthesis, while **smooth endoplasmic reticulum** is concerned with lipid synthesis and transport.

ER has the following functions in cells:

- it provides a large surface area for chemical reactions;
- it produces proteins (rough ER);
- it produces lipids and steroids (smooth ER);
- it collects and stores synthesised material;
- it provides a pathway for the transport of materials through cell;
- it provides a structural skeleton to maintain shape of cell.

◄ Golgi complex ►

ENDOPTERYGOTE INSECTS

Endopterygote insects are those which have a complete **metamorphosis** in their life cycle (e.g. butterfly).

◄ Butterfly ►

ENDOSKELETON

An endoskeleton forms an internal framework within an organism. It is best developed in the vertebrates, where it consists of the modified connective tissues, **cartilage** and **bone**.

◄ Skeleton ►

ENDOTHERMY

Mammals and birds are endothermic, able to maintain a constant body temperature independently of the environmental temperature. The heat is produced internally by metabolic activities. The body temperature of endotherms is usually in range of 35–44°C, and the higher the body temperature the higher is the metabolic rate of the animal.

Endothermic animals have the advantage of being more environmentally independent than ectothermic animals and consequently have been able to occupy a much wider geographical range.

◄ Temperature regulation ►

ENERGY, ENERGY FLOW IN ECOSYSTEM

All metabolic reactions in cells involve the gain or loss or energy, so the provision of energy is a fundamental requirement for life. Energy flow occurs through the ecosystem, with the movement of energy through the **trophic levels** of a food chain or web. The energy input for the system is light energy from the sun, which is absorbed by autotrophic organisms. This energy is gradually reduced by respiration, failure of assimilation (e.g. many animals cannot use cellulose cell walls of plants), heat loss, etc. at each level.

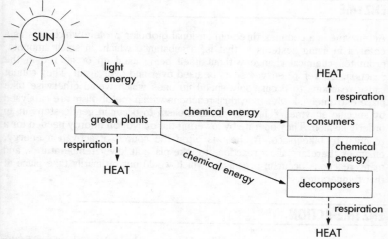

Fig. E.5 Energy

◀ Food chains, food webs, Pyramid of energy ▶

ENTOMOPHILOUS FLOWERS

Entomophilous flowers attract insects to convey pollen from one flower to another. Devices evolved to attract insects include the possession of brightly coloured petals and/or sepals, the secretion of nectar and the emission of scent. Elaborate mechanisms for promoting cross-pollination are often found (e.g. stigma higher than surrounding stamens so that pollen is unlikely to fall on stigma in same flower; also stigma in such a position that visiting insect will brush pollen it has picked up on to it).

ENVELOPE

An envelope is a double membrane surrounding an organelle, such as that found around the **nucleus** and **mitochondria**.

ENVIRONMENTAL VARIATION

Characteristics that are controlled by several genes (**polygenes**) are often subject to environmental variation. Different selection pressures imposed on different populations may cause the expression of the polygenes in the phenotype to vary. This is particularly true for characteristics such as height, which may be affected by many external factors. The combined effects of the polygenes and the environment result in **continuous variation**.

ENZYME

An enzyme is a complex three-dimensional **globular protein** which acts as a **catalyst** in living systems – that is, a substance which, in small amounts, promotes chemical change without itself being used up or altered in the reaction. Therefore enzymes can be used over and over again. They cannot cause reactions to occur, only speed up ones which would otherwise take place extremely slowly. Individual reactions within **metabolism** are catalysed by specific enzymes. This allows metabolism to occur in gentle steps in an orderly fashion. They operate by lowering the **activation energy** needed for a reaction to take place. As heat is often the source of activation energy, enzymes therefore allow reactions to take place at lower temperatures, and many reactions occur in organisms which would not ordinarily take place at that temperature.

ENZYME ACTION

All enzymes operate only on specific substrates, those whose shape will fit the **active site** of an enzyme ('lock and key' hypothesis). Recent evidence (induced-fit hypothesis) suggests that the active site may change in order to suit the substrate's shape (i.e. the enzyme is flexible and moulds to fit the substrate molecule). Once combined, the enzyme and substrate form the enzyme-substrate complex. The products produced have a different shape from the substrate and so, once formed, they escape the active site. Chemical reactions are reversible; the direction in which the reaction moves is dependent upon conditions such as pH, moving in one direction in acid conditions and the other in alkaline conditions. In time, reactions reach a point where the reactants and the product are in equilibrium with one another. Enzymes catalyse the forward and backward reactions equally and therefore do not alter the equilibrium itself, only the speed at which it is reached.

ENZYME CLASSES

Enzymes are classified according to the type of reaction they catalyse. For example, transferases (e.g. transaminases and phosphorylases), transfer a chemical group from one substance to another; lyases (e.g. carboxylases) add or remove a chemical group; oxidoreductases (e.g. oxidases and dehydrogenases) occur in all oxidation-reduction reactions where O and H atoms are transferred between substances; hydrolases (e.g. peptidases, lipases and phosphatases) carry out hydrolysis reactions; ligases (e.g. synthetases) form bonds between two molecules using energy provided by the breakdown of ATP; and isomerases (e.g. isomerases and mutases) rearrange groups within a molecule.

ENZYME INHIBITION

Enzyme activity is controlled by a variety of mechanisms which depend not only on physical parameters, such as temperature, pH, substrate concentration or enzyme concentration, but also on chemical agents which mask, block or alter the active sites of the enzymes they help to regulate. One common form of enzyme control, called **competitive inhibition**, involves an inhibitor substance sufficiently similar to the normal substrate of the enzyme binding to its active site to prevent the substrate becoming attached to the active site. Another type of inhibition, called **non-competitive inhibition**, depends on the presence of binding sites in the same enzyme molecule – one for the substrate (active site) and one for the inhibitor. When the inhibitor is bound to the enzyme, it is thought to interfere with the access of the substrate to the active site.

In some metabolic pathways the end product itself may act as an inhibitor. This occurs when there is an excess of the end product, which then combines with one of the enzymes responsible for its production, therefore further end-product formation is slowed down or stopped (an example of **negative feedback**).

Allosteric inhibition occurs in a group of enzymes which exist in two forms (active and inactive). The inhibitor molecules combine with a part of the enzyme that prevents it changing into its active form.

EPIDEMIOLOGY

Epidemiology is the study of diseases that are prevalent in a community at a specific time (epidemic).

EPIDERMIS

Epidermis is the outermost layer of cells of a plant or animal. In plants the epidermis consists of a single layer of flattened, often irregularly shaped cells, forming a protective layer covering the more delicate tissues beneath. They lack chloroplasts and the outer cellulose walls are often thick and impregnated with waxy materials, forming a **cuticle** that is impermeable to water and prevents excessive evaporation.

In mammals the epidermis forms the outer portion of the **skin**, while in arthropods the epidermis is a single layer of cells responsible for secreting the cuticle.

EPISTASIS

◀ Gene interaction ▶

ER

◀ Endoplasmic reticulum ▶

ERYTHROCYTES

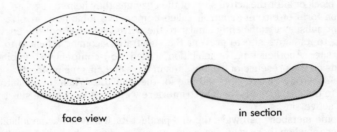

face view

in section

Fig. E.6 Erythrocytes

Erythrocytes are the red blood cells (Fig. E.6). Their main function is to carry oxygen from surface gaseous exchange to respiring tissues. There are approximately 5 million per cubic millimetre of blood. Each cell is about 8 μm in diameter and 3 μm thick. There is no nucleus, which enables more haemoglobin to be carried by the cell, and the biconcave disc shape provides a high surface–volume ratio for the absorption of oxygen. Red blood cells have a life span of about 120 days. New cells are produced in the bone marrow at a rate of about 1.5 million per second.

ESSENTIAL NUTRIENTS

Essential nutrients must be taken in by organisms because they are unable to synthesise them for themselves. An absence of these nutrients can result in disease and death. The essential nutrients fall into three groups:

- mineral elements (plants and animals);
- vitamins (animals);
- essential amino acids and fatty acids (animals).

◀ Mineral nutrition ▶

ETHANOL

Ethanol (ethyl alcohol – CH_3CH_2OH) is produced as a result of anaerobic respiration in plants and yeast (alcoholic fermentation).
◀ Fermentation ▶

ETHENE (ETHYLENE)

Ethene is a metabolic by-product of most plant organs. It stimulates the ripening of fruits, influences many auxin-induced responses, ends dormancy of buds (in some plants) and, in pineapples, promotes flowering.
◀ Auxin ▶

EUKARYOTIC CELLS

Eukaryotic cells have a nucleus that is separated from the cytoplasm by a nuclear membrane and the genetic material is carried on a number of chromosomes. Nuclear division is by mitosis or meiosis.

The cytoplasm contains membrane-bound organelles, notably the mitochondria for respiration and, in plants, chloroplasts for photosynthesis. Flagella or cilia that may be present have the typical 9 + 2 arrangement of longitudinal microtubules running down their length.
◀ Prokaryotic cells ▶

EUTROPHICATION

◀ Detergents, Nitrate pollution, Sewage micro-organisms ▶

EVAPORATION

This is the conversion of liquid into vapour. Water has a high heat of vaporisation, which means that in the evaporation of water much heat energy is required. This has a marked cooling effect, and consequently, has become an important mechanism by which excessive heat can be lost by an organism (e.g. sweating, panting). The evaporation of water is affected by such factors as temperature, humidity and air currents.
◀ Terrestrial life, adaptations for ▶

EVOLUTION

Evolution is the continuous change from simple to complex organisms. Prior to the eighteenth century, the scientific belief was that all the millions of species of living organisms arose as a result of some form of special creation along biblical lines. During the eighteenth century, however, two major themes emerged. The first was put forward by Jean-Baptiste Lamarck, who suggested that evolutionary change had resulted from minor alterations in individuals during their lifetime that were then inherited by their offspring. His views were not widely accepted, but did influence Charles **Darwin**, who modified the idea, putting forward his own theories of evolution occuring as a result of **natural selection** and **speciation**.

Processes of natural selection and speciation may certainly account for many of the changes that have occurred. They do not, however, explain the 'big steps' in organisation – from unicellularity to multicellularity, for example, from acoelomate to coelomate organisation, from ectothermy to endothermy, and so on.

Current understanding of the evolutionary process is that it has occurred in 'jumps' or punctuated equilibria, each jump occurring because of some (undocumented) massive change in the environment. Between the punctuations, development during the equilibria stages has been by natural selection and speciation.

EXCRETION

Excretion is the removal from the body of waste products that have been produced by chemical activity inside cells. These metabolic waste products are known as excretory products, and the organs concerned with their removal are called excretory organs.

Plants produce few excretory products, because they synthesise only the organic compounds they require. What organic waste they do have is often simply stored in an inert form. Compounds such as calcium pectate and calcium oxalate may be stored as insoluble crystals in the cytoplasm, for instance. The storage area may be in non-living parts of the plant, such as heartwood, where they do not affect living tisue. Alternatively, excess ions such as manganese and organic acids like tannic acid may accumulate in 'disposable' parts such as leaves, petals, fruits or seeds. The waste products will then be eliminated from the plant when leaves and petals fall or when the fruits and seeds are dispersed.

In animals excretory organs vary from contractile vacuoles in some protoctists, to flame cells in flatworms, nephridia in earthworms and malpighian tubules in insects.

In mammals the principal excretory organ is the kidney, which removes nitrogenous waste and excess salts and water from the body. Excretion of carbon dioxide occurs in expired air and bile pigments are discharged in the faeces via the bile, Sweat glands in the skin extract water, sodium chloride and a little urea from the blood and this is removed as sweat.

◀ Deamination, Kidneys, Ventilation ▶

EXOSKELETON

An exoskeleton is a more or less complete body covering characteristic of arthropods. It provides protection for internal organs and a rigid attachment for muscles. The outer three-layered cuticle is secreted by the epidermal cells beneath it. The cuticle forms a waxy, waterproof covering and is strengthened by chitin impregnated with tanned proteins. In crustaceans, the exoskeleton is further strengthened by the addition of salts, such as calcium carbonate.

To allow efficient movement, the inflexible parts of the exoskeleton are separated by flexible regions where the rigid chitin is absent. The exoskeleton is unable to expand, consequently growth is achieved by its periodic shedding.

◀ Cuticle, Ecdysis ▶

EYE

The eye is the sense organ involved with the transduction of light rays into nerve impulses. In mammals each eye is a spherical structure found in a bony socket of the skull called the orbit and may be rotated within the socket by the rectus muscles, which attach it to the skull (Fig. E.7).

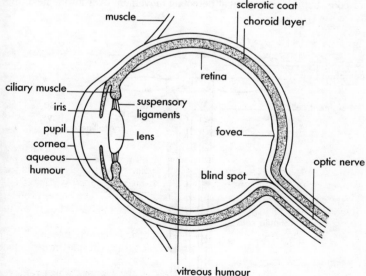

Fig. E.7 Structure of the mammalian eye

The spherical shape of the eyeball is maintained by the jelly-like vitreous humour in the posterior chamber and by the collagen fibres in the sclerotic coat. The photoreceptor cells, rods and cones, are concentrated in the retina, which lines most of the interior of the eye. The pigmented choroid prevents internal reflection of light and is rich in blood capillaries, which nourish the retina.

At the front of the eye, the sclera is transparent, allowing the entrance of light into the eye. This region is the cornea and it is here that most refraction of light occurs. The cornea is covered and protected by the transparent conjunctiva, an extension of the eyelid epithelium. Tears from lachrymal glands lubricate and nourish the cornea and conjunctiva. Behind the cornea is the anterior chamber, filled with a transparent liquid called aqueous humour. The amount of light entering the eye is controlled by the iris, a diaphragm of circular and radial muscles which function to alter the diameter of the pupil. The light is then focused on to the retina by the transparent, biconvex lens. The lens is flexible and elastic. Its shape is continually altered by the ciliary muscles which surround it, as it works to focus incoming light.

As light hits the retina, nerve impulses are fired. These leave the eye via the optic nerve, which carries them to the brain. At the point where the optic nerve joins the eye there are no photo-receptive cells, and it is this that gives rise to the blind spot.

The compound eye of arthropods is composed of numerous separate elements called ommatidia, each with light-sensitive cells (rhabdom) and a refractive system which can form an image. The ommatidia are separated from each other by pigment cells. The visual acuity of the compound eye is rather poor, but it is very good at detecting movement over a wide field (Fig. E.8).

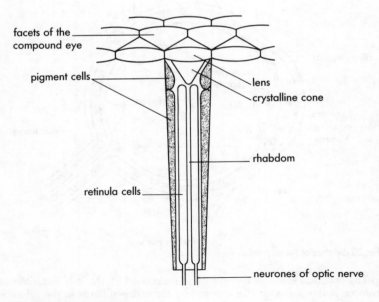

facets of the compound eye

pigment cells

lens

crystalline cone

rhabdom

retinula cells

neurones of optic nerve

Fig. E.8 Ommatidium compound eye

FACILITATED UPTAKE, FACILITATED DIFFUSION

Diffusion of **glucose** and **amino acids** into cells is very slow. This is because they are relatively large molecules. The process may be assisted, or facilitated, by the presence of a protein-carrier molecule, to which the glucose or amino acid can bind. The proteins span the plasma membrane and are similar to the carriers that operate together with sodium-potassium pumps in **active transport**. Adenosine triphosphate (ATP) is not required for facilitated uptake, however, so the process is a passive one; what is required is a diffusion gradient, with a higher concentration of glucose or amino acids outside the **cell** than inside.
◄ Molecule, Proteins ►

FAD

◄ Flavine adenine dinucleotide ►

FAECES

Faeces is the indigestible waste matter that remains after the processes of **digestion** and **absorption**. It leaves the gut or digestive tract by **egestion**. In most animal groups (Protozoa, Cnidaria and Platyhelminthes excepted) this occurs through the anus.

FATS

Fats are **lipids** that are solid at normal temperatures. They contain a high proportion of saturated **fatty acids**, which have high melting points.
◄ Saturated fats ►

FAT SOLVENTS

◄ Lipids ►

FATTY ACIDS

Fatty acids are components of **lipids**, and the nature of a particular lipid depends on which fatty acids it contains. The general formula of a fatty acid is $CH_3(CH_2)_nCOOH$, consisting of a methyl group, a hydrocarbon chain of varying length and a carboxyl group. If the hydrocarbon chain contains the maximum number of hydrogen atoms, then the fatty acid is said to be saturated. An example of a saturated fatty acid is stearic acid. If some hydrogen atoms are absent and there are one or more double bonds connecting the carbon atoms, then the fatty acid is described as unsaturated. An example of an unsaturated fatty acid is oleic acid (Fig. F.1).

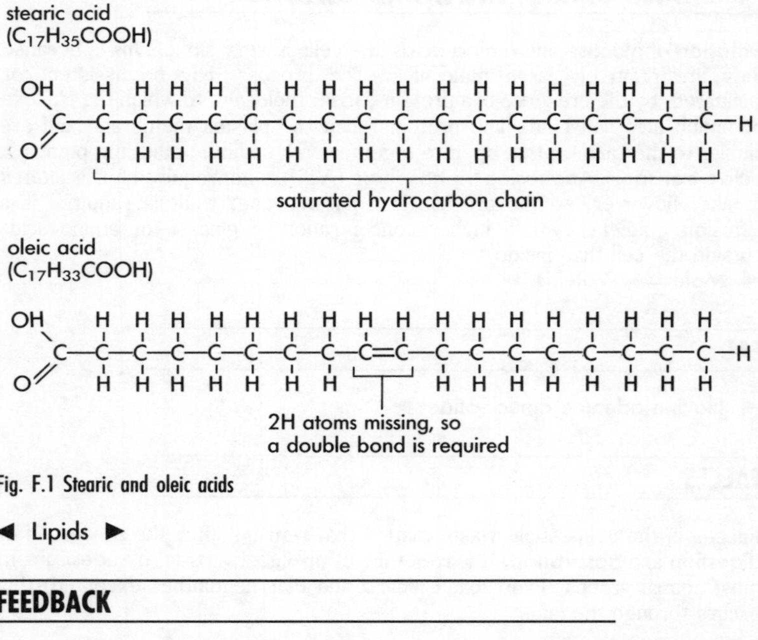

stearic acid
$(C_{17}H_{35}COOH)$

saturated hydrocarbon chain

oleic acid
$(C_{17}H_{33}COOH)$

2H atoms missing, so
a double bond is required

Fig. F.1 Stearic and oleic acids

◀ Lipids ▶

FEEDBACK

Many control mechanisms are regulated by the very effects that they bring about. In biological systems, this usually takes the form of **negative feedback**, in which an increase in the effect results in a decrease in the mechanism causing it, or vice versa. A typical example would be the control of blood osmotic level (Fig. F.2) by the secretion of **ADH** (anti-diuretic hormone). Negative feedback maintains stability, or 'norm' conditions, and therefore plays an important role in **homeostasis**.

Positive feedback may also occur in certain circumstances when control mechanisms fail. It increases the deviation from the norm and creates instability. If the environmental temperature rises so high that the body's cooling mechanisms fail, then the metabolic rate will start to increase. This generates more heat internally, which causes the metabolic rate to rise further by positive feedback.

Fig. F.2 Control of blood plasma osmotic level

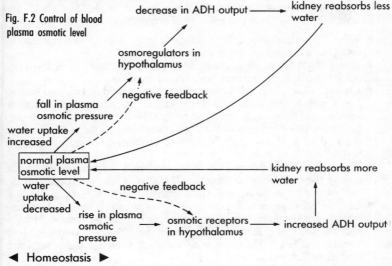

◄ Homeostasis ►

FEEDBACK INHIBITION

Feedback inhibition is an example of **negative feedback** applied to **enzyme** activity in a series of enzyme-controlled reactions such as occurs in a metabolic pathway. If the end-product of the pathway begins to accumulate, then it may regulate its further production by inhibiting the activity of an enzyme controlling one of the first steps in the pathway. An example occurs in **respiration**, where citric acid inhibits the enzyme for fructose-1, 6-diphosphate.

◄ Enzyme inhibition ►

FEMUR

The femur is the long **bone** from the hind limb of a vertebrate. It forms a ball and socket joint with the pelvic girdle at the hip, and a **hinge joint** at the knee.

◄ Vertebrates ►

FERMENTATION INDUSTRY

The **fermentation** process is exploited in industry to produce many useful **organic compounds**. These substances include pharmaceuticals such as **steroid** drugs and antibiotics, products for agriculture such as gibberellic acid and animal feed, human beverages and foods such as beer and wine, cheese, yoghurt and vinegar.

The starting material for fermentation is known as the feedstock. The chemicals used vary, but are usually either sugars or alcohols.

- Wine – The feedstock is the fructose in grape juice. It is fermented by wild yeasts present on grape skins.
- Beer – **Maltose** in germinating barley grains is fermented by the yeast *Saccharomyces* (e.g. *Saccharomyces carlsbergensis*).
- Cheese – Lactose in milk is fermented to **lactic acid** by **bacteria** such as *Lactobacillus*. The resulting low **pH** causes the milk protein casein to separate into solid curds and liquid whey. The curds are then fermented further by other bacteria and/or fungi, depending on the type of cheese required (e.g. the fungus *Penicillium camemberti* produces Camembert).
- Vinegar – The feedstock is an alcohol, which is fermented to ethanoic acid by the bacterium Acetobacter. The alcohol varies according to the type of vinegar required (e.g. spirit vinegar, cider vinegar).
- Silage – Fresh green material such as grass cuttings is sprinkled with the 'waste' carbohydrate, molasses. The mixture is fermented first by bacteria such as *Escherichia*, and then by obligate anaerobes, both bacteria and fungi. The process takes about a month, and results in a food mass that will keep for years.

◀ Yeast ▶

FERNS

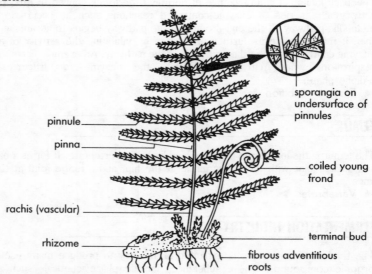

Fig. F.3 External features of the sporophyte of a fern (*Dryopteris felix-mas*)

Ferns are plants belonging to the phylum Filicinophyta. The main features of the phylum are as follows.

- They show **alternation of generations**, with the diploid **sporophyte** generation the most prominent.
- The sporophyte is a vascular plant – that is, it contains **xylem** and **phloem** tissues. True roots, stems and leaves are present. **Sporangia** are found in clusters, or sori, on the under surface of the leaves.
- The haploid gametophyte is reduced to a simple **prothallus**, without vascular tissue, and without a waterproofing cuticle. It bears archegonia and antheridia, the female and male reproductive structures.

A typical example of a fern is the male fern *Dryopteris felix-mas* (Fig. F.3). The stem of the sporophyte is an underground rhizome, which bears adventitious roots and large leaves known as fronds.

◄ Vascular plants ►

FERTILE OFFSPRING

When **sexual reproduction** occurs between two individuals of the same **species**, the resulting offspring are fertile. This means that they are themselves capable of reproducing. Occasionally, individuals of similar but different species may mate successfully, but the offspring is infertile. An example is the sterile mule that results from a cross between a horse and a donkey.

FERTILISATION

Fertilisation occurs when the haploid nuclei of two gametes fuse to form a diploid **zygote**. It is the essential process and aim of **sexual reproduction** since the mixing of genetic material allows for **variation** in the offspring. The amount of variation will be very small if self-fertilisation (the fusion of gametes from the same parent) occurs. In animals, therefore, this method is only used by certain internal parasites, such as tapeworms, whose chances of locating another individual for cross-fertilisation are limited. Most flowering plants have devices which encourage cross-fertilisation, or **out-breeding**, but may permit self-fertilisation, or **in-breeding**, to occur as a last resort.

In **moss** and **fern**, fertilisation requires 'rain-splash', or a film of water over the surface of the **gametophyte**. The male gametes, antherozoids, possess a **flagellum**, enabling them to swim to the female oosphere present in the archegonium.

In flowering plants the gametes are nuclei within the pollen grain and embryosac. After **pollination**, a pollen tube grows out from the pollen grain down the style by digesting the tissues of the style. Inside the tube there is a tube nucleus and also a generative nucleus, which divides by **mitosis** to give two male nuclei. The pollen tube enters an ovule through the micropyle and then ruptures to release the male nuclei. A double fertilisation (Fig. F.4) now takes place, in which one male nucleus fuses with the functional egg cell, while the other fuses with two polar nuclei in the centre of the embryosac to form an endosperm nucleus which contains 3n **chromosomes** (i.e. it is triploid).

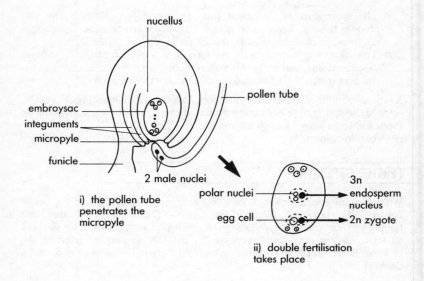

i) the pollen tube penetrates the micropyle

ii) double fertilisation takes place

Fig. F.4 Double fertilisation in an angiosperm

In animals the male gametes are small motile **sperm** cells and the female gametes are large, non-motile egg cells or **ova**. The gametes are brought together by either external or internal fertilisation.

External fertilisation occurs in aquatic invertebrates, most **fish** and many **amphibia**. Vast numbers of gametes are released into the water of a stream or lake; many will be lost but some may meet and fuse. The chances of fertilisation may be enhanced by specific forms of behaviour, such as the use of spawning grounds, where many individuals release their gametes in close proximity and at the same time. Elaborate **courtship behaviour** may also be employed.

Most land animals, vertebrate and invertebrate, use internal fertilisation. The female gametes are retained inside the female's body and the male gametes are transferred directly, surrounded by fluid. Far fewer gametes are required since there is far less wastage. Gamete release is synchronised by hormones, with the aid once again of courtship behaviour. In reptiles and **birds** the fertilised egg is enclosed in a waterproof protective shell and then passed out of the female reproductive tract (they are oviparous). In **mammals** the fertilised egg develops internally until the young mammal is born (they are viviparous).

◀ Hormone, Reptilia ▶

FERTILISER APPLICATION

Healthy plant growth requires a supply of inorganic mineral nutrients from the soil. In natural environments, nutrients are recycled. Dead plants (and animals) are decomposed by soil **bacteria** and **fungi** and their constituents are made available for new plant growth. In agriculture, however, crops are harvested, and so removed from the system. The mineral content of the soil will be reduced, and future crop **productivity** will decrease. Fertiliser application may then become necessary to replace minerals that are deficient.

Organic fertilisers such as manure and compost are the most beneficial. This is because they add to the humus content of the soil, and so increase its water-retaining capacity.

Inorganic fertilisers add minerals only, principally **nitrate** (N), **phosphate** (P) and **potassium** (K). If the soil is low in humus, these minerals may dissolve in rainwater and leach out of the soil. Soils low in humus are also liable to erosion.

◀ Mineral nutrition, Leaching ▶

FERTILISER POLLUTION

Where agricultural land is close to fresh water, excess applications of inorganic fertiliser may result in **pollution**. The fertiliser dissolves in rainwater and runs off into the pond or lake, where increased **nitrate** levels in the water result in **eutrophication**.

FETAL CIRCULATION

The pattern of **blood circulation** in a **fetus** differs from that in an adult (Fig. F.5). This is mainly due to the fact that the **lungs** and digestive system of a fetus are non-functional, though other organs such as the **kidneys** and liver do not have full adult function either. The fetus obtains its **oxygen** and **nutrients** by **diffusion** across the **placenta**, where the maternal blood **capillaries** and the umbilical capillaries of the fetus lie close together. Oxygenated blood is conveyed to the fetus by the umbilical vein, and the waste products of fetal metabolism are carried in the opposite direction to the placenta by the two umbilical arteries.

Most of the oxygenated blood of the umbilical vein reaches the **vena cava** along an extra vessel called a ductus venosus that by-passes the fetal liver. The vena cava then leads into the right atrium of the **heart**, from where most blood passes directly into the left atrium through a hole called the foramen ovale, and the remainder passes through another extra vessel, a ductus arteriosus. This connects the pulmonary artery with the aorta, so the lungs and **pulmonary blood circulation** are also by-passed.

Shortly after **birth**, the foramen ovale, ductus venosus and ductus arteriosus should close so that the adult pattern of blood circulation can take over. Occasionally the foramen ovale remains partly open, a defect known as 'hole in the heart' and surgery may be necessary to close it.

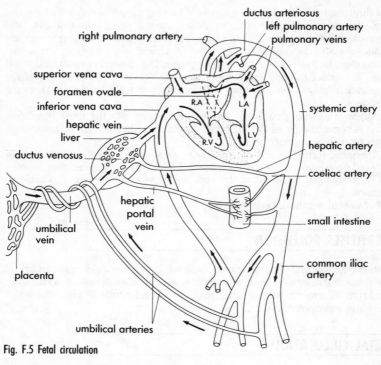

Fig. F.5 Fetal circulation

◀ Arteries, arterioles, Heart, Veins ▶

FETAL DEVELOPMENT, EFFECTS OF MOTHER'S ACTIONS ON

The closeness of maternal and fetal blood **capillaries** in the **placenta** is an essential requirement so that the **fetus** may obtain sufficient **oxygen** and **nutrients** for its growth. It does mean, however, that any substance able to pass through capillary walls can be transferred from the mother to the fetus, so the mother's diet and actions have a direct influence on the growth and development of her fetus.

If the mother smokes, for example, then the fetus will receive nicotine, which is an addictive drug, and it may also be starved of oxygen. This is because cigarette smoke contains carbon monoxide, which combines readily with **haemoglobin** and prevents further carriage of oxygen. Up to 10 per cent of the haemoglobin in the blood of smokers may be poisoned in this way. A reduced oxygen supply to the fetus increases the chances of a baby being born underweight and suffering impaired mental development in later childhood.

Alcohol and most other drugs will also pass to the fetus and may harm it, particularly during the first twelve weeks of development. Babies born with 'fetal alcohol syndrome' because of the mother's excessive drinking are retarded both physically and mentally, and have deformities of the face and heart.

Maternal illness during pregnancy may affect the fetus directly since some bacterial toxins and certain viruses can cross the placenta. A notable example is the rubella virus that causes German measles. If the mother is infected with rubella during the first twelve weeks of pregnancy, there is a risk that the baby will be born blind and deaf, with congenital heart disease.

◀ Alcoholism, effects of, Smoking, effect of, Virus, Viral replication ▶

FETAL MEMBRANES, FUNCTIONS OF

The fetal or embryonic membranes develop very early in pregnancy, either from the outermost layers of the embryonic tissue or as projections of the embryonic gut. There are four membranes: a yolk sac, which is largely non-functional in mammals, an amnion, an allantois and a chorion. The amnion and chorion grow to completely enclose the embryo in a fluid-filled amniotic cavity. This fluid acts as a shock absorber and allows the embryo to move about during growth. The chorion and a third membrane, the allantois, form a vascular structure called an allantochorion, which makes up the fetal part of the placenta. The chorionic villi provide a large surface area for exchange of materials between the maternal and fetal blood. Another function of the chorion is that it acts as an endocrine organ, secreting the hormones chorionic gonadotrophin, oestrogens, progesterone and placental lactogen.

FETUS

A fetus (sometimes spelt foetus) is the stage of growth of a mammalian embryo when recognisable features can be seen. In humans, this stage is reached at eight weeks.

FIBRE, IN HUMAN DIET

A certain amount of fibre, or roughage, is required in the human diet to maintain good health. The term refers to matter that we are incapable of digesting, in particular cellulose from plant cell walls. Fibre contributes bulk to the gut contents, and in providing some resistance for the smooth muscle of the gut wall it assists the process of peristalsis.

Without fibre, the movement of the gut contents is too sluggish. This causes constipation and may be the indirect cause of a number of diseases of the colon and rectum (e.g. Burkitt's lymphoma).

◀ Digestion ▶

FIBRES

In plants fibres are elongated cells with lignified walls. They occur in sclerenchyma and xylem, and their function is support.

In animals the term fibre may refer to elongated cells, particularly in muscle and nerve tissue. It may also refer to fibrous proteins such as collagen and elastin in connective tissue.

FIBROUS PROTEINS

Fibrous proteins are those which have little or no tertiary structure, so their shape and hence their function depend on their secondary structure. They consist of long, parallel polypeptide chains which are cross-linked at intervals, forming long fibres or sheets. They are insoluble in water and very strong, so have important structural functions.

Examples of fibrous proteins include keratin in hair, nails and feathers, collagen in tendons, bone and other connective tissues, silk fibroin in the cocoon of silkworms, and myosin in muscle tissue.

Keratin has single polypeptide chains, each in the form of an extended spiral spring or alpha-helix. The chains are cross-linked with a number of disulphide bridges – fewer in hair, which is elastic, and more in nails, which are relatively inelastic.

Collagen has its polypeptide chains in threes, wound round each other to form triple helices. This structure cannot be stretched, hence its importance in tendons.

Silk-fibroin takes the form of a beta-pleated sheet. Adjacent polypeptide chains run in opposite directions to each other, with a hydrogen bond between all the NH groups and the C=O groups. The arrangement makes silk inelastic but very supple.

◀ Tendon ▶

FIELD CROPS

In agricultural terms technically anything that is produced on a farm, whether animal or vegetable in nature, is a 'crop'. Field crops are plants, grown in a field, for harvesting (e.g. wheat, cabbages, strawberries).

FILAMENTOUS ALGAE

Some green algae, or chlorophytes, are unicellular or colonial. Others have a simple thallus, which is either filamentous or flattened. A common filamentous alga is *Spirogyra* (Fig F.6), which consists of an unbranched chain of identical cells, coated in slimy mucilage. It occurs, free-floating, in bodies of still, fresh water such as ponds.

The main photosynthetic pigment is chlorophyll, and each cell contains a single, spiral chloroplast. Growth is not limited to the apices as in most plants. All cells in the filament are capable of dividing by **mitosis**, then each daughter cell grows to full size to increase the length of the filament. Reproduction may be asexual or sexual. **Asexual reproduction** is by **fragmentation**, in which the filament breaks into two or more pieces. **Sexual reproduction** is by **conjugation**, in which a bridge forms between two adjacent filaments and an entire cell's contents passes from one filament to the other.

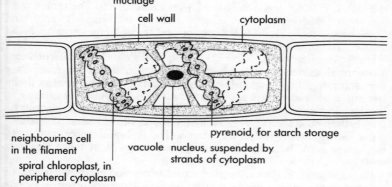

mucilage
cell wall
cytoplasm
neighbouring cell in the filament
vacuole nucleus, suspended by strands of cytoplasm
pyrenoid, for starch storage
spiral chloroplast, in peripheral cytoplasm

Fig. F.6 Structure of Spirogyra

◀ Chlorophyta ▶

FILICINOPHYTA

Filicinophyta is a phylum of the kingdom **Plantae**, containing the ferns.
◀ Fern ▶

FILTER FEEDING

Filter feeding is a feeding method used by animals whose food consists of tiny particles suspended in water. It is particularly useful for **sessile** animals. The method requires a water current, which is created either by beating **cilia**, by waving appendages or by the animal's own forward locomotion. Having brought the food particles into the water current, some means of filtering them out of the water is then required.

Bivalve molluscs such as the mussel are filter feeders, their food being microscopic **algae** and **protozoa**. The water current is created by cilia, which direct water into the animal through an inhalent siphon and out through an exhalent siphon. Filtration occurs through two pairs of gill-like structures, called ctenidia, which contain pores. Food particles of the right size become trapped in **mucus** on the surface of the ctenidia, and cilia direct them towards the mouth. The food is then sorted to some extent by ciliated palps on either side of the mouth, before being ingested.

◀ Mollusca ▶

FISH

Fish is a term that is used ecologically to cover all gill-breathing, scaled chordates. It is no longer considered a taxonomic group. The term covers two quite different classes, Chondrichthyes (cartilaginous fish) and Osteichthyes (bony fish). Individuals of both groups are streamlined and aquatic, and possess jaws and paired fins.

Cartilaginous fish (Fig. F.7a) have an endoskeleton made of cartilage. They are all marine, and examples include dogfish, sharks and rays. They have separate gill openings, without an operculum, and they possess fleshy fins with a heterocercal tail fin. Spiracles are present, but there is no swim bladder. The mouth is in a ventral position. Cartilaginous fish concentrate urea in their blood in order to become iso-osmotic with sea water, so avoiding water loss from their bodies by osmosis. The embryos cannot do this, so fertilisation must be internal, and eggs are enclosed in tough, leathery shells.

Bony fish (Fig. F.7b) have a skeleton of bone, and include dipnoans, or lung-fish, and the marine and fresh water teleosts. Examples of teleost include carp, trout and stickleback. They lack spiracles and possess a bony flap called the operculum covering their four pairs of gills. They have a swim bladder, which enables them to alter their buoyancy in the water, and their mouth is in a terminal position. Their fins are supported by rays, and the tail fin is homocercal. Although their scales are impervious to water, the gill membranes are not, so fresh-water bony fish experience continual influx of water, while marine fish suffer water loss. Osmoregulation is therefore essential. Fertilisation is external, and a larval stage is present.

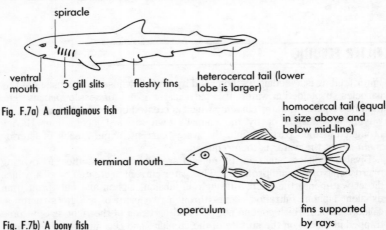

Fig. F.7a) A cartilaginous fish

Fig. F.7b) A bony fish

FISHERIES

The term fishery refers to an expanse of water, or aquatic **ecosystem**, that supports a **population** of a particular type of fish. Population numbers are high enough to permit the removal of fish by man for pleasure or profit. Fisheries may be found in fresh-water, marine-coastal or marine-oceanic locations, with the marine-coastal ones being of the greatest economic significance.

Important fisheries include those of the North Sea, where herring, cod, haddock and plaice are abundant, and those of the Mediterranean Sea, where sardines and mackerel predominate.

FISHING REGULATIONS

With the growth in technology and in numbers of people, the possibility of **overfishing** and exhausting fish stocks is a real one. Fish have a high reproductiv potential, with thousands of eggs laid by each female, but even without man's intervention, relatively few can be expected to survive to adulthood. Regulation of the fishing industry is therefore essential for successful fishery management.

One technique is to restrict the mesh size of nets. If the mesh size is large enough, only the biggest adult fish will be caught. Small, immature fish escape to continue their development.

It may also be necessary to impose quota restrictions, limiting the total numbers of fish of whatever size that may be caught per unit time. A quota may apply to anything from a single boat to a company or a nation and the time unit is usually a year.

Many fisheries are protected by having specified 'close seasons' when all fishing is prohibited. This covers the breeding season, when large numbers of fish congregate to release their gametes into the water at the same time. The close season ends when the young fish, the fry, reach a certain minimum size.

A fourth technique to regulate fishing is for each country to establish exclusion zones around its coast, in which only the fishing boats of that country may operate. The distance of an exclusion zone will depend partly on the extent of the continental shelf and partly on the current size of the fish population. If fish stocks are becoming depleted, then it may be necessary to increase an exclusion zone.

FISHING TECHNIQUES

Fishing techniques vary according to the type of fish to be caught, their location and the quantities required. Small-scale fishing by sport and hobby anglers is mainly done with a line connected to a fishing rod. The line usually has a float attached and may be baited, with maggots, or artificial flies may be used (fly-fishing).

Large-scale fishing for economic gain is mainly done with nets from boats.

Fish that move around on the sea floor, such as sole and plaice, can be caught using a trawl net. This is a bag-like net that is dragged along the bottom by a boat called a trawler. Fish that swim around in shoals away from the sea bed, such as herrings, are caught using a seine net – a vertical net that hangs from floats on the surface. The ends are brought together and it is hauled in by a seine boat. The mesh size of both types of net can be varied. Clearly, a larger mesh size will allow small or immature fish to escape and continue their development in the sea. If herring fry are required, however (to make whitebait), then a very fine mesh size will be used.

FISSION

In the single-celled organisms, or protoctistans, mitotic cell division results in two new individuals, so a form of **asexual reproduction** has taken place. This is known as fission, and it occurs in all types of **bacteria** and in many **protozoa** and unicellular **algae** and **fungi**. Replication of **DNA** and division of the **cytoplasm** give rise to daughter cells genetically identical to the parent cell. The relative simplicity of this method of reproduction means that a colony of bacteria, for example, may double its numbers every twenty minutes.

'FITNESS'

The word 'fitness' is often used to describe either physical prowess, particularly at sport, or general good health. In biology it has a rather different meaning, however, as illustrated by the well-known phrase of **Darwin** 'survival of the fittest'. Fitness is a measure of the ability to produce mature offspring which will themselves be able to reproduce. The fittest individuals in a **population** are those that are best able to pass on their genes to succeeding generations and are not necessarily those that simply live longest. These individuals require adaptations enabling them to avoid **predation** and **disease**, to mate and to produce a sufficient number of healthy offspring. They are then said to have been 'selected'.

◀ Gene, Natural selection ▶

FIXATION (1)

The conversion of any substance into a biologically more usable form is known as fixation. **Nitrogen** gas forms 79 per cent of the atmosphere but can only be used in its pure gaseous form by certain **bacteria**. All other organisms require it first to be incorporated into **organic compounds** such as **amino acids**. Nitrogen-fixing bacteria include *Azotobacter*, which is free-living in the soil, and Rhizobium, which is symbiotic in the root nodules of leguminous plants.

Carbon dioxide gas requires fixation by green plants before it can be used by animals. In the **dark reaction** of photosynthesis, carbon dioxide is reduced to form carbohydrate.

FIXATION (2)

The process of treating living tissue for microscopic examination is also termed fixation. The tissue must be killed with the minimum distortion, so that the preparations can then be stained and mounted. Suitable fixatives include 10 per cent formalin, aqueous methanol and Bouin's fluid.
◀ Stains ▶

FLAGELLATES

Flagellate is a non-taxonomic term describing unicelled organisms that possess at least one **flagellum** for **locomotion**. The kingdom **Protoctista** includes two phyla of flagellates, the phylum Zoomastigina, which are all heterotrophic, and the phylum Euglenophyta, which includes photosynthetic and non-photosynthetic members with their own distinctive biochemistry. The phylum **Chlorophyta** also includes a few members that are flagellate (e.g. *Chlamydomonas*).

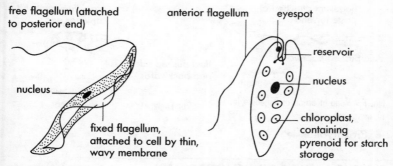

free flagellum (attached to posterior end)

nucleus

fixed flagellum, attached to cell by thin, wavy membrane

anterior flagellum   eyespot

reservoir

nucleus

chloroplast, containing pyrenoid for starch storage

Fig. F.8a) *Trypanosoma*   Fig. F.8b) *Euglena gracilis*

A typical member of the Zoomastigina is *Trypanosoma* (Fig. F.8a), which is a blood parasite that causes sleeping sickness. It feeds by **absorption** of dissolved **nutrients** from the blood in which it lives. Other zoomastiginans are free-living and feed by **phagocytosis**.

The Euglenophyta includes several species of **Euglena**, some of which contain **chlorophyll** for feeding by **photosynthesis** while others are colourless and feed saprophytically on decaying material. Green species of Euglena may also lose their chloroplasts and feed saprophytically if deprived of light for long enough (Fig. F.8b).

FLAGELLUM

A flagellum (plural: flagella) is a long hair-like structure concerned with **locomotion**. They are found on the surface of cells, both of **bacteria**, which are prokaryotes, and of the eukaryote flagellate **protozoa** and some green **algae**.

The prokaryotic flagellum resembles a single microtubule. It is only 20 nm in diameter and not enclosed by the plasma membrane. Some bacteria have a single flagellum (e.g. **Rhizobium**) others have many (e.g. Azotobacter).

In eukaryotes flagella have an identical internal structure to **cilia** with a '9+2' arrangement of **microtubules**. They are surrounded by the plasma membrane so may be considered true organelles. Their mean length is approximately 100 μm, which is about ten times longer than cilia, and they usually occur singly or in pairs, while cilia are numerous.

In both cilia and flagella, the mechanism of movement appears to involve microtubules sliding past one another in a **ratchet mechanism**, similar to that found in muscle cells. The resulting action is very different, however. Unlike a cilium, a flagellum has a symmetrical beat, with several undulations running from base to tip at any given moment. This wave-like motion is usually in one plane, with the flagellum attached at the posterior end of the cell, as for example in **sperm** cells (Fig. F.9a) and *Paranema*. A notable exception is **Euglena**, which has an anterior flagellum which beats in a corkscrew manner, causing the organism to rotate about its own axis (Fig. F.9b).

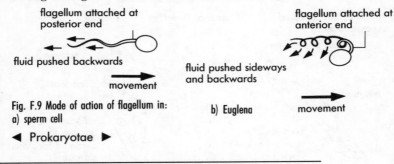

flagellum attached at posterior end

fluid pushed backwards

movement

flagellum attached at anterior end

fluid pushed sideways and backwards

Fig. F.9 Mode of action of flagellum in:
a) sperm cell

b) Euglena

movement

◀ Prokaryotae ▶

FLAVINE ADENINE DINUCLEOTIDE (FAD)

FAD is a dinucleotide that contains Vitamin B_2, riboflavine, combined with **adenosine monophosphate**. It is easily reduced and oxidised and it acts as a hydogen acceptor for **dehydrogenase enzymes** in **Krebs cycle** and the electron transport system (ETS). It is often described as a **co-enzyme**, though since it forms a complex with the dehydrogenase enzyme, it is strictly a **prosthetic group**.

- In Krebs cycle:
  dehydrogenase
  succinic acid + FAD ⟶ fumaric acid + $FADH_2$

- In the ETS:
  dehydrogenase
  $NADH_2$ + FAD ⟶ NAD + $FADH_2$

◀ Electron transfer, ETS ▶

FLAVOPROTEIN

When **FAD** combines with a dehydrogenase enzyme, the resulting complex may also be known as a flavoprotein. In **Krebs cycle** the flavoprotein consists of FAD and succinic dehydrogenase, while in the electron transport system, the flavoprotein consists of FAD and NAD dehydrogenase.

FLEXOR MUSCLE

When a flexor muscle contracts, it pulls two bones closer together, and so causes the bending of a limb. For every flexor muscle, there is an antagonistic extensor muscle that contracts to straighten the limb.

In a mammal's forelimb, the flexor muscle is the biceps.
◀ Antagonistic muscles, Forelimb of mammal ▶

FLIGHT

Flight may be defined as **locomotion** through the air with the use of wings. It has evolved quite separately in two main classes, the **insects** and the **birds**. One group of **mammals**, the bats, also has the ability to fly, and flying fish can glide over the surface of the water for up to 50 metres.

FLIGHT IN INSECTS

Insect wings are flattened extensions of the thoracic **exoskeleton**, supported by a system of hollow veins. They are not muscular, and all the muscles involved in flight are contained within the **thorax**. Large-winged insects such as butterflies and locusts have direct muscles attached to the base of the wing. These muscles contract once for each **nerve impulse**, resulting in a relatively slow wing-beat. In insects with smaller wings, the flight muscles are attached to the thoracic wall and operate a lever system; small distortions in the shape of the thorax result in large movements of the wing. These muscles are able to cause up to forty wing-beats per nerve impulse, because they are able to contract in between in response to a stretch reflex.

FLIGHT IN BIRDS

In birds the wing is a modification of the pentadactyl limb. This means that it is supported by bones and is muscular. It also possesses **joints**, enabling it to flex, or bend, at the 'wrist', reducing air resistance on the upstroke of the wing.

The wing acts as an aerofoil. Greater pressure on the under surface of the wing tends to 'push' it upwards, so creating an upthrust which is known as 'lift'. The amount of lift depends on the shape and size of the wing, the angle it is held at, relative to the bird's body, and the speed of flight. Slow-flying birds usually have short, wide wings, while fast-flying birds have longer, narrow wings. The feathers also affect the degree of lift. On the downstroke of the wing, they interlock to increase air resistance, so increasing lift, while on the upstroke they separate, allowing air to flow between them, offering minimum resistance (Fig. F.10).

Flight may be active or passive. In active flight the wings are flapped up and down, using the powerful pectoral flight muscles between the sternum and humerus. These large muscles are rich in myoglobin, and the sternum is extended into a keel to provide sufficient space for their attachment. Flapping flight requires considerable energy expenditure, and in many birds it is interspersed with periods of passive flight.

In passive flight, or gliding, the wings are held out from the body. They act as fixed aerofoils, creating lift, which is opposed by gravity forces acting on the mass of the bird. Since the latter forces are usually greater, the bird loses height during gliding flight. Birds with particularly large wings for their body size, such as eagles and buzzards, can gain height by gliding in circles, using thermals and other upcurrents of air. This is also known as soaring flight.

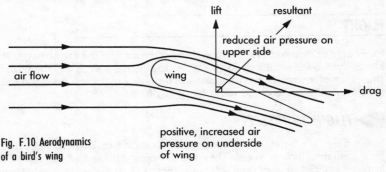

Fig. F.10 Aerodynamics of a bird's wing

FLORAL MORPHOLOGY

Flower structure is closely linked to the reproductive function of flowers, and to the way in which they are pollinated. An enormous range of variation exists in the form of flower parts, but there is consistency within a species, so floral morphology is used extensively in classification.

Each flower is borne on its own stalk, called a pedicel. Flowers may be solitary or grouped together as an inflorescence, in which case the pedicels are attached to an inflorescence-stalk called a peduncle. The tip of the pedicel

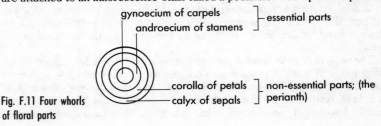

Fig. F.11 Four whorls of floral parts

is swollen to form the receptacle, on which four sets of floral parts are arranged in spirals or whorls (Fig.F.11). In **monocotyledon** flowers the floral parts are usually in threes or multiples of three, while in **dicotyledon** flowers the floral parts are in fours fives or multiples of these.

The sepals protect the rest of the flower during the bud stage. They are usually green, though they may be coloured like the petals. The main function of petals is to attract **insects** to the flower for **pollination**, so in **entomophilous flowers** (insect-pollinated) the petals are brightly coloured and often scented, while in **anemophilous flowers** (wind-pollinated) they are either small and green or absent altogether. Petals may be joined, in which case the flower is described as **sympetalous**, or separate, as in **polypetalous** flowers.

Though some flowers are single-sexed, most flowers are hermaphrodite, containing both stamens, the male reproductive structures, and carpels, the female reproductive structures. Each stamen is made up of an anther and a filament. Each carpel consists of an **ovary** containing one or more ovules, a style and a stigma, though in many flowers the carpels are completely or

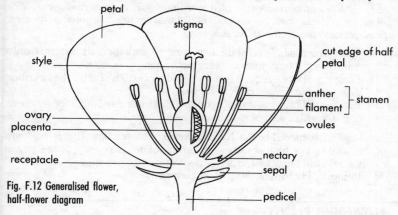

Fig. F.12 Generalised flower, half-flower diagram

partially fused. The arrangement of flower parts is best illustrated in a half-flower diagram (Fig. F.12).

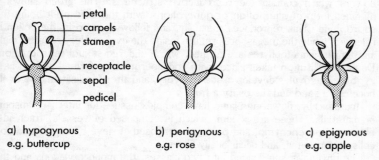

a) hypogynous
e.g. buttercup

b) perigynous
e.g. rose

c) epigynous
e.g. apple

Fig. F.13 Arrangements of flower parts

The ovary may be described as superior or inferior, depending on whether its position is above or below the point of origin of the petals. Flowers may be described as hypogynous, perigynous or epigynous, depending on whether the other flower parts are attached to the receptacle below, around or on the top of the gynoecium (Fig. F.13).

◀ Anthers, Stamen ▶

FLOWERING, CONTROL OF

The production of flowers in each plant species is controlled by various plant **hormones**, which are themselves affected by environmental factors. Plants of the same species should therefore flower together, making **cross-pollination** more likely, and can flower at about the same time every year, to coincide with such factors as the seasonal activity of pollinating **insects**.

The most important environmental factor is the photoperiod, which affects the relative proportions of **phytochrome** 665 and phytochrome 725. Flowering plants can be divided into three groups, according to their photoperiodic requirements for flowering.

- Short-day plants – require exposure to dark periods longer than a critical length (e.g. tobacco, chrysanthemum, poinsettia).
- Long-day plants –require exposure to dark periods shorter than a critical length (e.g. cabbage, clover, petunia).
- Day-neutral plants – do not require a particular day length for flowering (e.g. tomato, cucumber, begonia).

Another environmental factor that can induce or hasten flowering is exposure of the seed to low temperatures, or **vernalisation**. Short-day, long-day and day-neutral plants may all require periods of cold before they will flower.

◀ Hormone, Photoperiodism, Phytachrome ▶

FLOWERING PLANTS

Flowering plants belong to the phylum **Angiospermophyta**. They bear flowers which contain the reproductive structures. The group shows a modified form of **alternation of generations**, with the main plant being the **sporophyte**. This reproduces asexually, and following **meiosis**, the pollen is released, while the megaspores remain inside the ovules. Very reduced male and female gametophytes are formed, which undergo **sexual reproduction**. Double **fertilisation** takes place, with endosperm tissue formed as well as a **zygote**. The ovules develop inside an **ovary**, and after fertilisation, the ovule becomes a **seed** and the ovary a **fruit**.

Anatomically, flowering plants have complex tissues for internal transport of materials. These are **xylem**, which is composed of vessels, tracheids, fibres and **parenchyma**, and **phloem**, composed of sieve tubes, **companion cells**, parenchyma, and occasionally fibres.

The phylum is sub-divided into two classes, the monocotyledons and the dicotyledons. Overall, it is an extremely diverse group of plants with representatives in a wide range of habitat.

◄ Dicotyledon, Floral morphology, Monocotyledon, Pollination ►

FLUID MOSAIC MODEL OF CELL-MEMBRANE STRUCTURE

The fluid mosaic model for cell-membrane structure was suggested by Singer and Nicholson in 1972. Investigations using the electron microscope had indicated that three layers of molecules were involved; a lipid bilayer covered by protein layers. Experiments on membrane functioning, however, implied that these layers were not as fixed as originally thought. The only explanation that could satisfy all the results was the suggestion that the protein molecules formed a mosaic pattern in the fluid lipid part of the membrane. Some protein molecules would extend through the depth of the membrane, some move from one side to the other and some form pores through the membrane. The technique of freeze fracturing, which splits the membrane along lines of weakness, supports this model.

The lipid forms a bilayer because each molecule possesses a phosphate group, (so it is actually a phospholipid), giving it a polar 'head' with two non-polar 'tails'. Sterols, or steroid alcohols, such as cholesterol, are also incorporated into the membrane structure. Carbohydrate molecules may be attached on the outer surface of the membrane, forming glycolipids and glycoproteins with membrane lipids and proteins. This layer is referred to as the glycocalyx and it functions in recognition mechanisms. The proteins in the membrane have very many functions. These include forming part of the structural framework and acting as enzymes (e.g. permeases). They can also be carriers for transporting specific molecules through the membrane, and in metabolic reactions they can be electron carriers.

◄ Cell membranes, Electron carrier, Lipids, Phospholipids, Proteins ►

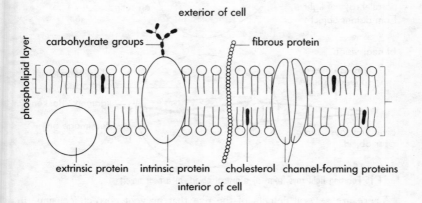

Fig. F.14 Fluid mosaic model

FLUKE

A fluke is a parasitic flatworm in the class Trematoda, phylum Platyhelminthes. Examples include the liver fluke, *Fasciola hepatica*, and the blood fluke, *Schistosoma*.

FOCUSING (ACCOMMODATION)

Focusing means the bending, or refraction, of light rays entering the eye so that they are brought to a point on the retina. The image is actually inverted on the retina, but the brain is able to interpret the impulses received so that objects appear the correct way up. Refraction of light occurs at three surfaces within the eye, these being the cornea, the front surface of the lens and then the back surface of the lens. The curving bulge of the cornea is maintained by the aqueous humour and produces a constant angle of refraction. The lens is elastic, however, and its curvature can be altered by the ciliary muscle so that both distant objects and close objects can be focused. For distant vision, the ciliary muscle is relaxed. This pulls the suspensory ligaments taut and the lens is flattened, so reducing the amount of refraction (Fig. F.15a). For near vision, the ciliary muscle contracts, allowing the ligaments to slacken (Fig. F.15b). The elasticity of the lens causes it to assume an almost spherical shape, enabling it to bend the light rays sufficiently to focus them.

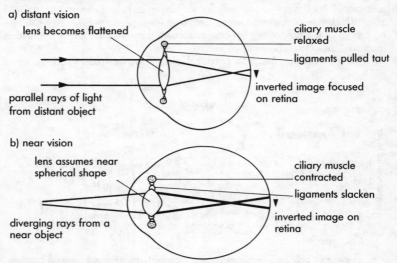

a) distant vision

lens becomes flattened

ciliary muscle relaxed

ligaments pulled taut

parallel rays of light from distant object

inverted image focused on retina

b) near vision

lens assumes near spherical shape

ciliary muscle contracted

ligaments slacken

diverging rays from a near object

inverted image on retina

Fig. F.15 Focusing light rays from; a) a distant object, b) a near object

There are several defects of the eye that prevent correct focusing. In near-sightedness, or myopia, close objects can be seen clearly but rays from far objects focus in front of the retina. Spectacles with concave lenses are required in order to make the light rays diverge slightly. In far-sightedness, or hypermetropia, distant objects can be focused but rays from close objects focus behind the retina. Convex lenses are needed to converge the light rays before they enter the eye.

FOETUS

◀ Fetus ▶

FOLLICLE STIMULATING HORMONE (FSH)

FSH is a **hormone** secreted by the anterior lobe of the **pituitary gland**. Together with **luteinising hormone** (LH) and hormones secreted by the **ovary**, it helps to regulate the **menstrual cycle**.

FOOD

◀ Nutrients ▶

FOOD ADDITIVES

Additives are substances added to food to preserve it or change it in some way. There are very many additives used by food manufacturers, some extracted from nature, some synthetic copies of 'natural' products and others completely artificial. The four main categories of additives are controlled by legislation, and those substances that are permitted under European Community laws are given 'E' numbers. The main categories are as follows.

- Preservatives which help food to keep longer, prevent wastage of food through spoilage and provide protection against bacteria such as *Salmonella*, which cause food poisoning. Their use also means that foods are available out of season, so a wider diet becomes possible. Examples include saltpetre (E252), used to preserve cooked or cured meat, and sorbic acid (E200), used to preserve fruit yoghurt.
- Antioxidants, which stop **lipids** and fat-soluble **vitamins** from oxidising and going rancid or deteriorating. Commonly used antioxidants include ascorbic acid (E300) and butyl hydroxytoluene (E321).
- Colours, which are used to make food look more appealing. There are over fifty permitted colours: natural ones include caramel (E150) and beta carotene (E160a), and artificial ones include tartrazine (E102).
- Emulsifiers and stabilisers, which cause emulsions to form from ingredients such as oil and water and then prevent them from separating again. They also add to the smoothness and creaminess of texture in many foods. Examples include gum arabic (E414) in confectionery and methyl cellulose (E461) in low-fat spreads.

Other categories of additives are not covered by EC legislation and some are controlled in the UK alone. These include flavour enhancers such as monosodium glutamate (MSG), sweeteners such as saccharin, pH buffers, crisping agents, moistening agents, flour improvers and bleachers, glazing agents, anti-caking agents, propellants and many more.

◀ Salmonella poisoning ▶

FOOD CHAINS, FOOD WEBS

A food chain is a sequence of feeding relationships in an environment. At the base of the chain are the **producers**. These are autotrophic able to synthesise complex organic molecules using energy from the sun in most cases. Producers form the first trophic level, and they are fed upon by primary **consumers** on the second trophic level. These in turn are fed upon by secondary consumers, which comprise the third trophic level in the chain, and so on. For example,

grass	→	sheep	→	human being
PRODUCER		FIRST CONSUMER		SECOND CONSUMER

The number of links in the chain is normally limited to four or five. This is because although there is a flow of **energy** through the chain, a high percentage of the energy input is lost at each stage, through **respiration**, **excretion** and other body activities.

A detritivore food chain is slightly different from the one already described.

Fig. F.16 Simplified pond food web

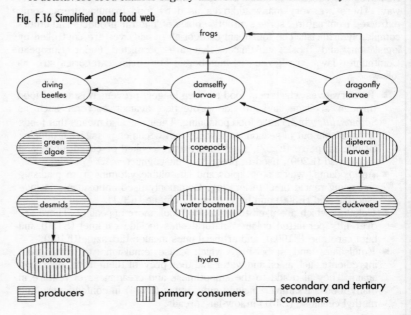

It occurs where there is dead organic material which is fed on by **decomposers** and turned into detritus. This detritus may then act as the base of a food chain of consumers.

Single food chains in fact rarely exist, and a food web is a more realistic representation of feeding relationships. This is because most primary consumers feed on more than one kind of autotroph, and most secondary consumers rely on more than one type of prey. The more varied the organisms in an environment, the more complex a food web is formed (the one illustrated in Fig. F.16 is very simplified). Studies of feeding relationships have become extremely important in modern ecological research and can be extended to provide data on **biomass, productivity** and ecological energetics.

◄ Trophic levels ►

FOOD SPOILAGE

Food spoilage means that food is spoiled or wasted, and is no longer edible. It may result from invasion by **bacteria** or **fungi**, or may be due to physical changes in the food, such as dehydration or loss of crispness, or to chemical changes because of processes such as oxidation.

Food additives such as preservatives and antioxidants can be used in order to prevent or delay food spoilage.

FOOD TESTS

Food tests are biochemical tests which can easily be performed in the laboratory to show the presence of the various basic constituents of food. They all rely on simple techniques, usually with a specific colour end-point. In most cases the food is first crushed with some distilled water and filtered, then a known volume of filtrate is used in the test. The most common tests are as follows.

 IODINE TEST FOR STARCH

The reagent used is a brown solution of iodine in potassium iodide. A couple of drops added to a filtrate containing starch will produce a blue-black colour. If no starch is present the filtrate will remain brown.

 BENEDICT'S SOLUTION TEST FOR REDUCING SUGARS (E.G. MALTOSE AND GLUCOSE)

A known volume of the blue reagent is added to the same volume of filtrate and boiled in a water bath for two minutes. If no reducing sugar is present, the liquid remains blue; if a small amount is present, the liquid becomes green; if much reducing sugar is present, it turns red. The red colour is due to a precipitate which settles out on standing. The amount of this precipitate is an indication of the amount of original reducing sugar in the food sample.

▶ *TEST FOR NON-REDUCING SUGARS (E.G. SUCROSE)*

This is a modification of the last test. Since many foods will contain both reducing and non-reducing sugars, it is a good idea to carry out the two tests using equal volumes of the same food filtrate and to retain the red precipitate from the reducing sugar test for comparison. For this test, an equal volume of sodium hydroxide is added to the filtrate with two drops of concentrated hydrochloric acid. The mixture is boiled in a water bath for five minutes, then allowed to cool down, before adding an equal volume of Benedict's solution and proceeding as for the reducing-sugar test. The precipitate in this case will represent both reducing and non-reducing sugars and should be compared to the precipitate retained earlier.

▶ *BIURET TEST FOR PROTEINS*

Potassium hydroxide is added to the filtrate a little at a time until the solution becomes clear. One drop of copper sulphate is then added down the side of the test tube. If the filtrate contains protein, a dark-blue ring will form at the surface of the solution, and on shaking the blue ring will disappear and the solution turns purple. Another test for protein involves heating the filtrate with Millon's reagent to obtain a brick-red colour. This causes Millon's reagent to give off poisonous mercury vapours however, so the biuret test is preferable.

▶ *ETHANOL TEST FOR LIPIDS*

Equal volumes of absolute ethanol and water are used for this test, and the undiluted ground up food sample is tested instead of a filtrate. The food is first shaken vigorously with the ethanol to dissolve any lipid present, then the water is added. Lipid is indicated by a cloudy white precipitate, the whiteness of which is proportional to the concentration of lipid in the food sample. A simpler test is the **grease-spot test for fats**, in which the food sample is rubbed on filter paper. The presence of fat is indicated by a transparent greasy mark which disappears if washed with alcohol.

◀ Benedict's solution, Ethanol, Glucose, Lipids, Maltose, Non-reducing sugars, Proteins, Reducing sugars, Starch, Sucrose ▶

FORELIMB OF MAMMAL

The forelimb of a mammal can be used to illustrate how bones, **joints**, muscles and the **nervous system** all work together to produce movement (Fig. F.17).

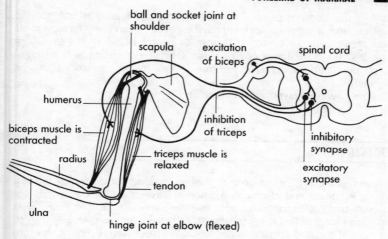

Fig. F.17 Forelimb of a mammal as a working unit

► BONES AND JOINTS

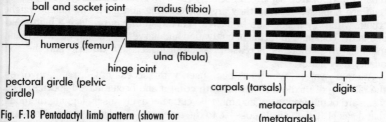

Fig. F.18 Pentadactyl limb pattern (shown for forelimb, with hind limb bones given in brackets)

The limbs of a mammal are built on the pentadactyl limb pattern that is characteristic of all four-legged **chordates** (Fig F.18). This pattern requires a single long bone which fits into a socket of the limb girdle at its head and forms a hinge joint with a pair of long bones at the other end. After the long bones, comes a group of nine small bones, called the carpals in the forelimb (tarsals in the hindlimb), then five metacarpals (metatarsals in the hindlimb) and the bones of the five digits. The ball and socket joint at the shoulder allows movement in all planes and some rotation, but very heavy loads may cause dislocation. The hinge joint at the elbow is restricted to movement through 180 degrees in one plane only, but can bear heavy loads without damage.

► MUSCLES AND NERVES

The forelimb shown in the Fig. F.18 is being raised by the contraction of the flexor muscle of the upper arm, the biceps. At the same time, the triceps, which is the extensor muscle, is relaxed. They are known as **antagonistic muscles**, since if both muscles contracted together, then clearly no movement could result. Nervous control is thought to involve inhibitory and excitatory synapses. While excitation occurs in the synapse connecting to the biceps' motor neurone, the synapse to the triceps' motor neurone must be inhibited.

◀ Bone, Synapse, synaptic transmission ▶

FORESTRY

Forestry is the art, or science, of planting, tending and managing forests. Forest is the natural **climax** vegetation in large areas of the world, but although most of Europe was once forested, less than 30 per cent still is today, and much of that is in Scandinavia. In Britain, for example, less than 10 per cent of the land remains under forest, as trees have been cut down to clear land for agriculture, urbanisation and communications. There are major reforestation programmes in areas such as the Scottish highlands, however, so the situation should improve.

There are two main approaches to forest management. One is to plant a monoculture of tree saplings in orderly rows on cleared land. Spruce, pine or teak are popular, because they are fast-growing and have one main straight trunk, with only minor side branches. This system can produce a high yield and is the cheapest in terms of cultivation and harvesting costs, but as with all monocultures, there is increased risk from **insects** and **disease** and the soil quality may suffer.

Another system, which has been used with success in Germany, involves the planting of mixed forest with both **conifer** and broad-leaved species. The trees are of different ages and must be cut selectively, using logging methods that do as little damage as possible to the trees still standing. New saplings are planted in the spaces and allow for sustained production. A major advantage of this system is that it provides enough timber to be commercially viable and yet the land remains forested.

The advantages of retaining forest land are considerable. Timber is used for construction purposes and to make plywood, paper and other products. Forests are home to a great diversity of plant and animal **species** and are sources of many medicinal herbs. They are also valuable for recreational purposes.

In the long-term, forests hold the land together, keep water cycles functioning and maintain the balance of gases in the atmosphere. The land is protected from wind and water erosion, by trees acting as windbreaks and 'rainbreaks' and by roots binding the soil particles. Soil fertility is also improved due to litter decomposition and reduced **leaching**. Water cycles are maintained by the forest transpiration, which assists cloud formation, and by the trees intercepting moisture-laden winds and so influencing rainfall. Finally, trees replenish the oxygen supply of the air by their **photosynthesis**. Indeed, the vast Amazon jungle has been described as the lungs of the earth.

FRACTIONATION

◄ Cell fractionation ►

FRAGMENTATION

Fragmentation is a form of **asexual reproduction** that can occur in plants and certain animal groups, such as **sponges** and nemertine worms. It means literally dividing up into fragments, or small pieces, each of which can grow into a new individual.

In plants **filamentous algae** such as *Spirogyra* reproduce by fragmentation. All cells in the filament can divide by **mitosis**, so even tiny fragments can regenerate into long strands. Most forms of vegetative **reproduction** in **flowering plants** are also based on the principle of fragmentation.

In animals the marine nemertine worm *Lineus* fragments into hundreds of pieces, each of which can grow into a new worm.

FREQUENCY, OF SPECIES

Frequency is an ecological term giving information on the relative abundance of different species in a **habitat**. It is usually expressed as a percentage. As an example, if a species had a frequency of sixty per cent, it must have been recorded present in sixty out of 100 observations. **Quadrat frames** can be used for making these observations.

FRESH MASS

The fresh mass means the mass including the water content. All living things contain water, and evaporation and other factors mean that this water content is variable, so **dry-mass** measurements may be more reliable. Fresh mass is often preferable, however, since dried organisms are also dead organisms.

FRESH-WATER ECOSYSTEMS

Fresh-water ecosystems include bodies of still water such as ponds and lakes, and bodies of flowing water such as rivers and streams. In comparison with terrestrial and marine habitats, fresh water provides a relatively stable environment with clearly defined limits, and the species diversity is small enough to ease the problem of identification.

Still water may be subject to distinct climatic variations, particularly if it is shallow. **Climatic factors** affecting species distribution include light penetration, temperature, oxygen concentration, pH and dissolved mineral content.

In most bodies of still water, the species distribute themselves in three main zones. At the bottom is the mud layer, home of aerobic micro-organisms and of detritivores such as the swan mussel, *Anodonta cygnea*. Next comes the vegetation zone and the open water. The majority of pond plants are totally submerged (e.g. Canadian pondweed, *Elodea canadensis*), but others such as bullrushes may have just their lower stems in water. The plants support a wide range of herbivorous animals such as snails and bugs, which in turn support carnivores such as water beetles and sticklebacks. In the open water, vast numbers of planktonic micro-organisms are also present. The third zone is the surface film, or interface between air and water. The most common plants here are the free-floating duckweeks such as *Lemna minor*, and most animals are specialised air-breathing insects (e.g. pond skaters, whose weight is supported by the surface tension).

Flowing water has many of the characteristics of still water but there are important differences. Climatic factors such as oxygen concentration, pH and mineral content show much less variation, while physical factors such as current can vary enormously. Most plants and animals that colonise a stream possess adaptations for surviving in a current, examples being attachment mechanisms, streamlining and specific behaviour patterns.

◀ Carnivore, Ecosystem, Habitat, Herbivore, Marine environment ▶

FROGS

Frogs are fresh-water representatives of the class **Amphibia**, phylum Chordata. As adults they have no tails and are hence classified as the order Anura. Their hindlimbs are elongated and muscular for leaping, and bear webbed digits as an adaptation for swimming, most species being amphibious. **Gaseous exchange** occurs by diffusion through the moist skin and buccal cavity as well as via the sac-like lungs. This is one reason why frogs are restricted to moist or humid environments.

Reproduction begins when the frogs gather at spawning grounds in the mating season. Male frogs attach themselves to the back of the females, holding on with the nuptial pads on their thumbs. **Sperm** are then shed on to the eggs as they are laid, resulting in external **fertilisation**. The eggs hatch out into tadpole larvae, which later undergo **metamorphosis** from a tailed aquatic form to a four-legged adult amphibian.

◀ Larva, Metamorphosis ▶

FRUIT, FRUIT DEVELOPMENT

A fruit forms from the **ovary** of a **flowering plant** after **fertilisation** of the ovules has taken place. Considerable changes occur during the development of the fruit before it, or the seeds it contains, are dispersed. This development is under the control of the plant hormones, **auxin** and **gibberellin**, secreted by the fertilised ovules. Commercial fruit growers can exploit this fact by applying external auxin treatment to encourage parthenocarpy, the formation of fruits without seeds. Parthenocarpy does, however, occur naturally in selected varieties of certain fruits (e.g. bananas and pineapples). Towards the completion of fruit development, auxin production decreases and **abscisic acid** (ABA) is secreted instead. This functions as in **leaf fall** and allows the fruit to be shed.

During fruit formation, the ovary wall develops into the pericarp, or fruit wall. Fruits may be classified into groups according to whether their pericarp is dry or fleshy.

Dry fruits may be dehiscent or indehiscent. Indehiscent fruits are shed whole, and the seeds are eventually released by decay or **germination** (e.g. dandelion, Fig. F.20a). Most indehiscent fruits are dispersed by wind or on animals. In other fruits, such as broom (Fig. F.20b) the pericarp dries out unevenly and eventually splits open along the dorsal and ventral edges, flinging the seeds out by mechanical dispersal.

Fleshy or succulent fruits are usually dispersed by being eaten by animals. The pericarp is divided into three layers: a thin outer epicarp, which is coloured to attract animals such as birds, then a thick fleshy mesocarp, and on the inside an endocarp, which may be soft or hard. Succulent fruits with a soft endocarp that encloses many seeds are called berries (e.g. tomato, Fig F.20c). Fruits with a hard, stony endocarp, enclosing a single seed, are called drupes (e.g. plum, Fig. F.20d).

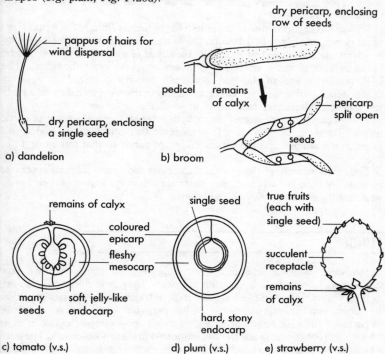

Fig. F.20 Fruits

All the examples described so far are simple true fruits. Compound fruits are formed by some plants, where several separate carpals combine to form a single fruit. A raspberry, for example, is a collection of tiny drupes. In false fruits, some part other than the ovary becomes swollen and fleshy. A strawberry fruit is composed of an enlarged, fleshy receptacle with tiny indehiscent true fruits embedded in the surface (Fig. F.20e).

◀ Floral morphology, Seed dispersal ▶

FUCUS

◀ Phaeophyta ▶

FUNGAL CROP DISEASES

Fungi include some of the most destructive parasites of crop plants, being fast-growing and able to spread rapidly across large agricultural areas. Fungal spores are extremely light and may be carried long distances by wind or water. They are also very persistent and can lie dormant in the soil for many years.

Among the zygomycetes is the potato blight fungus *Phytophthora infestans*. Wind-dispersed spores first land on the leaves, then germinate into hyphae, which invade the whole leaf and kill it. Hundreds of spores are released to be blown to other plants or washed into the soil by rain to infect the tubers. The Irish potato famine of the mid-nineteenth century occurred as a direct consequence of this disease. Other zygomycete diseases include white rusts and downy mildews and damping-off of seedlings.

The ascomycetes are mainly saprophytic, though there are some parasitic forms. These include the powdery mildews that attack roses and cereal grains, for example, and the fungus *Claviceps purpurea* that causes ergot of rye.

The basidiomycete phylum contains the rusts and smuts, serious economic parasites of corn and wheat crops. Rusts parasitise the leaves of their hosts, while smuts invade the developing grains.

FUNGI

Fungi were originally classified as a sub-group of plants but are now considered to constitute a separate kingdom. They lack chlorophyll so are non-photosynthetic, and must acquire their nutrition heterotrophically, either by parasitism or saprophytism. Many parasitic fungi are of economic importance because fungal diseases, of crops for example, result in poor yields. Saprophytic fungi are the decomposers in many food chains. They are essential for nutrient recycling, but can cause harm by causing food spoilage. A few types of fungi form specialised symbiotic, or mutualistic, relationships (e.g. in lichens, where the fungus provides a framework within which green **algae** can photosynthesise, and in mycorrhizae with the roots of pine trees and other plants, where the fungus improves **mineral uptake**).

The nutritional requirements of fungi are often very specific. Most require a source of organic nitrogen as well as a source of organic carbon, and some may require other organic nutrients such as **vitamins**. In all fungi, **ingestion** occurs by **absorption** of soluble food products. This is a simple matter for parasites since the host tissues already contain dissolved nutrients, but saprophytic fungi may have to secrete hydrolytic enzymes on to their substrate first so that external **digestion** can take place.

A few fungi are single-celled, such as the **yeast** *Saccharomyces*, but the structure of most is a mycelium of branched hyphae. The hyphae may be coenocytic, with no internal dividing walls, or septate, in which perforated septa sub-divide the hypha into uni- or multi-nucleate cells. Fungal cell walls are made of **chitin**, and their storage carbohydrate is usually **glycogen**. Reproduction is mainly by resistant spores, resulting from **asexual reproduction** or **sexual reproduction**, though yeasts can reproduce asexually by budding.

Fungi are found in all types of **ecosystem** and feature in many advantageous and disadvantageous associations with humans. The kingdom is sub-divided into three phyla: Zygomycota (e.g. *Mucor*), Ascomycota (e.g. *Neurospora* and *Saccharomyces*) and Basidiomycota (e.g. *Agaricus*).

◀ Basidiomycete, Saprophytes, saprophytism, Zygomycete ▶

FUSED BONES

The mammalian **endoskeleton** includes some bones that are fused together, with no clear dividing line where one bone ends and the next one begins. The sacrum, for example, is composed of the sacral **vertebrae** (five in man) fused into a broad plate at the back of the pelvic region. The bones of each side of the pelvic girdle are also fused together to make a single structure, and many bones of the skull are fused or form immovable **joints**. The functions of fused bones are to protect and to support.

GALACTOSAEMIA

Galactosaemia is a hereditary condition characterised by the presence of high levels of galactose in the blood and also urine. It is caused by a **gene (point) mutation** that prevents the metabolism of galactose to **glucose**, and if undetected it will result in severe liver and **brain** damage. The urine of new-born babies is therefore routinely tested for the presence of galactose, which is a **hexose** sugar normally found in milk and yoghurt.

GAMETE

A gamete is a **haploid** reproductive cell produced by eukaryotes during **sexual reproduction**. Two gametes fuse at **fertilisation** to produce a **diploid** zygote. In plants, gametes are produced by the haploid **gametophyte** stage as a result of **mitosis**, but most animals are diploid so gametes must be produced by **meiosis**.

A small number of plant groups form isogametes, which are identical in both size and motility, but other plant groups and all animals produce non-identical gametes. The female gametes are few in number, large and stationary, while the male gametes are numerous, small and motile. Conifers and angiosperms, however, have a greatly reduced gametophyte stage, and their gametes are reduced to little more than nuclei.

◄ Angiospermophyta, Conifer, Haploidy, Ovum, Sperm ►

GAMETOGENESIS

Gametogenesis means the formation of gametes, a process which occurs in the testes in males and the ovaries in females. Male gametes are formed by spermatogenesis, which does not start until puberty, and female gametes by oogenesis, the first stage of which occurs in the female **fetus** several months before **birth**. Gametogenesis has three stages, as illustrated in Fig. G.1.

1. ■ Both processes begin with a multiplication phase in which **diploid** germ cells in the **testis** and **ovary** divide repeatedly by **mitosis**. The resulting diploid cells are called either spermatogonia or oogonia.
2. ■ Most of the oogonia degenerate, but one oogonium per germ cell and

all spermatogonia, undergo a growth phase. They increase in size to form a large primary oocyte or smaller primary spermatocytes.

3 ■ The maturation stage is when **meiosis** occurs. In spermatogenesis, the first meiotic division, results in two haploid secondary spermatocytes, and the second in four spermatids, which differentiate into spermatozoa or **sperm** cells. In oogenesis, the process is irregular. Nuclear division occurs as expected for meiosis 1, but cytoplasmic division is unequal, giving a large secondary oocyte and a very much smaller first polar body. The second meiotic division does not then occur until after a sperm cell has pierced the vitelline membrane in **fertilisation**. Again it is unequal, giving a large functional egg cell, called an **ovum**, and a small second polar body.

Formation of sperm (spermatogenesis)   Formation of egg (oogenesis)

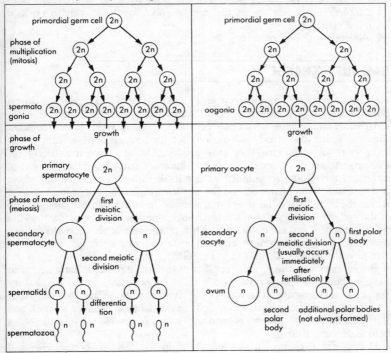

Fig. G.1 Gametogenesis

GAMETOPHYTE

A gametophyte is the stage in the life cycle of a plant when gametes are formed by **mitosis**. It alternates with a **sporophyte** and is haploid since it develops from the germination of a **spore** that was produced by **meiosis**. One gametophyte may contain both male and female sex organs, as in ferns, or separate male and female gametophytes are formed, as in the **flowering plants**.

The gametophyte is the dominant phase in bryophytes. In **liverwort** it is a thin sheet of relatively undifferentiated photosynthetic tissue called a thallus, restricted to very damp habitats. The **moss** gametophyte has a stem and leaves but lacks a **cuticle**. It can therefore take up water over its whole surface, but it can also lose water rapidly, so the plants usually mass together in cushions to slow down the rate of evaporation. The gametophyte of ferns is a heart-shaped **prothallus**, also restricted to damp habitats. Both bryophyte and fern gametophytes develop male sex organs called antheridia, and female sex organs called archegonia.

In angiosperms the male gametophyte forms inside the pollen, while the female gametophyte develops inside the embryosac in the **ovule**. Both gametophytes lack sex organs and are non-photosynthetic, relying on food from the sporophyte.

◀   Alternation of generations   ▶

GASEOUS EXCHANGE

Aerobic respiration requires **oxygen** as a raw material and produces **carbon dioxide** as a waste product. These gases must be exchanged with the environmental medium, which may be water or air. If water is the medium, then the gases are already in solution, but for terrestrial organisms a fluid layer is required so that they may dissolve. In all organisms, therefore, exchange takes place across a moist respiratory surface by the process of **diffusion**, though the respiratory surface itself varies. It could be the whole body surface, as in **protozoa** and the **earthworm**, or an area protected deep within the body, as are the alveoli of mammals. In **insects** gas exchange occurs at the end of the tracheoles of the **tracheal system**, in **fish** it occurs across the gill membranes, and in **flowering plants** it takes place at the **stomata** (where exchange for **photosynthesis** also occurs). Gaseous exchange across the alveoli in the lungs is illustrated in Fig. G.2.

Blood arriving at the alveolar **capillaries** is only 70 per cent saturated with oxygen, but as it leaves saturation is up to 95 per cent, so the respiratory surface is very efficient. The walls of the alveolus and capillary both consist of a single layer of flattened pavement cells so the diffusion distance is small, and the epithelium of the alveolus is lined with moisture in which oxygen dissolves before diffusing through.

During gas exchange in the lungs and in the tissues, certain chemical changes take place. The low partial pressure of carbon dioxide in the alveoli causes hydrogencarbonate ions to pass back from the **plasma** into the **red blood cells**. Here they combine with hydrogen ions released from **haemoglobin**, and the carbon dioxide and water formed can then diffuse out of the capillary. At the same time, oxygen from the alveolar air diffuses into the red blood cells and combines with haemoglobin for carriage round the body.

For gas exchange between oxygenated blood and respiring tissues, these events are reversed. Carbon dioxide from the tissues diffuses into the red blood cells and combines with water under the influence of carbonic anhydrase enzyme. The carbonic acid formed then dissociates into hydrogencarbonate ions and hydrogen ions. Hydrogencarbonate ions diffuse out to the plasma in exchange for chloride ions (the chloride shift) and hydrogen ions displace oxygen from the haemoglobin. The oxygen can then diffuse to the respiring cells and gas exchange is complete.

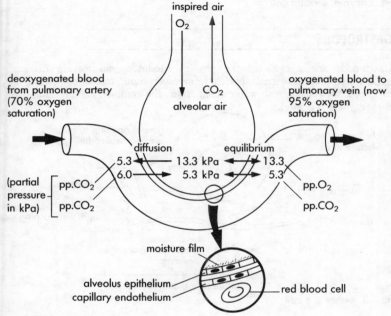

Fig. G.2 Gas exchange in an alveolus

◄ Blood, Gills of fish, Respiratory surfaces and systems ►

GASTRIC JUICE

Gastric juice is an acidic mixture of enzymes and mucus secreted by glandular cells in the stomach, the initial stimulus for secretion being the presence of food in the mouth, which triggers an autonomic reflex response. The mucosa of the stomach wall contains goblet cells which secrete mucus, as well as tubular gastric glands made up of two types of cell:

■ oxyntic cells, which secrete hydrochloric acid, making the pH of the stomach about pH2. This is the optimum pH for the stomach enzymes, and the acid conditions also help kill many pathogenic bacteria.

■ peptic cells, which secrete pepsinogen and pro-rennin, which are activated by acid to become the enzymes **pepsin** and **rennin**. Pepsin hydrolyses proteins to polypeptides, while rennin coagulates milk protein.

The continued secretion of gastric juice for the time the food is in the stomach is under hormonal control. The presence of food in the stomach causes endocrine cells in the stomach lining to secrete the **hormone** gastrin. This is conveyed by the blood to the gastric glands.

◄ Enzyme, Goblet cell ►

GASTROPODS

Gastropoda are a class of the phylum **Mollusca** and include marine, fresh-water and terrestrial species (e.g. *Buccinium*, the whelk, which is marine; *Planorbis*, a fresh-water snail; *Helix*, the common garden snail; and *Limax* which is a slug).

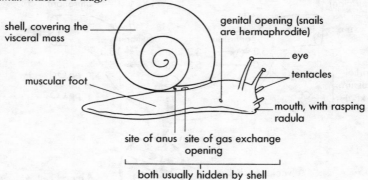

Fig. G.3 Structure of a snail

The body of a gastropod (Fig. G.3) is divided into a distinct head, with eyes on tentacles and a rasping radula for feeding, a visceral mass covered by a single shell (greatly reduced in slugs) and a large muscular foot for locomotion. The shell is coiled due to the torsion, or rotation, of the visceral mass during development.

GENE

A gene is a unit of heredity that is located on and transmitted by a **chromosome** from one generation to the next. Either by itself or together with other genes, it is responsible for determining a characteristic of the individual possessing the gene. It has been defined as 'that portion of a chromosome which codes for one enzyme', or more recently as 'the portion of a chromosome, equivalent to a **cistron**, which codes for a single polypeptide'.

A more general definition that covers all interpretations is that it is 'a specific length of a DNA molecule, made up of a sequence of nucleotides, to which a specific function can be assigned (e.g. a nucleotide sequence coding for a specific polypeptide, or a nucleotide sequence specifying a mRNA molecule)'.

GENE EXPRESSION

Gene expression is the way in which characters under the control of a specific gene appear in the phenotype. The simplest situation involves one pair of alleles which code for contrasting phenotypic characteristics. One allele is dominant and one recessive, and in a heterozygote, the dominant condition is always expressed and appears in the phenotype. Many genes have a more complex relationship with the phenotype, where more than one pair of alleles may be controlled, for example, or where the expression of one gene is dependent on the presence or absence of another gene. The rule is that although alleles are always present in the genotype, they may or may not be expressed in the phenotype.

Gene expression can also be affected by mutation. Gene (point) mutation alters the chemical nature of an allele, so may have a direct affect on the character that appears in the phenotype. Chromosome mutation may alter the position of the gene and so change its interaction with other genes.

◄ Dominant alleles, Gene interaction, Genotype, Heterozygous, Mutation, Recessive alleles ►

GENE INTERACTION

All the genes of an organism work together to determine the specific form and life cycle of an organism. They control a complex set of phenotypic characters as well as physiological and behavioural features.

A relatively small number of characters are controlled by single non-interacting genes. These include wing size in *Drosophila* and tongue-rolling in humans, where the gene appears as just two distinct contrasting characteristics. For most genes there is some form of interaction, so their expression is less precise.

The simplest form of interaction occurs between the alleles of a particular gene. This may take the form of codominance, where the heterozygote shows a phenotype intermediate between those of the homozygotes, or there may be multiple alleles, where any two of a group of alleles interact, resulting in three or more different phenotypes.

Gene interaction more commonly involves a gene complex, consisting of several genes and their alleles interacting to determine a phenotypic character. A well-documented example is the inheritance of comb shape in poultry. This involves the interaction of two genes that occur on different chromosomes so are transmitted independently. There are four possible phenotypes. (Fig. G.4).

phenotype	single comb	pea comb	walnut comb	rose comb

genotype	pprr homozygous recessive alleles for both genes (gives single shape)	PPrr or Pprr dominant allele P present (gives pea shape)	PPRR, PPRr, PpRr, or PpRR codominance of P and R alleles (gives walnut shape)	ppRR or ppRr dominant allele R present (gives rose shape)

Fig. G.4 Comb shape in poultry

Other forms of gene interaction include **epistasis**, where one gene controls the expression of another gene. An example of this is the inheritance of black, white and grey fur colours in mice. Polygenic inheritance involves the interaction of many different genes, and gives rise to **continuous variation** of the phenotypic characters. This type of gene complex is responsible for determining height, mass and so on, where a normal distribution curve may be drawn from the data.

◄ Heterozygous genotype, Homozygous genotype, Polygenes, Polygenic inheritance ►

GENE MAPPING

A gene map is a diagram showing the relative positions of genes on a particular **chromosome**. All the genes on a given chromosome form a **linkage** group and can be inherited together. During prophase I of **meiosis**, however, **chiasmata** formation leads to the **crossing over** of **homologous chromosomes**. This results in new combinations within the linkage groups of the maternal and paternal chromosomes, and recombinant phenotypes appear in the offspring. The number of recombinant types is expressed as a percentage of the total number of offspring, and termed the **cross-over value** (COV).

Gene mapping is based on the assumption that the closer two gene loci are, the less likely they are to be separated by a chiasma, so the lower the COV they will have. A series of breeding experiments is carried out to determine the COVs for all the combinations of a set of genes. Each percentage point is taken to be one unit of the chromosome, and the smallest COV is mapped first.

Example: Take a set of genes, A, B, C and D.
COVs : A-B = 8%, A-C = 3%, A-D = 10%, B-C = 5%, B-D = 18%, C-D = 13%

A and C are 3 units apart, so map them first. C to B is 5 units, while A to B is 8 units, so their sequence is A – C – B. D is 10 units from A, but further away from C and B, so the final sequence and distances are as follows.

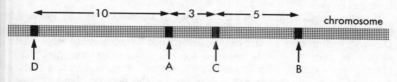

GENE (POINT) MUTATION

A gene or point mutation occurs at a single gene **locus**, and results from a change in the nucleotide sequence during DNA replication. Nucleotide bases may be added (insertion), lost (deletion), changed (substitution) or rearranged (inversion). Somatic mutations only affect the individual, but a **mutation** that takes place during **gametogenesis** can be inherited. If it is a dominant mutation it will be expressed immediately, while recessive mutations may remain masked or hidden for several generations.

An example of a gene mutation is the one that causes **sickle cell anaemia**. The substitution of one base for another changes just one amino acid in **haemoglobin**, but this is enough to distort the red blood cells and seriously lower the amount of oxygen that can be carried.

GENE POOL

The gene pool of a **population** is the sum total of all the genes present in that population. The term is particularly used with reference to demes, or genetically isolated breeding units of the population.
◄ Population genetics ►

GENETIC CODE

The genetic code is the base sequence on a strand of **DNA** or **mRNA**, which acts as the code for **protein synthesis**. Each triplet of consecutive bases on DNA translates into a **codon**, and each codon on mRNA represents an amino acid in the protein to be synthesised. For example, GUG codes for valine, while the triplet GAG codes for glutamic acid. Some triplets form nonsense or punctuation codons, because instead of coding for an amino acid, they act as stop and start signals.
◄ Protein synthesis ►

GENETIC COUNSELLING, GENETIC SCREENING

Genetic counselling is offered to couples with any family history of inherited diseases, such as **cystic fibrosis, haemophilia, sickle cell anaemia** and **phenylketonuria**. The counsellor can assess each partner's chances of being a carrier for the abnormal gene, and advise the couple of the possible risks of having children.

Genetic screening involves certain tests to assess whether an individual possesses an abnormal gene or a chromosome mutation. The presence of **Down's syndrome** in a fetus can be determined by amniocentesis. A small amount of amniotic fluid is removed for cell culture, and the metaphase chromosomes can be photographed and counted. A gene mutation that is screened for is one that causes a deficiency in the pentose shunt enzyme, glucose 6-phosphate dehydrogenase. The deficiency may not be apparent since energy can still be released by the glycolytic pathway, but drugs such as **synthetic sulphonamides** inhibit glycolysis, and so would cause death.

GENETIC DRIFT

Genetic drift is a way in which evolutionary change may occur in small populations. If the frequency of a particular **allele** is 20 per cent, for example, and only half of the individuals posessing that allele reproduce successfully, then the frequency could well be reduced to as low as 5 per cent. This alters the balance of phenotypes, and may result in evolutionary change which has not been dictated by **selection pressure**. In a large population, a dynamic equilibrium exists and the gene frequencies tend to remain constant from one generation to the next. Positive selection pressure is required before changes can occur.

◄ Evolution, Hardy—Weinberg equilibrium, Phenotype, Population ►

GENETIC ENGINEERING AND GENE MANIPULATION

Genetic engineering begins with the manipulation of eukaryotic DNA in the test tube. Recombinant DNA is then introduced into **bacteria** by a **vector**, which may be a bacterial plasmid or a **bacteriophage** virus (Fig. G.5).

A DNA strand containing the **gene** for the desired protein is sliced up into fragments by restriction endonuclease enzymes. These produce staggered cuts, leaving single-stranded 'sticky ends' at each end of a fragment. The same enzyme is used to open up a bacterial plasmid, and the complementary sticky ends of plasmid and eukaryotic DNA fragment and are joined using another **enzyme**, DNA ligase. DNA fragments can also be made from **mRNA**. Reverse transcriptase enzyme is used to produce a single strand of DNA, and DNA polymerase causes the double helix to form.

The recombinanat DNA plasmids are now introduced into the host bacterial cells, and the transformed bacteria are plated out to form colonies. Selection procedures are used to identify the bacteria that contain the required gene. These can then be cloned on an industrial scale and large amounts of the protein harvested. Proteins that are currently manufactured by this technique include **insulin** and human **interferon**.

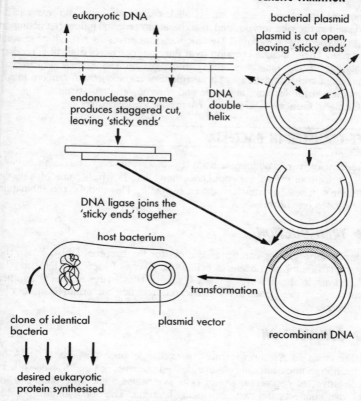

eukaryotic DNA

bacterial plasmid

plasmid is cut open, leaving 'sticky ends'

DNA double helix

endonuclease enzyme produces staggered cut, leaving 'sticky ends'

DNA ligase joins the 'sticky ends' together

host bacterium

transformation

clone of identical bacteria

plasmid vector

recombinant DNA

desired eukaryotic protein synthesised

Fig. G.5 Genetic engineering using a plasmid vector

GENETICS

Genetics involves the study of heredity and of variation. It encompasses the mechanics of inheritance, and the ways in which genetic information is expressed and controlled.

◀ Gene expression, Gene interaction, Jacob–Monod model of gene control, principles of ▶

GENETIC VARIATION

The term genetic variation describes the differences in the genes and chromosomes that make up the genomes of organisms. Every individual organism is totally unique, with its own particular 'genetic fingerprint', or combination of **alleles**. This genetic variation may not reveal itself as phenotypic variations, since many alleles are recessive so cannot be expressed in the **phenotype**, and also the environmental influences acting on the genotype may be variable. Genetic variation arises as a result of several processes. These include **crossing over** during prophase of **meiosis** I, random orientation of chromosomes and chromatids on the spindle equator in metaphase I and II, independent assortment of chromosomes, random fusion of gametes at **fertilisation**, and gene and chromosome mutations.

◄ Gamete, Genotype, Genome, Mutation, Variation ►

GENE TRANSFER IN BACTERIA

Bacteria usually reproduce asexually by binary fission. They also have a primitive form of **sexual reproduction**, however, in which some of a donor bacterium's genes are transferred to a recipient. This genetic recombination may occur in one of three ways.

 ### TRANSDUCTION

Bacteriophage viruses can act as vectors for the bacterial **DNA**. When the virus replicates inside a bacterial cell, small pieces of bacterial DNA may be enclosed inside the new virus coat. If one of these viruses infects another bacterium, it causes genes to be transferred from one bacterium to another by transduction.

 ### CONJUGATION

Bacteria such as *Escherichia coli* can exchange large portions of DNA by conjugation. Some bacterial cells are classed positive, or donors, while others are negative, or recipients. Donor cells synthesise a special protein rod, or pilus, that connects the two conjugating bacteria. The donor then replicates some, or occasionally all, of its DNA and passes one unwound strand through the pilus to the recipient.

 ### TRANSFORMATION

Transformation also involves donors and recipients, but the two cells do not make direct contact. The donor cell first releases a small piece of DNA into its surroundings. The recipient then absorbs the DNA fragment by **active uptake**, and uses it to replace part of its own DNA. This process occurs only in a few types of bacteria (e.g. some species of *Pneumococcus*).

GENOTYPE, GENOME

The genotype of an organism is its genetic constitution with respect to the **alleles** under consideration. It is given in the form of symbols, representing the alleles present at a given gene **locus** or loci. For example, in the inheritance of height in garden peas, there are three possible genotypes: TT (tall plant),

Tt (tall plant), tt (short plant). TT and tt are examples of **homozygous genotypes** while Tt is a **heterozygous genotype**.

In the dihybrid inheritance of height and pod colour in garden peas, there are nine possible genotypes: TTGG, TTGg, TTgg, TtGG, TtGg, Ttgg, ttGG, ttGg, ttgg.

The genome of an organism is its complete genetic constitution. It is the sum total of all its alleles on all its chromosomes, and is unique to that individual organism.

◀ Phenotype ▶

GENUS

A genus is a unit of **classification** used in **taxonomy**. It is the rank below family and consists of one or more closely related **species**. Organisms are givn two names under the binomial system introduced by Linnaeus. The genus, or generic name, is written first and always has a capital letter. It is followed by the species name, which begins with a small letter. Both names are either printed in italics or underlined.

Some examples include: the bacterium *Escherichia coli*, the grass *Festuca rubra*, the honey bee, *Apis mellifera*, and humans, *Homo Sapiens*.

GEOGRAPHICAL VARIATION IN HUMANS

The human populations of the world show quite marked differences in the gene frequencies of certain alleles, indicating that they are to some extent reproductively isolated. One example of such geographical variation is the relative proportions of the ABO blood groups in different parts of the world.

For the blood group B allele, there is a cline, or continuous change in gene frequency, along a line from the south-west of France to the north-west of the USSR, as shown in the table.

Region	Frequency of B gene
Pyrenees	0–5%
Western Europe	5–10%
Eastern Europe and the Baltics	10–15%
Ukraine and West USSR	15–20%
Kazakhstan and Soviet Central Asia	20–25%
North Urals	25–30%

GEOTROPISM

Geotropism is the growth movement made by part of a plant in response to the stimulus of gravity. Roots are positively geotropic, because they grow towards gravity, while stems are negatively geotropic, because they grow away from gravity. It can be demonstrated that gravity is the stimulus for this by attaching the seedlings to a klinostat. If the seedlings are then rotated so that all sides of the root and shoot receive equal gravity stimulus, they grow horizontally. If the seedlings are kept still, however, the plumule grows upwards and the radicle downwards (Fig. G.6).

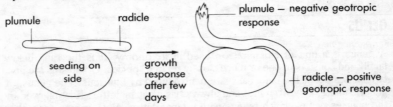

Fig. G.6 Geotropism in a seedling placed on its side in the dark

The stimulus is perceived by special starch grains called statoliths. These are denser than the remaining cell contents and fall under gravity to whichever is the lowest side of the cells. If the statoliths are removed, then the plant shows no further response to gravity. It seems likely that the statoliths affect the distribution of plant hormones, possibly by pulling them down also. There are two hormones that may contribute to the growth reponse: auxin and abscisic acid. In stems, a high auxin concentration stimulates increased cell division and cell elongation, so when auxin gathers on the lower side of a horizontal stem, more growth will occur here and the stem will bend upwards. In roots, high concentrations of auxin inhibit growth, so the root grows downwards. The inhibition may also be caused by accumulated abscisic acid, a growth inhibitor that is produced by root caps.

◄ Tropisms ►

GERMINATION

Germination is the initial growth of a seed or a spore which makes use of the stored food reserves, particularly in seeds. The germination stage ends when the seedling or gametophyte or mycelium is obtaining its own nutrients for growth, either by photosynthesis or heterotrophically.

◄ Heterotrophs, Seed germination ►

GIBBERELLIN

Gibberellin, or gibberellic acid, is a growth-promoting plant hormone. It was first discovered in a fungus, but it is synthesised by most plants in their seeds, flower and leaf buds, young leaves and stem tips. It is involved in **cell division** and tissue differentiation, but its best-known effect is to stimulate cell elongation in the internodes of the stem.

In seeds gibberellin is involved in the breaking of dormancy and start of **germination**. After water is absorbed into the seed, the **embryo** starts to produce gibberellin, which triggers the secretion of enzymes by the aleurone layer. These then hydrolyse the food reserves of the endosperm, releasing sugars and **amino acids** for growth.

◄ Seed germination, Stem elongation, Tissue/organ differentiation ►

GILLS OF FISH

The gills form the **respiratory surface** of a fish, so they are thin, permeable, highly vascular and have a large surface area.

Cartilaginous fish (Chondrichthyes) have five gills on either side of the head, each composed of a double stack of lamellae with gill plates on their surfaces. **Gaseous exchange** occurs between the blood in the gill plate capillaries and the water flowing over the gills. The water flow is parallel to the blood flow, so gas exchange is not that efficient and only about 50 per cent of the dissolved oxygen can be extracted.

Bony fish (**Osteichthyes**) have four gills on either side, covered by a protective bony plate called the operculum. As with cartilaginous fish, each gill consists of a double stack of lamellae with gill plates on their surfaces. A major difference, however, is that the two halves of the gill are free and fan out into the opercular cavity. This changes their orientation with respect to the water flow, so that the water is moving in the opposite direction to the blood flow. Counter-current exchange occurs, allowing about 80 per cent of the dissolved oxygen to be extracted.

◄ Counter-current mechanisms, Fish, Respiratory surfaces and systems, Ventilation mechanisms ►

GIRTH

Girth is a measure of the circumference of a solid object. Increase in the girth of a plant occurs by the division of the **cambium**, which results in **secondary thickening**. If the trunk of a tree is sliced across, the annual increments in girth are visible as concentric light and dark rings. Excessive increase in the girth of a human is referred to as **obesity**!

GLANDS, GLAND CELLS

A gland is an organ composed mainly of gland cells, and a gland cell is one which is modified for **secretion**. Some gland cells, such as goblet cells, occur on their own, as part of a glandular epithelium that has other functions, but most are found grouped into glands. There are two distinct types of gland.

Ductless or **endocrine glands** secrete hormones directly into the bloodstream, while ducted glands secrete enzymes, or other secretions such as sweat, into a duct or tube. Examples of endocrine glands include the **pituitary gland** and **thyroid gland**; examples of ducted glands include the salivary and sweat glands. The **pancreas** contains glandular cells of both types, with the islets of Langerhans secreting hormones into the blood, and other cells secreting pancreatic juice into the duodenum.

◄ Digestion, Goblet cell ►

GLOBULAR PROTEIN

Globular **proteins** are those which have a tertiary structure and, in some cases, quaternary structure as well. This determines their shape, and hence their function. The tertiary structure involves the folding-up of the **polypeptide** chain into a complex three-dimensional structure, held together by disulphide, ionic and hydrogen bonds. **Haemoglobin** is an example of a protein which has a quaternary structure, in that its globular shape is composed of separate polypeptide chains bonded together. All enzymes are globular proteins, as are antibodies and some hormones, such as **insulin**.

◄ Hydrogen bond ►

GLUCAGON

Glucagon is a **hormone** involved in the control of blood glucose. It is secreted by the alpha cells of the islets of Langerhans in the **pancreas** in response to a decreased glucose level in the blood plasma. It travels in the blood to the liver, where it causes the liver cells to break down stored **glycogen** into glucose. This results in an increase in blood glucose, which in turn inhibits further glucagon secretion by **negative feedback**.

◄ Blood glucose level ►

GLUCOSE

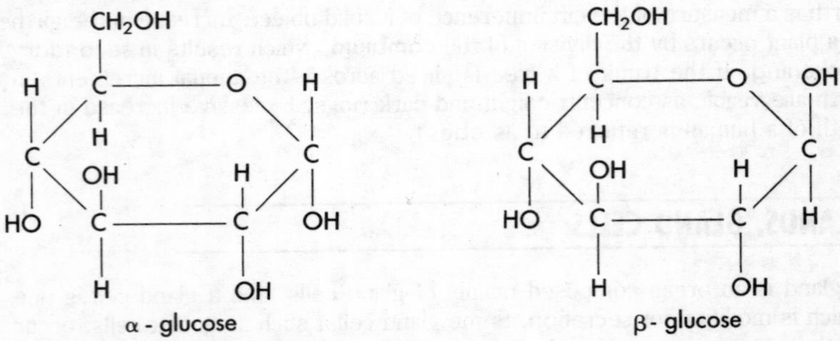

Fig. G.7 Structure of glucose

Glucose is a **hexose** monosaccharide, the most common **monosaccharide** in living organisms (Fig. G.7). It is the main respiratory substrate for **aerobic respiration**, and it is the monomer for the polymers **cellulose, starch** and **glycogen**. There are two forms or isomers, alpha-glucose and beta-glucose, which have differing positions of the H and OH groups on the first carbon atom.

GLYCERATE 3-PHOSPHATE (GP)

Glycerate 3-phosphate, or GP, was formerly referred to as phosphoglyceric acid, PGA. Similarly, phosphoglyceraldehyde, PGAL, should now be called glyceraldehyde 3-phosphate, or GALP. Both molecules are intermediates in **glycolysis** and in the **Calvin cycle** of **photosynthesis**.

GLYCOGEN

Glycogen is a storage polysaccharide, formed by the polymerisation of alpha-**glucose** molecules. It has long, highly branched chains which form tiny granules in the **cytoplasm** of animal cells and in some fungi. In chordates, it is mainly stored in liver and muscle, as a reserve energy store for their high metabolic activity.

◀ Blood glucose level, Muscle contraction, Polysaccharides, Storage polymer ▶

GLYCOLYSIS

Glycolysis is the first stage of **cellular respiration**, involving the breakdown of a hexose respiratory substrate (usually **glucose**) to pyruvic acid. It occurs in the **cytoplasm** of a cell and is essentially the same for both **aerobic** and **anaerobic respiration**.

The hexose molecule is first phosphorylated to make it more reactive. Two molecules of **adenosine triphosphate** (ATP) are used, to form hexose phosphate and then hexose diphosphate. This splits into two molecules of triose phosphate, each of which is converted to pyruvic acid, yielding a total of four hydrogen atoms and four ATP molecules. The net **energy** gain at the end of glycolysis is therefore two ATP molecules, $(- 2 + 4 = 2)$. The hydrogen atoms removed are taken up by the **co-enzyme nicotinamide adenine dinucleotide (NAD)**, which is a hydrogen acceptor (Fig. G.8).

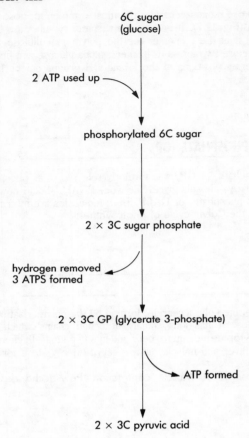

Fig. G.8 Summary of glycolysis

◀ Electron transfer, ET systems, Hydrogen acceptors, Hydrogen carriers, Krebs cycle ▶

GOBLET CELL

A goblet cell is a gland cell that secretes **mucus**. It occurs in the glandular epithelia that line the **alimentary canal**, trachea and bronchi. In the alimentary canal, mucus provides a protective lining for the stomach wall against the acid conditions, and also lubricates the passage of food. In the trachea and bronchi, mucus traps dust particles which can then be swept out of the **lungs** by cilia.

◀ Glands, gland cells, Smoking, effects of ▶

GOLGI COMPLEX

The Golgi complex, Golgi body and Golgi apparatus are all names for the same structure. It occurs in the cytoplasm of most plant and animal cells and is particularly well developed in secretory cells. In the electron microscope, it appears as a stack of flattened membrane-bound pockets called cisternae, with secretory vesicles fusing with them and budding off from them. Recent research indicates that the cisternae actually form a network made of smooth endoplasmic reticulum.

Golgi bodies are particularly concerned with the secretion of glycoproteins such as mucus. The vesicles fusing with the cisternae contain protein which has been synthesised in the rough endoplasmic reticulum. Polysaccharides are added to the protein while it is in the Golgi body, then vesicles containing the glycoprotein pinch off and migrate to the cell membrane. They fuse with the cell membrane to secrete the glycoprotein from the cell, and help to replenish the cell membrane at the same time.

Other vesicles formed from the Golgi body contain hydrolytic enzymes capable of dissolving the cell contents. These vesicles are called lysosomes and remain within the cytoplasm.

◀ Cell membranes, Ultrastructure ▶

GONADS

A gonad is a general term for an organ that produces sex cells or gametes, so the gonads are the ovary and testis, producing ova and sperm respectively.
◀ Gamete, Gametogenesis, Ovum ▶

GP

◀ Glycerate 3-phosphate ▶

GRAPHS

Most biological experiments involve the collection of data of some kind. In order to make sense of this data, it needs first to be organised. It may then be subjected to simple statistical analysis, or may be analysed using deductive reasoning.

Organisation of data involves tabulation and the use of graphs. There are several different kinds of graph, and the type chosen will depend on the data that has been collected.

▶ LINE GRAPHS

These are used for isolated points, where one set of figures is fixed and the other dependent. For example, a timed enzyme experiment might be conducted using thermostatically controlled water baths, set at 20°, 30° and 40° C. Here temperature is the fixed variable, and is plotted on the *x*-axis, while the time taken is the dependent variable and is plotted on the *y*-axis. When the points have been plotted, they can be joined up in different ways. A single straight line or a smooth curve implies that there is a gradual change of one variable with the other, while each point joined by a short straight line to the next indicates that no assumptions are made about values in between the plotted points (Fig. G.9a).

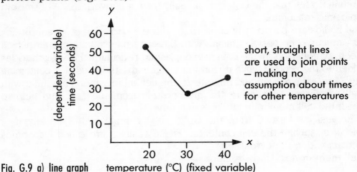

short, straight lines
are used to join points
— making no
assumption about times
for other temperatures

Fig. G.9 a) line graph   temperature (°C) (fixed variable)

SCATTER GRAPHS

These are used for isolated points where neither variable is fixed. For example, while investigating the effects of exercise, the pulse rate and breathing rate a number of people might be recorded. A scatter graph would indicate if there is any relationship or correlation between the two variables (Fig. G.9b).

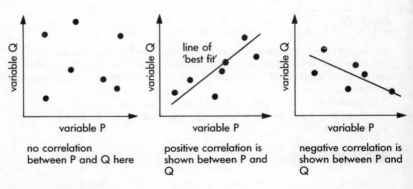

no correlation
between P and Q here

positive correlation is
shown between P and
Q

negative correlation is
shown between P and
Q

Fig. G.9 b) scatter graphs

▶ HISTOGRAMS AND BAR GRAPHS

These are used for grouped data which have been tabulated as a frequency distribution. For example, the heights of all pupils in the third year would have to be grouped before they could be plotted on a graph: 120–124 cm − 4 pupils, 125–129 cm − 7 pupils, etc. In this example, the bars touch one another, because one group leads on to the next, so a histogram should be drawn (Fig G.9c). In a bar graph, the bars are separate because each group is distinct. For example, numbers of boys and of girls in the third year would be plotted as a bar graph (Fig. G.9d).

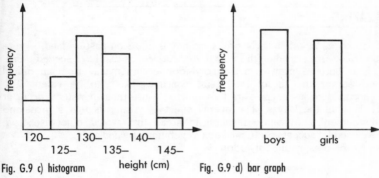

Fig. G.9 c) histogram   Fig. G.9 d) bar graph

GRASSLAND ENVIRONMENT

Grassland is an extremely common environment. In addition to parkland, playing fields, lawns and verges, about two-thirds of farmland is also occupied by grass. It is largely an artificial environment, however, maintained by **grazing**, mowing and trampling. Without such controls, most grasslands would gradually revert to scrub, and from scrub to woodland.

At first glance, grassland appears to be very uniform, but meadow pasture often contains a surprising variety of plant species. It is interesting to compare the species diversity and types present in grassland that has been grazed and trampled and grassland that has been left undisturbed. The frequency of different plants can be estimated by throwing **quadrat frames**. The **soil** type, depth and drainage may also affect the grasses growing, so hillside and low-lying pasture can be compared. If the grasses are fairly long, **insects** and other invertebrates living among them can be sampled using a sweep net.

◀ Sampling techniques ▶

GRAVITY

Gravity is a force exerted by the centre of the Earth that tends to pull objects towards it. The 'heaviness' or 'lightness' of an animal is a measure of the force of gravity acting on its mass (i.e. the greater the mass of an animal, the heavier it is).

Gravity is an essential environmental stimulus for plants, since it ensures that their roots grow downwards and shoots upwards. The response of plants to gravity is called **geotropism**.

Sensitivity to gravity is also essential for animals, in order for them to maintain their **balance**. In mammals, the utriculus and sacculus of the inner ear contain chalky otoliths on which gravity acts, distorting sensory hairs in the process.

GRAZING

When sheep or other herbivorous **mammals** graze on pasture land, severe constraints are placed on the growth of dicotyledons that have seeded there. This is because growth in a **dicotyledon** occurs mainly from an **apical meristem** at the tip of the stem, which is likely to be eaten. The monocotyledonous grasses are less affected, since their meristems occur at the base of the leaves. The overall effect of grazing is that a **grassland environment** is maintained, often in areas that would otherwise have developed by **succession** to a **climax** vegetation of woodland.

◀ Herbivores, Monocotyledon ▶

GREASE-SPOT TEST FOR FATS

◀ Food tests ▶

GREENHOUSE CULTURE

The commercial cultivation of flowers and food plants is increasingly being carried out in enclosed glasshouses, or greenhouses. The plants are grown in carefully controlled conditions, designed to increase their value economically. The optimum conditions can be provided for flower growth, or for fruit-setting, or for growth of leaves, and these conditions can be reproduced at any time of the year, allowing production out of season. Climatic factors that are controlled, often by computer, include light intensity, the photoperiod, temperature, humidity, ventilation and carbon dioxide concentration. The optimum supply of water and mineral salts is ensured by growing the plants hydroponically. Instead of using soil, the roots are anchored in a material called rock-wool and immersed in a slow-moving stream of oxygenated nutrient solution. Although harvesting of the flowers fruit or vegetables is still labour-intensive, the rest of their growth is not. With the aid of a computer, a single operator can oversee many acres. One disadvantage of greenhouse culture is that the favourable conditions may also encourage the rapid spread of pests and diseases, so regular spraying may be necessary.

◀ Photoperiodism ▶

GREENHOUSE EFFECT

The term 'greenhouse effect' likens the Earth and its atmosphere to an unventilated greenhouse on a sunny day. Light rays from the sun enter the greenhouse and warm the plants and trays, but heat rays rising from the plants cannot escape, so the internal temperature rises. In the same way, light rays from the sun warm the Earth's surface, and heat rays rising from the ground are reflected back by the presence of carbon dioxide in the atmosphere. The air temperature will therefore rise.

Some carbon dioxide in the atmosphere is absolutely essential, since if all heat was allowed to escape, the Earth would become too cold for life – meaning that if the 'greenhouse effect' did not exist at all, we would all die. The problem is that man's activities have caused a sharp increase in the amount of atmospheric carbon dioxide and other 'greenhouse gases', such as methane. This is partly due to **deforestation**, since the trees would have used up surplus carbon dioxide in their **photosynthesis**, but it is mainly due to the combustion of the fossil fuels – coal, oil and petrol. Running a car on unleaded fuel is not really a 'green' option, because the car still releases massive amounts of greenhouse gases in its exhaust fumes.

As more and more heat is reflected back to the Earth, the weather patterns of the Earth are likely to change, and there is a real danger that the polar ice caps will start to melt, causing the sea level to rise and flood low-lying regions.

(NB: A common misconception among A-level students is that **CFCs** cause the greenhouse effect; this is incorrect!)

GREEN PLANTS

Under the old system of **classification**, it was necessary to clearly state 'green' plants when referring to photosynthesisers, or to **producers** in food webs. This was to distinguish them from **fungi** in particular. In the five-kingdom classification system proposed by Margulis and Schwartz, and adopted by the Institute of Biology, the kingdom **Plantae** now includes only the green plants.

◄ Food chains, food webs, Kingdoms ►

'GREEN REVOLUTION', IMPLICATIONS OF

Over the past few years various environmental matters have moved to the forefront of politics. Young people in particular have become concerned about the sort of world they are inheriting, and their voting power has helped to force a change. This change has been described as a 'Green Revolution', in which the word 'green' stands for **conservation**, non-pollution, putting environmental priorities before economic ones and so on. Most European countries now have a Green Party, and all political parties aim to emphasise their 'greenness'. Public attitudes have also altered, such that many people are now prepared to pay more for 'green' goods like phosphate-free washing powders, recycled paper products and aerosols without CFC propellants.

GREY MATTER

Grey matter is nervous tissue that contains mostly neurone cell bodies. The Nissl's granules that they contain makes the tissue appear grey.
◄ Spinal cord ►

GROWTH

A permanent or irreversible increase in size is called growth. There are a number of criteria by which it can be measured:

- increase in **cell** size, or amount of **protoplasm**;
- increase in cell numbers;
- increase in **fresh mass**;
- increase in **dry mass**;
- increase in physical dimensions (height, length, etc.);
- increase in complexity.

GROWTH CURVES

A growth curve is constructed by plotting a parameter of growth against time. A common growth curve is sigmoid, or S-shaped, where there is slow growth initially, followed by rapid increase, then a final period of slower growth (Fig. G.10a). Sigmoid curves are obtained for the growth of populations as well as

Fig. G.10 Growth curves

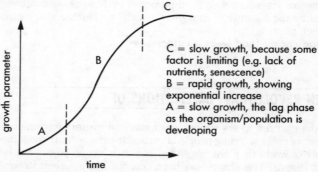

C = slow growth, because some factor is limiting (e.g. lack of nutrients, senescence)
B = rapid growth, showing exponential increase
A = slow growth, the lag phase as the organism/population is developing

a) sigmoid growth curve

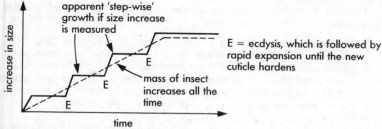

b) intermittent growth in an arthropod

individuals. A variation of this pattern is the growth of **arthropods**, which show intermittent growth if increase in fresh mass or physical dimensions are used as parameters (Fig. G.10b). When increase in dry mass or increase in biomass are considered, however, the curve appears sigmoid again. Growth in arthropods also involves **metamorphosis**.

Growth in **flowering plants** begins with **seed germination**, followed by the **primary growth** of the stem and root. This produces increase in length, and also **differentiation** into leaves, flowers, storage organs and so on. Certain plants may also experience **secondary growth**, involving increase in **girth**. Primary growth is carried out by the **apical meristems**, while secondary growth requires the lateral meristems, **cambium** and **cork cambium**. All plant growth is controlled genetically and by hormones, or plant growth substances, the main ones being auxins and gibberellins. Sufficient light, carbon dioxide, water and mineral nutrients are also required.

Growth in mammals is also under genetic and hormonal control, and subject to correct **nutrition**. The particular hormones involved are pituitary **growth hormone**, **thyroxine** and the sex hormones, **oestrogens** and **testosterone**.

◄ Gibberellin, Gene expression, Population

GROWTH HORMONE

Growth hormone, or somatotrophin, is secreted by the anterior **pituitary gland** under the influence of two **hypothalamus** hormones. It promotes growth in the tissues and organs of the body by causing liver cells to secrete another hormone, somatomedin. This stimulates the cellular uptake of **amino acids** and mineral ions, and increases synthesis of nucleic acids and **proteins**, probably by affecting **gene expression**.

Excess growth hormone in childhood leads to gigantism, while undersecretion causes dwarfism. Very little growth hormone is secreted normally in adults, and any oversecretion may result in acromegaly or enlarged facial bones.

GUT HISTOLOGY

Histology means the study of tissues, so gut histology refers to the tissues that make up the wall of the gut, or **alimentary canal** (Fig. G.11).

The wall of the mammalian gut has the same basic structure all along its length. There are five tissue layers:

- The mucosa is the innermost layer, closest to the lumen. It is highly folded to increase the surface area for **digestion** and **absorption**, particularly in the wall of the **small intestine**, where the villi occur. There is a thin epithelium over the surface with **goblet** cells for **mucus** secretion and other cells which secrete enzymes, some continue down into simple glands. Blood capillaries and lacteals extend up into the villi.
- A thin layer of **smooth muscle** separates the mucosa from the submucosa. The contractions of this muscle cause the villi and other folds of the mucosa to wave around in the lumen, and so come into contact with more of the gut contents.
- The submucosa is made of **connective tissue**, and contains arterioles, venules and lymphatics. In the duodenum, the submucosa also contains Brunner's glands, which secrete alkaline fluid and mucus into the crypts of Lieberkühn.
- A thick band of circular smooth muscle comes next. Contraction of the circular muscle constricts the gut and helps to squeeze the gut contents along.
- The outermost layer is a thick sheath of longitudinal smooth muscle, which is antagonistic to the circular muscle. The two layers work together to produce **peristalsis** which moves food along the gut.

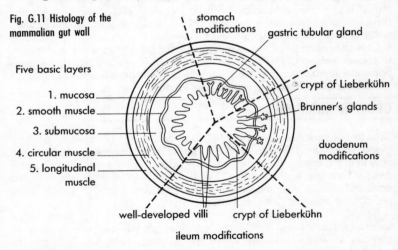

Fig. G.11 Histology of the mammalian gut wall

Five basic layers

1. mucosa
2. smooth muscle
3. submucosa
4. circular muscle
5. longitudinal muscle

stomach modifications
gastric tubular gland
crypt of Lieberkühn
Brunner's glands
duodenum modifications

well-developed villi   crypt of Lieberkühn
ileum modifications

GYMNOSPERMS

In the five-kingdom system of **classification**, the former class Gymnospermae has been renamed and elevated in status to phylum Coniferophyta, the conifers.

◄ Conifer ►

HABITAT

A habitat is the particular environment in which an organism lives. It has definable limits and characteristic climatic and edaphic conditions. It will also have a characteristic community of living organisms since most species have distinct habitat preferences. Examples of habitats include a pond, a rocky shore, a hedgerow and a woodland. Conditions may vary in different parts of a habitat, and if so it can be divided into a number of microhabitats.

◄ Communities ►

HAEMOCYTOMETER, USE OF

A haemocytometer is a special slide that is used to count the cells in a known volume of liquid. It is specifically intended for **red blood cells**, but is also used for others such as white blood cells and **yeast** cells.

A haemocytometer slide has two deep grooves across it. Between these grooves the surface of the slide is 0.1 mm lower than the rest of the slide. In the centre of the lower portion are ruled vertical and horizontal lines, and where the lines cross is a grid 1mm^2 in area (Fig. H.1a, b and c).

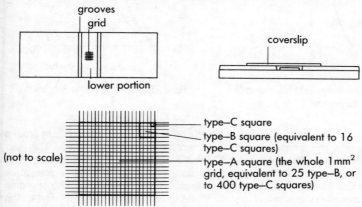

Fig. H.1 Haemocytometer:

The procedure for using the slide is as follows. A blood sample is first diluted 1/100 with 3 per cent saline. With the coverslip in place, a drop of diluted blood is placed on the lower portion of the slide alongside the coverslip, so that it is drawn under by capillary action. After allowing a few minutes for the cells to settle, the slide is examined under the low power of a microscope. The red blood cells in 100 type-C squares are counted, and the average calculated. Each type-C square represents a volume of 0.00025 mm^3, so the number of cells per cubic millimetre of diluted, and then undiluted, blood may be calculated.

HAEMOGLOBIN

Haemoglobins are iron-containing blood pigments that serve as oxygen carriers in many groups of animals. Mammalian haemoglobin has four sub-units, each of which can combine reversibly with a molecule of **oxygen**, resulting in the formation of oxyhaemoglobin, HbO_8 for short. Haemoglobin is an example of a conjugated protein, since each sub-unit is a **polypeptide** chain attached to a **prosthetic group**. The prosthetic group is called haem and consists of a central **iron** atom with rings of nitrogen and carbon atoms round the outside. Each polypeptide chain forms an alpha-helix for its secondary structure, and folds into a globular shape for its tertiary structure; two chains have 141 amino acids and are called alpha-chains, and two have 146 amino acids and are called beta-chains.

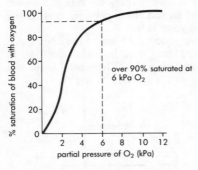

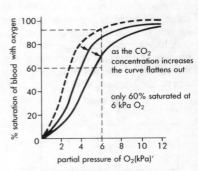

Fig. H.2a) Oxygen dissociation curve for human haemoglobin

Fig. H.2b) Graph showing the Bohr effect

The four chains are held only loosely to one another with weak hydrogen bonds and the overall shape of the molecule can be distorted. This fact explains why haemoglobin rarely carries less than its full complement of four oxygen molecules. When an oxygen molecule combines with the ferrous atom of the first haem group, the polypeptide chains shift position slightly, exposing the other iron atoms, which can then take up oxygen more readily. The fourth oxygen molecule is attached several hundred times more quickly than is the first. This means that haemoglobin has a high affinity for oxygen. Blood can become fully saturated at relatively low partial pressures of oxygen and, conversely, can give up oxygen rapidly when the partial pressure falls sharply in the respiring tissues. Fig. H.2a shows the oxygen dissociation curve for human haemoglobin.

When the partial pressure of carbon dioxide is high, haemoglobin is less efficient at taking up oxygen and more efficient at releasing it. This is called the Bohr effect, and is illustrated in Fig. H.2b. The Bohr effect is probably due to hydrogen ion concentration. During gaseous exchange in the tissues, carbon dioxide diffuses into red blood cells and causes an increase in hydrogen ions. These then combine with haemoglobin, displacing the oxygen molecules.

The ability of haemoglobin to accept hydrogen ions also means that it has an important role in the blood as a buffer.

◄ Buffers, Hydrogen bond, Proteins ►

HAEMOPHILIA

Haemophilia is an inherited blood disorder in which a substance needed for clotting, called Factor 8, cannot be synthesised. At one time many sufferers would have bled to death, but the disease can now be treated with injections of Factor 8 extracted from donated blood. The condition is a sex-linked trait, due to a recessive gene (point) mutation that is transmitted by the X-chromosome. Usually it is only males who suffer from the disease, since a female haemophiliac can be produced only by a haemophiliac father and a carrier mother and genetic screening should prevent this happening. Fig. H.3 illustrates the possible offspring if a normal man marries a woman who is a carrier of the abnormal haemophilia allele.

Let X^H represent X-chromosome carrying dominant allele for blood clotting.
Let X^h represent X-chromosome carrying recessive allele for haemophilia.

parental phenotypes:	normal male	×	carrier female	
parental genotypes (2n):	X^HY	×	X^hX^H	
gametes (n):	X^H $\quad$ Y		X^h	X^H
F1 genotypes (2n)	X^HY $\quad$ X^HY		X^HX^h	X^HX^H
F1 phenotypes	haemophiliac $\quad$ normal male $\qquad$ male		carrier female	normal female

Fig. H.3 Inheritance of haemophilia

◄ Gentic counselling, genetic screening ►

HAPLOIDY

Haploidy is a condition in which chromosomes are single, without their homologous partner chromosomes, and it is denoted by the symbol 'n'. In most animals, haploidy only occurs as a result of **meiosis** during **gametogenesis**. Only the secondary spermatocytes and secondary oocytes, and the functional gametes themselves, are haploid. At **fertilisation** the diploid state is restored.

Among plants which show **alternation of generations**, the diploid **sporophyte** produces haploid spores by meiosis. The spores then develop into a haploid **gametophyte**, which is the dominant form in **algae** and bryophytes. The gametes are also haploid, but diploidy is restored at fertilisation. In **flowering plants**, meiosis occurs within the pollen grain and embryosac to form haploid nuclei which fuse to form a diploid **zygote**.

◀ Bryophyta, Gamete, Spore ▶

HARDY–WEINBERG EQUILIBRIUM

The Hardy–Weinberg equilibrium is based on the principle that, provided the **population** is large enough and there are no disruptive influences, then the frequency of **alleles** in the population remains constant. Disruptive influences include such factors as environmental change, **natural selection** and **mutation**. It is called an equilibrium because movement of genes, or gene flow, does continue within the population, although the overall situation is stable.

The frequency of a given **genotype** in a population is calculated as follows. Let the pair of alleles have the symbols Aa, and the frequency of A be p, and the frequency of allele a be q. If the frequencies of these alleles are constant, then $p+q = 1$ for all males and females in the population.

Assuming random mating occurs, then gametes will fuse to give AA, Aa, aA, and aa in equal numbers, and these genotypes have the following frequencies.

$$AA = p^2, \text{ Aa and aA} = 2pq, \text{ aa} = q^2$$
$$\text{So } p^2 + 2pq + q^2 = 1.$$

HARVESTABLE DRY MATTER, HARVESTABLE PROTEIN

The harvestable dry matter or harvestable protein are two ways of measuring the productivity and value of a field crop. Crops such as peas, beans and soya beans, for example, contain good-quality protein, but there is also a lot of leafy growth that is not harvested, so the harvestable dry matter is fairly small. A fodder crop such as hay, on the other hand, has enormous harvestable dry matter but less protein.

◀ Proteins ▶

HEALTH

Health has been defined by the World Health Organisation as an absence of disease, though being 'healthy' also involves generally feeling well in body and mind, with all the body organs working properly. Regular vigorous exercise, sufficient regular sleep and relaxation and a balanced diet are all important in maintaining good health.

◄ Infectious diseases ►

HEART

The heart is a muscular organ that pumps **blood** round the body of an animal. The size, complexity and efficiency of hearts vary in different animal groups. **Insects**, for example, possess simple tubular hearts, while **fish** have a heart divided into two chambers, and **mammals** possess a complex four-chambered heart. These four chambers are shown in the simplified diagram, Fig. H.4.

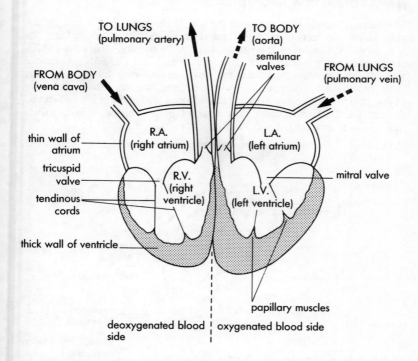

Fig. H.4 Simplified diagram of a mammalian heart

► BLOOD FLOW

Deoxygenated blood from the body enters the right atrium via the vena cava, while oxygenated blood enters the left atrium via the pulmonary vein. There is no mixing of blood between the two halves of the heart. Atrial contraction moves the blood through the tricuspid and mitral valves into the ventricles. After a slight delay, the ventricle muscles contract, forcing blood out into the arteries through the semilunar valves. Contraction of the ventricle muscles also forces the tricuspid and mitral valves to close, so preventing backflow of blood to the atria. The valves do not turn inside out because they are 'anchored' in place by the tendinous cords. The right ventricle pumps blood into the pulmonary circulation to the lungs, while the left ventricle pumps blood into the systemic circulation to all other parts of the body. The thicker wall of muscle in the left ventricle enables it to generate sufficient force for this. When the ventricle muscles relax, the semilunar valves close, preventing backflow of blood into the ventricles. More blood can then pass into the ventricles from the atria.

▶ CONTRACTION MECHANISM

The **cardiac muscle** that makes up the wall of the heart is myogenic, which means it can contract and relax rhythmically by itself without external nervous stimulation. Rhythmic contractions are initiated by the sino-atrial node (SAN), or pacemaker, in the wall of the right atrium (Fig. H.5). The SAN generates a wave of depolarisation, or excitation, which spreads over the atria, causing them to contract. The depolarisation reaches the atrio-ventricular node (AVN), and from there impulses are passed along the bundle of His and spread through the Purkinje fibres to the apex of each ventricle. The ventricle muscles then contract together, from the apex upwards.

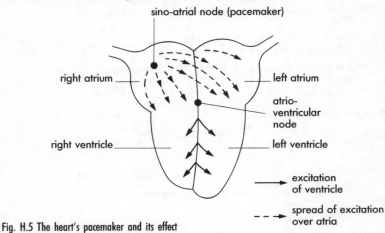

Fig. H.5 The heart's pacemaker and its effect

◀ Cardiac cycle, Cardiac output, Pulmonary blood circulation ▶

HEAT GAIN AND LOSS

◀ Thermoregulation ▶

HEATHLAND ENVIRONMENT

Heathland is a uniform environment with two dominant **indicator species**, *Calluna vulgaris*, or ling, and *Erica cinerea*, or bell heather. It may often represent the **climax** vegetation if the area is too windswept to allow the growth of trees. Heathland usually develops in upland areas with porous acid soils, so the plants that grow there must be tolerant of acidity and resistant to wind, rain and temperature fluctuations. Many plants also possess xeromorphic features, because the porous soil dries out easily, and may have adaptations to supplement **nitrogen** shortage, such as mycorrhizae, since the soil is subject to leaching.

Since the plant and animal **communities** on heathland are fairly uniform, they may be studied effectively with the use of quadrat sampling. If a heathland has developed from an area of bog close by, the **succession** from bog through wet heath to heath can be followed using a belt or line transect.

◄ Quadrat frames, Sampling techniques, Xerophytes ►

HEAVY METALS

A heavy metal is defined as one which has a specific gravity greater than 5, and examples include lead, mercury and silver. Heavy metals are toxic to most forms of life because their ions act as irreversible enzyme inhibitors. They do so by combining permanently with sulphydryl groups in protein, causing the enzyme to precipitate, and distorting the **active site**. They are not specific in their action and block very many enzymes, so careless **pollution** of the land and waterways with heavy metals can have serious consequences (e.g. lead poisoning in swans).

Certain grasses, such as *Agrostis tenuis* and *Festuca ovina*, have developed tolerance to heavy metals and can colonise polluted land. These plants have been found growing on old spoil tips near where zinc, copper and lead ores were once mined. They provide a clear example of **natural selection**, in which the **selection pressure** is the presence of the toxic heavy metal ions in the soil. A **mutation** giving tolerance to these ions has been selected for and passed on to subsequent generations.

◄ Enzyme inhibition ►

HEDGEROWS

A hedgerow is a closely growing row of bushes or small trees acting as a fence enclosing fields. The majority of existing hedgerows in Britain are about 200 years old, though some may be over 1,000 years old. Such hedges are complex ecosystems, containing a great diversity of plant species, especially of woody perennials. They also serve as windbreaks for plants growing in the verges, and provide food and sanctuary for many animal species that might otherwise die out. These include butterflies, such as the Meadow Brown and

the Common Blue, and many bird species that nest in hedgerows. Unfortunately, the economic use of modern agricultural machinery, such as combine harvesters, depends on having large, uninterrupted fields. Hedges are therefore being removed at an alarming rate, and the plant and animal communities that used to inhabit them are being eliminated or reduced. It is an important task for conservation to try and preserve the hedgerow habitat.
◀ Ecosystem ▶

HELICAL STRUCTURE OF DNA

◀ DNA ▶

HEPATIC ARTERY, VEIN, PORTAL VEIN

The hepatic artery carries oxygenated blood to the liver, while the hepatic vein carries deoxygenated blood away from the liver. The hepatic portal vein is an extra blood vessel that carries blood from the gut to the liver. This blood has been deoxygenated by the gut tissues, but contains instead all the soluble products of digestion that have been asborbed into the villi blood capillaries. The liver can then regulate the amounts of glucose, amino acids and other substances that pass on into the general blood circulation.
◀ Blood vessels, Villus ▶

HERBACEOUS PLANTS

Herbaceous plants are those whose aerial parts usually die down in winter. They mostly survive the winter as seeds or as underground perennating organs. Their stems are always green and do not undergo secondary thickening.
◀ Perennation, Seed ▶

HERBICIDES

Herbicides are chemical substances that kill weeds and other unwanted plants. They can be divided into two broad groups: those that are non-selective and those that are selective in their action. Non-selective herbicides, such as paraquat, kill a wide variety of plants, so are used mainly for total land clearance. Selective herbicides, such as 2,4-D (2,4-dichlorophenoxyacetic acid), kill certain species only, in this case broad-leaved species, so can be used on lawns and on grain field crops. 2,4-D is a synthetic auxin that works by promoting growth to such an extent that the plant outgrows its resources. It is biodegradable, leaving no toxic residues, and is effective in very low concentrations, so is cheap to use.

There are many disadvantages to using herbicides, however. They upset the balance of nature, both by depriving animals of their natural habitat and by removing essential links in food chains. They may harm plants other than those to be destroyed and some herbicides, such as paraquat, are also toxic to animals.

HERBIVORES

Herbivores are animals that eat plants. They occupy the second trophic level in a food web, acting as primary consumers. Typical herbivores include molluscs and crustaceans in aquatic ecosystems, and insects, birds and mammals in terrestrial ecosystems.

The main problem with plants as a food source is that the nutrients are enclosed within a tough cellulose cell wall. Particular adaptations are therefore required to release these nutrients. Herbivorous molluscs such as the snail possess a radula for this purpose. This is a rasping organ covered in tiny, backwardly pointing teeth. Leaves are held in the mouth while the radula rubs backwards and forwards over them, tearing off minute fragments. Herbivorous insects such as the locust have biting and chewing mouthparts, which include a pair of strong mandibles with ridged cutting edges and broad grinding surfaces to cut and crush leaves. The other mouthparts propel the food towards the mandibles. Herbivorous mammals such as sheep have grinding teeth with chisel-shaped lower incisors which bite against a horny pad to cut the grass and broad ridged molars to grind it.

A second problem for herbivores is the digestion of the cellulose so that its consituent monosaccharides can be absorbed and used. The only organisms able to synthesise cellulase enzymes are certain bacteria, fungi and protoctistans, so many herbivores have acquired symbiotic micro-organisms in their guts. Wood-eating termites contain a flagellate called *Trichonympha* in their intestine. The flagellate hydrolyses cellulose for the termite, and receives food and shelter in return, so the relationship is an example of mutualism. *Ruminants* such as sheep and cattle contain mutualistic bacteria in a special chamber called the rumen. The bacteria digest cellulose for the mammal and receive food, shelter and an ideal temperature in return. Partially digested material from the rumen is regurgitated and chewed again before passing into the true stomach.

◀ Crustacea, Flagellates, Flagellum, Food chains, Food webs, Mollusca, Protoctista ▶

HEREDITY

Heredity is the transmission of characteristics to descendants. The units of heredity are genes, located on chromosomes, and the science or study of gene transmission is called genetics. The first breakthrough in the understanding of heredity was made by Gregor Mendel through his studies of monhybrid and dihybrid inheritance in garden peas. His laws of heredity still hold true for many situations. Exceptions include inheritance of linkage groups, cases of **gene interaction, codominace** of **alleles** and inheritance in haploid organisms.

◄ Haploidy ►

HETEROSPORY

Heterospory means the formation of two distinct types of **spore**. In club mosses such as **Selaginella**, the **sporophyte** bears two types of **sporangia**. Microsporangia produce many tiny microspores, which germinate into small male gametophytes, while megasporangia produce just four large megaspores that germinate into the larger female gametophytes. Conifers and **flowering plants** are also heterosporous.

◄ Conifer, Gametophyte, Homospory ►

HETEROTROPH, HETEROTROPHIC NUTRITION

Heterotrophs are organisms which cannot synthesise their own organic molecules from simple inorganic raw materials and must obtain them by feeding on other organisms. All animals and fungi, and the majority of bacteria, are heterotrophic, and insectivorous plants obtain some of their nutrients heterotrophically. There are three types of heterotrophic nutrition.

 ### HOLOZOIC NUTRITION

This involves feeding on solid organic matter obtained from the bodies of other organisms. This food is ingested into the body and then digested by enzymes into smaller soluble molecules that can be absorbed and used in metabolism.

 ### SAPROPHYTIC (OR SAPROTROPHIC) NUTRITION

This involves feeding on soluble organic compounds from dead and decaying plants and animals. Enzymes are secreted on to the substrate for external digestion, then the products are absorbed and used in metabolism.

 ### PARASITIC NUTRITION

This involves feeding on the organic compounds in the living tissues of a host organism. In most cases the nutrients are already in solution, so can be absorbed and used by the parasite without the need for further digestion.

◄ Holozoic nutrition, Parasitism, Saprophyte ►

HETEROZYGOUS GENOTYPE

A heterozygous **genotype** is one in which the **alleles** occupying a given **locus** on **homologous chromsomes** are different. The cell or organism possessing this genotype is described as a heterozygote. Unless there is **codominance**, one of the pair of alleles will be dominant and the other recessive, and the dominant allele will be expressed in the **phenotype**. For example, in the inheritance of height in garden peas, a heterozygote will have the genotype Tt. The allele for tallness, T, is dominant over the allele for shortness, t, so the plant will be tall.

◄ Dominant alleles, Homozygous genotype, Recesive alleles ►

HEXOSE

A hexose is a monosaccharide with six carbon atoms. The general formula is $C_6H_{12}O_6$, and examples include **glucose**, **fructose**, galactose and mannose, with glucose the most common.

◄ Monosaccharides ►

HEXOSE DIPHOSPHATE, HEXOSE PHOSPHATE

◄ Glycolysis ►

HIBERNATION

Hibernation is a mechanism used by certain small endotherms to enable them to survive periods of low temperatures. Examples of true hibernators include insectivores such as shrews and hedgehogs, and rodents such as dormice and hamsters. The word comes from the Latin verb 'to winter', *hiberno*, but very small birds or mammals, such as humming birds and small insectivorous bats may hibernate every night. The problem for small endotherms is that they have a very large surface area with respect to their volume and consequently lose heat rather quickly. In order to maintain their core temperature, they require very high metabolic rates, and hence need to eat almost continually to provide sufficient fuel. In winter not only do they lose heat faster but also there is less food available, so hibernation becomes a necessity.

Hibernation in most species is influenced by hormones and is triggered by a drop in temperature and a shorter photoperiod, although only if the animal has adequate supplies of stored food. Most animals overeat before hibernating and store the surplus as fat. They may also prepare a nest or a burrow to provide some insulation during hibernation. The core temperature then falls to one or two degrees above the environmental temperature, and the metabolic rate and all other body processes are reduced to an equivalent level. Stored **lipids** are used at a steady rate all through the winter, then as the animals begin to come out of hibernation, there is a sharp increase in metabolic activity in the brown fat cells. The lipid in these cells is stored in the form of oil droplets in the cytoplasm. When respired, these release energy, primarily as heat. This heat warms the animal enough to start it shivering, and it soon returns to its original temperature without having to absorb heat from the environment.

Strictly speaking, ectotherms such as tortoises and frogs do not hibernate but enter a state of torpor or extended sleep. Bears are also not true hibernators because their body temperature drops only very slightly.

◄ Endothermy, Hormone, Photoperiodism ►

HINGE JOINT

Hinge joints are **synovial joints** that occur at the **elbow** in the forelimb, and at the knee in the hindlimb. They permit movement through 180 degrees in one plane only, allowing the arm or leg to bend, or flex, and then straighten. Further movement of the limbs is prevented by the way the ends of the bones fit together in the joint. In the elbow, for example (Fig. H.6), the olecranon process extends beyond the articular surface, so that when the arm is straightened it makes contact with the **humerus** and prevents the arm bending backwards.

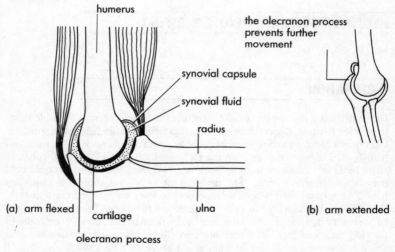

Fig. H.6 Hinge joint at the elbow (in cross section)

◄ Elbow joint, Forelimb & mammal, Synovial joints ►

HISTOLOGY

Histology is the study of **tissue** structure and function. Most A-level syllabuses require knowledge of the following plant and animal tissues.

▶ PLANTS

- **Parenchyma** consists of unspecialised living cells with thin cellulose cell walls. It serves as packing tissue and storage tissue. Parenchyma cells may become modified to form the **epidermis** and **endodermis**, the root pericycle and the **mesophyll** in leaves (sometimes referred to as chlorenchyma).
- **Collenchyma** cells are also living, but have additional cellulose deposited at the corners to provide support.
- **Sclerenchyma** is a dead tissue, made up of fibres and sclereids with lignified walls. It provides support and mechanical strength for the plant.
- **Xylem** tissue contains more than one type of cell. There are living parenchyma cells and dead lignified vessels, tracheids and fibres. The two major functions of xylem are the transport of water and mineral salts and support.
- **Phloem** is also a mixed tissue. It contains dead, lignified fibres and sclereids for strength, and living sieve tube elements, companion cells and parenchyma for translocation.

▶ ANIMALS

- Epithelial tissue covers the external and internal surfaces of the organism. It lines and protects, and may become specialised to also either absorb, secrete, excrete or receive stimuli. Glands are composed of modified epithelial tissue.
- **Connective tissue** is a packing and connecting tissue. It is modified to form **bone, cartilage** and ligaments for support, tendons for muscle attachment, **adipose** tissue for insulation and haemopoietic tissue which makes red and white blood cells.
- Muscle tissue contains specialised contractile cells. **Skeletal muscle** is concerned with locomotion and body movements, while **smooth muscle** assists the movement of substances in the alimentary canal, blood vessels and genital and urinary systems. **Cardiac muscle** occurs only in the heart.
- Nervous tissue is made up of receptor cells and neurones, specialised for the conduction of nerve impulses. The tissue is concerned with the co-ordination and control of all body functioning.

HISTONE

Chromatin in the nucleus is composed of a DNA-protein complex, the proteins being histones. These are positively charged, basic proteins that combine with DNA, which is acidic and has negative charges all along it. It is believed that the DNA helix wraps itself round groups of eight histone molecules, forming structures called nucleosomes. The presence of protein increases the overall diameter of each chromosome and may serve to provide a protective coat for the DNA. Histones may also play a part in the control of **gene expression,** by masking certain genes along the chromosome.

◀ Chromosomes ▶

HIV

◀ Human Immuno-deficiency Virus ▶

HLA SYSTEM

The HLA system covers about forty antigenic proteins that may be present on the surface of human cells. These **antigens** are the means by which the body's immune system recognises self and non-self. HLA antigens are not normally identified for blood transfusions because they are present in much smaller amounts on red blood cells than are the type A and type B antigens of the ABO system. They do need to be known for organ transplants, however, where tissues must be matched as closely as possible. Clearly, if a transplanted kidney has many non-self antigens on its cell membranes, then the body's immune system will produce antibodies to kill those cells, and the organ will be rejected.

◀ Antibody, Immunity ▶

HOLOZOIC NUTRITION

Holozoic nutrition is a form of heterotrophic nutrition found in most animals and in insectivorous plants. It literally means 'feeding like an animal'. Complex organic molecules are ingested into the body, often into a mouth. They may then be broken up mechanically by structures such as **teeth** or **mandibles,** before being digested chemically by hydrolytic enzymes. **Digestion** usually occurs in some sort of gastro-intestinal tract or **alimentary canal,** and results in small soluble molecules such as **amino acids** and **monosaccharides.** These molecules are absorbed into the body tissues, and either used directly by the absorbing cells or transported elsewhere in the body by a **blood** system. The utilisation of these molecules as respiratory substrates or for **biosynthesis,** is called **assimilation.**

There are three categories of holozoic feeding methods.

- Microphagous animals feed on tiny particles that are often suspended in water. These particles are ingested by means of pseudopodia, as in **Amoeba,** or using **cilia,** as in *Paramecium,* or by **filter feeding,** as in mussels.

- Macrophagous animals feed on large food particles. These may be ingested using tentacles, as in **Hydra**, a rasping radula, as in **gastropods**, jointed mouthparts, as in **insects**, or **teeth**, as in herbivorous and carnivorous **mammals**.
- Fluid feeders ingest liquid food, either by sucking, as in the **butterfly**, or by piercing and sucking, as in **aphids**.

◀ Absorption, Ciliates, Carnivores, Herbivores, Heterotrophs, Heterotrophic nutrition ▶

HOMEOSTASIS

Homeostasis is the maintenance of a stable internal environment in which conditions are maintained at the optimum level for life. Animals, such as mammals, that possess efficient homeostatic mechanisms can thus become more independent of their external environment. The internal environment is usually taken to mean the **intercellular fluid** and the bloodstream though homeostasis also occurs within cells (e.g. in the control of **gene expression** according to the **Jacob-Monod model of gene control**). Most homeostatic mechanisms are co-ordinated by hormones and involve **negative feedback** control. This means that an increase in a given condition triggers a corrective mechanism leading to its decrease.

The physiological processes of a mammal are all either involved in homeostasis or depend on its existence. Examples of homeostatic processes include **thermoregulation**, control of **respiration** and **gaseous exchange**, **osmoregulation** and the **excretion** of nitrogenous waste by the **kidneys**, and regulation of blood glucose and **amino acids** in the liver. The **hypothalamus** and **pituitary gland** provide a control centre for many of these.

◀ Blood glucose level ▶

HOMOLOGOUS CHROMOSOMES

The **chromosomes** in a **diploid nucleus** occur in pairs, one of the pair being the maternal chromosome and the other the paternal chromosome. The chromosomes are exactly the same length and contain the same gene loci arranged in the same sequence. They are described as a homologous pair.

HOMOSPORY

Homospory means the formation of identical spores. In **moss, liverwort** and **fern**, the **sporophyte** bears just one type of sporangium, in which one type of spore develops. These spores germinate into a **gametophyte** that bears both male and female gamete-forming organs.

◀ Heterospory, Sporangia ▶

HOMOZYGOUS GENOTYPE

A homozygous **genotype** is one in which the **alleles** occupying a given **locus** on **homologous chromosomes** are identical. The cell or organism possessing this genotype is described as a homozygote, or a pure-breeding line. The pair of alleles are either both dominant or both recessive. For example, in the inheritance of height in garden peas, a dominant homozygote will have the genotype TT and will be tall, while the recessive homozygote will have the genotype tt and will be short.

◄ Dominant alleles, Genotype, Heterozygous, Phenotype, Recessive alleles ►

HORMONE

A hormone is a chemical substance secreted by an endocrine gland directly into the blood system. It is transported by the **blood** to its target cells in some other part of the body, where it attaches to specific receptor sites on the **cell membrane**. It then exerts an effect on the cell **metabolism** either by altering membrane permeability, by activating enzymes associated with the membrane or by activating or inhibiting genes.

The amount of hormone secreted is usually under **negative feedback** control, and it may be influenced by the **hypothalamus** and **pituitary gland** via releasing factors and trophic hormones. Undersecretion or oversecretion of any hormone will generally result in some kind of defect or disorder. Examples of these include diabetes mellitus, caused by undersecretion of **insulin** by the **pancreas**, and gigantism, caused by oversecretion of **growth hormone** by the anterior pituitary gland.

◄ Endocrine glands, Enzyme, Gene ►

HORTICULTURE

Horticulture means literally 'the cultivation of gardens'. It covers the cultivation of parks and gardens of all sizes, as well as market gardens and glasshouses where plants are grown for profit. Most commercial horticulture takes place in the south of Britain, where the photoperiod is not a limiting factor. Horticulture occurs on a smaller scale than agriculture, but many of the same principles apply. Suitable plants should be grown for the climatic and soil conditions, and they should be planted far enough apart to minimise **competition** without giving space to weed species. In many glasshouses plants are grown hydroponically so their mineral requirements are always met. Weed and pest management may be by chemical or biological means or by employing cultivation techniques such as intercropping. Some plants may require pruning or separating, and consideration should be given to **harvesting** methods and times.

◄ Greenhouse culture, Photoperiodism ►

HUMAN IMMUNO-DEFICIENCY VIRUS (HIV)

The Human Immuno-Deficiency Virus is the pathogen that causes AIDS, Acquired Immuno-Deficiency Syndrome. It is a **virus** of the blood system and body fluids so can be transmitted only by direct contact between the blood or body fluids of an infected person and those of a non-infected person. It can be spread by sexual contact, particularly if anal sex is involved, since the anal epithelium is less robust and hence more likely to bleed than the vaginal epithelium. It can also be spread if intravenous drug users share the same hypodermic needles. All donated blood is now screened for the HIV virus, but blood transfusions and injections to haemophiliacs that were given before 1985 may have transmitted the virus. There is often a considerable time delay between infection with HIV and the development of AIDS, so the virus may be passed on unwittingly.

◀ AIDS, Haemophilia, Pathogens ▶

HUMERUS

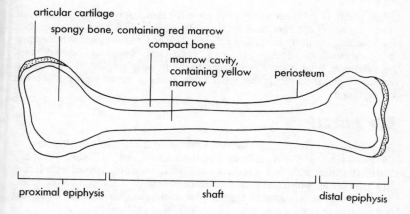

Fig. H.7 Humerus structure

The humerus (Fig. H.7) is the single long **bone** in the upper part of the forelimb. The main body of the bone is called the shaft and the ends are called the epiphyses. The entire bone is covered by a sheath of tough **connective tissue** called the periosteum. Internally, the shaft is composed of a cylinder of compact bone surrounding a marrow cavity containing fatty yellow marrow. The epiphyses are composed mainly of spongy bone to withstand compression, with just a superficial layer of compact bone for added strength. The spongy bone contains some red marrow.

◀ Forelimb of mammal ▶

HUMORAL RESPONSE

The humoral immune response is carried out by specific antibodies produced by B-lymphocytes.
◀ Immunity ▶

HYALINE CARTILAGE

Hyaline cartilage is the most common and also the simplest type of cartilage. It forms the articular cartilage at the ends of the limb bones where they form hinge joints and ball and socket joints. Here it protects the bones from friction damage and acts as a shock absorber. The tissue consists almost entirely of chondrin matrix with chondrocytes scattered through it, though there are a few fine collagen fibres embedded in it to give added strength.
◀ Bone, Hinge joint ▶

HYBRIDS, HYBRIDISATION

When plants of different varieties or closely related species are crossed, or when animals of different breeds or closely related species are crossed, then the resulting offspring are called hybrids. The process is called hybridisation or out-breeding. There are two main advantages associated with hybridisation. It introduces new genes to the population, thereby increasing variation, and the hybrids themselves may possess hybrid vigour which can be exploited.

▶ ANIMALS

An example of hybridisation that has occurred in animals was the breeding of the Santa Gertrudis beef cattle for hot, dry regions such as Texas. European Hereford cattle, with their excellent beef qualities, were crossed with Indian Brahman cattle, which had good resistance to heat, drought and insect pests. After several generations of rigorous selection, any undesirable traits had been eliminated and the new breed of cattle was established.

▶ PLANTS

Hybridisation in plants not only produces new combinations of desirable features but also results in hybrid vigour, or heterosis. The hybrids show characteristics that are superior to those of either of the parent plants, in height, yield, disease resistance, earlier maturity and so on. Homozygous parents are produced first, by a programme of in-breeding to select the most desirable qualities. The best inbred strains from different populations are then crossed to give heterozygous F1 hybrids. In maize plants, for example, F1 hybrids have been produced that give a yield up to two and a half times that of the parent plants.
◀ Gene, Heterozygous genotype, Homozygous genotype ▶

HYDRA, HYDROIDS

Hydroids belong to the class Hydrozoa, in the phylum **Cnidaria** (formerly Coelenterata). Most hydrozoans, for example *Obelia* (Fig. H.8) are marine but the genus *Hydra* lives in fresh water. Hydra takes the form of a solitary, semi-sessile polyp with no medusa stage. Obelia has sessile polyps which form colonies, some polyps for feeding and some for **asexual reproduction**, and a motile, simple medusa which reproduces sexually and serves as a dispersal stage. This is not the same as **alternation of generations** in plants, because both the polyp and medusa are **diploid**, and the male and female medusae produce gametes by **meiosis**.

◄ Sexual reproduction ►

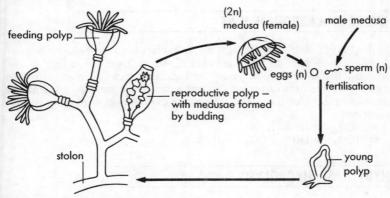

Fig. H.8 Life cycle of Obelia (simplified)

HYDROGEN ACCEPTORS, HYDROGEN CARRIERS

Hydrogen acceptors and hydrogen carriers also function as electron acceptors and carriers. Their molecules lack an electron, making them electropositive, so they can carry an electron as well as a hydrogen atom. They are easily reduced and oxidised and act as co-enzymes for **dehydrogenase enzymes**. Examples include **NAD**, **FAD** and **cytochromes**, the carriers which make up the **electron transfer** system in **aerobic respiration**.

◄ Co-enzyme ►

HYDROGEN BOND

A hydrogen bond is a weak electrostatic attraction between a slightly positive hydrogen atom and a slightly negative oxygen atom. They occur between water molecules, and between -NH or -OH groups and -C=O groups (Fig. H.9). Hydrogen bonds play an important role in holding organic molecules together. Examples include cellulose, whose chains are cross-linked by many hydrogen bonds to form microfibrils, and DNA, in which the base pairs are joined by hydrogen bonds.

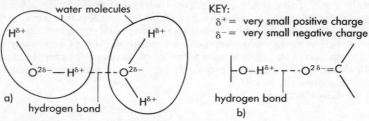

Fig. H.9 Hydrogen bonding a) water b) in organic molecules

HYDROGENCARBONATE IONS

Hydrogencarbonate ions (HCO_3^-) act as **buffers** because they can remove hydrogen ions from an aqueous solution and so lower the acidity of the solution. If the alkalinity becomes too high, they can also react with free hydroxyl ions to form carbonate ions and water. Their presence in a fluid will therefore mean that the **pH** of the system can be maintained more or less constant.

- $HCO_3^- + H^+ = H_2CO_3$
- $HCO_3^- + OH^- = CO_3^{2-} + H_2O$

HYDROLASE, HYDROLYSIS

Hydrolysis occurs when the bonds between the sub-units of a molecule are broken by the addition of water. Hydrolases are enzymes that catalyse this reaction. Many biological molecules are built up by condensation, or water removal, and broken down by hydrolysis. These include polypeptides, polysaccharides, nucleic acids and lipids. The enzymes involved in **digestion** are hydrolases (e.g. **amylase**, **pepsin** and **lipase**).

◀ Condensation reactions, Enzyme, Polypeptide, ▶

HYDROSTATIC SKELETON

In a hydrostatic skeleton, the 'skeletal' material that provides support is a fluid. Herbaceous plants and structures such as leaves do not have secondary thickening. They rely instead on a hydrostatic skeleton of turgid **parenchyma** tissue. If the cells lose water, then the plant wilts.

In the animal kingdom hydrostatic skeletons are characteristic of soft-bodied animals. The supporting fluid is enclosed by a muscular body wall, composed of antagonistic circular and longitudinal muscles. The fluid presses against the wall and the muscles in turn can contract against the fluid. This maintains the shape of the animal, and allows for **locomotion** – sometimes known as hydrostatic locomotion. In annelids such as the **earthworm**, this type of locomotion is very effective. The segmented body of an annelid is divided by septa into discrete, fluid-tight compartments, each with its own muscles. This means that some segments can be elongated by contraction of their circular muscles, while others are shortened by contraction of their longitudinal muscles. The chaetae of the shortened segments are protracted in order to anchor against the soil, while the chaetae of the extended segments are retracted, or pulled in. The alternate muscle contraction is controlled by nerve impulses (Fig. H.10)

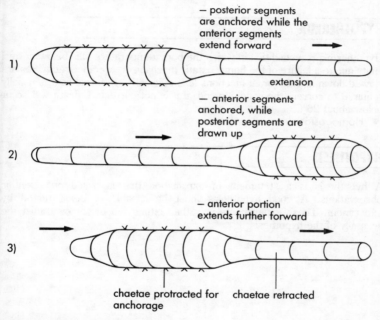

Fig. H.10 Locomotion in an earthworm

◄ Annelida, Antagonistic muscles ►

HYPOTHALAMUS

The hypothalamus is found in the ventral part of the 'tween-brain and participates in many homoeostatic processes. It is the main coordinating centre for the autonomic nervous system, and it contains centres controlling such functions as feeding and drinking, sleep and wakefulness, speech, **temperature regulation** and **osmoregulation**. In temperature regulation, the hypothalamus acts directly, through the autonomic nervous system. For many of its other efffects, however, it acts indirectly by influencing the **pituitary gland**. It is connected to the pituitary by a stalk through which run blood vessels to the anterior lobe, and nerve axons to the posterior lobe. The blood vessels carry hormone-releasing factors from the hypothalamus to the anterior lobe, stimulating the pituitary to secrete the appropriate hormones. The nerve axons carry **ADH** from the hypothalamus to the posterior lobe, where it is liberated into the bloodstream by neurosecretion. Stimulation of the hypothalamus occurs either by nerve impulses from the rest of the brain or as a result of its own receptor cells, which monitor blood temperature and the levels of hormones and metabolites in the blood.

◀ Autonomic nervous control, Homoeostasis ▶

HYPOTHERMIA

Hypothermia is a condition in which the body temperature falls below normal limits due to a failure of the homoeostatic mechanism. Metabolic activities are slowed down and the brain functions less efficiently. External heat is usually required to correct the condition and, if it is not corrected, death will occur below about 26°C.

◀ Homoeostasis ▶

HYPOTHESIS

A hypothesis is a statement of explanation that is based on scientific observations. A good hypothesis must be capable of being tested by experiment. These experiments may then either support or contradict the accuracy of the hypothesis.

ILEUM

The small intestine consists of a short upper tube, the duodenum, which leads into a much longer and much folded tube, which is the ileum. The ileum has two functions: the completion of digestion and the absorption of the soluble end-products of digestion.

For digestion the mucosal lining of both the duodenum and the ileum secrete intestinal juice, or **succus entericus**, which contains a number of hydrolytic enzymes.

The ileum is structurally adapted for absorption. It is very long and it has a large internal surface area, due to the numerous villi and the fact that the **villus** epithelium is covered in **microvilli**. Also, the villi are richly supplied with blood capillaries and contain lacteals, so the absorbed products can be quickly transported away. Monosaccharides and amino acids are absorbed into capillaries by diffusion and active transport. These capillaries then unite to form the hepatic portal vein, which goes to the liver. Fatty acids and glycerol pass into the villus epithelium, where they recombine to form fats. These fats then enter the lacteals and become coated with protein, forming lipoprotein droplets called chylomicrons. The chylomicrons enter the bloodstream in the neck from the thoracic lymphatic duct.

◄ Gut histology ►

IMMUNE SYSTEM

Immunity involves two initial processes: the recognition of foreign material when it enters the body and the mobilisation of cells and antibodies capable of removing the foreign material, or **antigens**, quickly and effectively. A further process involves the formation of memory cells, which carry out the secondary immune response.

► IMMUNE SYSTEMS IN MAMMALS

There are two systems of immunity in mammals: a cell-mediated immune response and a humoral immune response. Two types of **lymphocytes** are involved, both of which have receptor sites on their membranes for recognising antigens. Both types are formed in the bone marrow and then complete their development in either the thymus gland, in which case they are known as T-lymphocytes or T-cells, or in lymphoid tissue, producing B-lymphocytes or B-cells.

Cell-mediated Immune Response

The thymus gland is active from birth until a mammal is weaned. During this time it causes lymphocytes to mature and become 'immunologically competent', and capable of synthesising new receptor molecules and incorporating them into the plasma membrane. T-lymphocytes leave the thymus and circulate in the blood and body fluids. If a T-cell meets an antigen for which it has a receptor site, it is stimulated to divide many times by mitosis, forming a clone. Each cell in the clone can attach to a complementary antigen and destroy it.

A further function of T-cells is that their presence is required for the maturation of specific B-lymphocytes.

Humoral Immune Response

B-lymphocytes complete their development in the lymph nodes, or spleen. There are many thousands of different B-lymphocytes, each with just one type of receptor on its cell surface. If an antigen is recognised, the B-cells are stimulated to divide by mitosis forming a clone of plasma cells in the lymph node, and also forming memory cells. The plasma cells live only a few days but can synthesise and secrete vast quantities of specific antibody molecules – nearly 2,000 per second. (These antibodies are of the IgM type.)

The memory cells persist for a long time, sometimes for life. They are responsible for the secondary immune response and confer active immunity against the specific antigen. If that antigen is encountered again, the memory cells can recognise it and stimulate the immediate production of massive quantities of antibody, some IgM as for the primary immune response and also large amounts of IgG.

◄ Antibody ►

IMMUNITY

There are three types of immunity.

► HEREDITARY IMMUNITY

This occurs passively due to the inheritance of genes for disease resistance.

NATURALLY ACQUIRED IMMUNITY

This may occur passively or actively. Natural passive immunity may be due to the transfer of antibodies from mother to fetus across the placenta, or from mother to new-born offspring via colostrum, the first secretions of the mammary gland. The immunity is only temporary, since no memory cells have been formed.

Natural active immunity is achieved as a result of exposure to infection. The body manufactures its own antibodies in response to the presence of antigens on the infectious agent and also forms specific memory cells. If the same agent is encountered again, it can be flooded with antibodies and eliminated before it causes disease.

ARTIFICIALLY ACQUIRED IMMUNITY

This may also occur passively or actively. Artificial passive immunity results from the injection of ready-made antibodies into the body, and again, since there are no memory cells, it is only temporary. It is useful as a preventative measure for diseases that are difficult to immunise against, such as tetanus and diptheria. It may also be used as a treatment for certain diseases, such as rabies, where infection has already occurred which is too dangerous to leave to the body's natural immune system.

Artificial active immunity is achieved by **immunisation** or vaccination, in which **vaccine** is injected into a healthy individual. The body is stimulated to produce antibodies and memory cells against the antigen in the vaccine, and thus acquires immunity to subsequent infection by that disease organism.

◀ Vaccine ▶

IMPLANTATION

After **fertilisation** the **zygote** travels down the oviduct to the **uterus**. As it does so, it divides many times by **mitosis** to form a hollow ball of cells called a blastocyst. This blastocyst then becomes embedded in the endometrium, or uterus lining, a process known as implantation.

One treatment for human infertility involves **in vitro fertilisation**, in which an embryo is developed in the laboratory and may then be inserted into the uterus for implantation.

◀ Pregnancy ▶

IMPRINTING

Imprinting is a form of **learned behaviour** in which young animals will follow their parents, or any substitute animal or moving object, provided it is the first thing they see after birth or hatching. The classic example of imprinting was described by Konrad Lorenz using young ducks, which imprinted on him as though he was their mother.

IMPULSE

◀ Nerve impulse ▶

IN-BREEDING

The fusion of gametes from the same or closely related parents results in in-breeding. It may be used in the breeding of 'show' dogs and cats, but since the genetic material is limited there is very little variation in the offspring, so it is uncommon in natural populations. Prolonged in-breeding may result in reduced fertility, poorer disease resistance and a general loss of vigour.

◀ Genetic variation, Outbreeding ▶

INCIPIENT PLASMOLYSIS

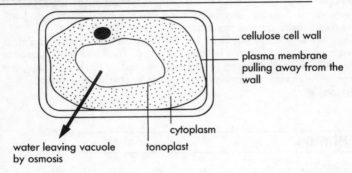

cellulose cell wall

plasma membrane pulling away from the wall

cytoplasm

water leaving vacuole by osmosis

tonoplast

Fig. I.1 Incipient plasmolysis

Incipient plasmolysis (Fig. I.1) is defined as the stage in which the cytoplasm just begins to pull away from the cell wall due to water being drawn out of a plant cell by **osmosis**. At this point the **pressure potential** of the cell wall can be taken as zero, so the **water potential** of the cell is equivalent to the water potential of the surrounding solution. In experimental work incipient **plasmolysis** is taken as the point when 50 per cent of all cells are plasmolysed.

INCOMPATIBILITY

Plant breeders are increasingly using **out-breeding** techniques in order to obtain improved yields and healthier plants. Plants of different varieties and even different species are crossed, resulting in hybrid offspring. The main problem is that of incompatibility between such plants: chemical differences may prevent pollen grain germination or pollen tube growth, and different chromosome numbers may result in sterility. Special methods of overcoming incompatibility include polyploidy and induced mutations.

◀ Hybrids, hybridisation, Mutation outbreeding, Polyploidy ▶

INCOMPLETE DOMINANCE

◀ Codominance ▶

INCUBATION PERIOD

The incubation period is the time delay between initial infection by a disease-causing organism and the appearance of symptoms of the disease. With viruses, this corresponds with the latent phase of virus replication.

INDEPENDENT ASSORTMENT OF TWO PAIRS OF ALLELES

Mendelian inheritance of two pairs of alleles results in a 9:3:3:1 ratio in the F2 generation because of Mendel's Second Law of Independent Assortment. This states that of a pair of contrasting alleles, each allele of one pair may combine with either of the other pair in a gamete.

◀ Mendelian inheritance ▶

INDICATORS

Indicators are solutions used in experimental work to determine pH levels (e.g. the pH of soil samples).

INDICATOR SPECIES AND COMMUNITIES

One way of defining the community associated with a certain habitat is in terms of indicator species. These are species of plants or animals that tend to predominate in the particular ecological conditions associated with the habitat. A good example might be *Calluna vulgaris* as indicator species for a heather moor.

Another application of indicator species is in determining the extent of water pollution, by biological means rather than by chemical analysis. The presence or absence of certain species or **communities** in a body of water will indicate how polluted it is. Fish such as trout are particularly intolerant of poor water quality and low oxygen content (hence the relevance of the reappearance of salmon in the River Thames). At the other end of the scale, the oligochaete annelid worm *Tubifex* can live in almost oxygen-free water, and the presence of sewage fungus indicates that there are organic pollutants in the water.

INDIVIDUALITY

Individuality is an essential characteristic of living things. It means that every individual plant and animal is unique, possessing a genetic blueprint that differs from the **genome** of all other plants and animals. The exception to this occurs when micro-organisms, such as bacteria, reproduce asexually, forming a clone.

INDUCTIVE AGENTS OF DISEASE

◀ Pathogens ▶

INDUSTRIAL EFFLUENTS

Industrial effluents are the liquid and gaseous discharges of waste from factories, power stations and other industrial units. They cause **pollution** of the atmosphere and of aquatic ecosystems.

INDUSTRIAL MELANISM

Industrial melanism is the darkening of animal coloration in areas of high industrial activity where smoke and soot are atmospheric pollutants. The best-known example is the peppered moth, *Biston betularia*. This shows **polymorphism**, existing in two varieties: the light-coloured 'peppered' form and a mutant black form which first appeared near Manchester in 1848. The peppered form predominates in areas with clean air, where they are camouflaged on the lichen-covered tree trunks on which they rest during the day. If air pollution is severe, however, the lichen dies and trees become blackened. The black moths are less visible to their bird predators and thus become more abundant.

This is an excellent illustration of environmental **selection pressure** acting on variations in **phenotype** and resulting in population change. As yet **speciation** has not occurred, since the two varieties of peppered moth can still

interbreed, producing **fertile offspring**.
◀ Adaptation, Variation ▶

INFECTION

Infection occurs if pathogenic micro-organisms manage to invade the body, despite the passive defences of the skin, respiratory cilia, stomach acid, blood clotting and so on. The body reacts to this infection in several ways.

For a surface wound, the first mechanism is **inflammation**, in which blood flow to the area is increased, bringing **opsonins** and phagocytes to the wound to fight infection. Opsonins attach to bacteria, making it easier for the phagocytes to engulf them. The phagocytes operating in a wound area are neutrophils, because they are capable of squeezing out through the walls of blood capillaries. **Phagocytosis** also occurs in lymphoid tissue, where the large fixed macrophages are present.

For a deep wound or for an internal infection, the **immune system** of the body is activated. Antibodies are manufactured by **lymphocytes** in response to specific **antigens** on the surface of the pathogen, and the body can become immune to further infections by that particular organism. Antitoxins are also produced to neutralise the toxins produced by many bacteria.
◀ Antibody, Immune system ▶

INFECTION, PREVENTION OF

It is not possible to prevent infection completely, but a number of measures can be taken which make certain infections less likely. **Sterilisation**, in which all micro-organisms and their spores are killed, is used for surgical instruments and syringes, where the risk of infection of internal tissues is high. The spread of water-borne diseases such as cholera can be largely prevented by good personal hygiene and by **water purification**. Most of the serious or life-threatening diseases of humans and domesticated animals can now be protected against by the use of **vaccine**. Large-scale vaccination against smallpox has eradicated the disease, and immunisation against childhood diseases such as measles has greatly reduced infant mortality.

INFECTIOUS DISEASES

An infectious **disease** is one which is caused by a pathogen of some kind, frequently **bacteria** or a **virus**, but also some **fungi** and **protoctista**. The **pathogens** can be transmitted from one host organism to another and so the disease is also passed on. Infectious diseases that are spread by direct contact are known as contagious diseases. If an infectious disease spreads rapidly and widely through the population, then the situation is described as an epidemic.
◀ Disease transmission ▶

INFERTILITY

The term infertility may be applied to a lack of nutrients in **soil**, which is therefore unable to support plant growth. It may also apply to **sexual reproduction** and the inability to produce viable offspring.

INFLAMMATION

Inflammation is the response of tissue to injury. When tissue is damaged in a wound, it releases chemicals such as histamine that cause localised swelling, redness and pain (i.e. inflammation) around the wound. They do so by causing **vasodilation** of the **capillaries**, which increases blood flow and raises the temperature of the wound area. They also make the capillaries more permeable, so that plasma containing **phagocytes** and antibodies can reach the damaged tissues and help combat any infection. It is this leakage of plasma into the area that causes the localised swelling. Inflammation ends as fibroblasts enter the wound area and synthesise collagen, which is built up into scar tissue.
◀ Antibody, Infection ▶

INFLUENZA

Influenza is a viral infection that is characterised by a range of symptoms, including high temperature, aching joints, sore throat and stuffy nose. It is caused by a group of myxoviruses, which can be divided into three types, viruses A, B and C, with A the most virulent. Influenza A virus is capable of frequent mutations, so **immunity** to it can only be short-lived. It can spread rapidly through the population, causing many deaths. The 'flu outbreak in England in autumn 1989 was caused by a type-A virus called English A.
◀ Immunity, Virus ▶

INGESTION

Ingestion is the taking in of food into the body. In protoctistans solid food particles are ingested into the cytoplasm in the form of a food **vacuole**, with the aid of pseudopodia or **cilia**. In higher animals food is ingested into a gut or **alimentary canal**, with the aid of a variety of structures such as claws, jointed mouthparts, tentacles and **teeth**. Many internal parasites have no need of such mechanisms and ingest their already soluble food substances by simple absorption across the body surface.
◀ Protoctista ▶

INHERITANCE, PARTICULATE NATURE OF

In 1866 Gregor Mendel suggested that the characteristics of organisms were determined by discrete units or 'factors' that were passed on from one generation to the next. Inheritance is not, therefore, a matter of blending parental characteristics, but is based on particles transmitted by gametes. We now call these particles genes.

◄ Genes, Mendelian inheritance ►

INHIBITION

Inhibition is the blocking or slowing down of a process by substances known as inhibitors. It is an essential part of homoeostatic mechanisms in the body and most hormones have both stimulatory and inhibitory effects. The control of biological processes such as **growth** and **germination** involves a balance between promoters and inhibitors. The inhibition of **enzyme** activity is of particular importance, and may underline the above processes.

◄ Enzyme inhibition, Homeostasis, Hormone ►

INNATE BEHAVIOUR

Innate behaviour is inborn and characteristic of the species concerned. It is involuntary and inflexible in that a certain stimulus will always produce the same response, and the nature of that response is inherited from one generation to the next. Plant **tropisms, nastic responses** and **turgor** movements are innate, as are **tactic responses** in micro-organisms. Other forms of innate behaviour are reflexes, instincts, and **biorhythms**.

▶ REFLEXES

A reflex is a simple automatic response of one part of the body to a given stimulus, and it requires a **nervous system**. The route taken by the nervous impulse from **receptors** to **effectors** is called the **reflex arc**. Examples of reflexes include blinking, sneezing and coughing, stretch reflexes and withdrawal from pain or heat. All these are protective responses, designed to reduce the risk of damage to the part of the body concerned.

▶ INSTINCTS

Instincts are complex, stereotyped behaviour patterns that involve the whole body and have important survival value. Insect behaviour is based largely on instinct, as is the behaviour of most vertebrates, though mammals also depend on **learned behaviour**. Examples of instinctive behaviour include swarming in termites, **courtship behaviour** in sticklebacks and nest-building in birds.

Biorhythms

Biorhythms are instinctive behaviour patterns that are repeated at regular time intervals, regardless of changes in the external environment. Examples include laboratory rats feeding every two hours even if food is present all the time, nocturnal animals being active at the same time each night even when kept in constant light and migratory birds flying south in autumn even if the weather is mild.

◄ Migration, Reflex action ►

INORGANIC IONS

With the exception of carbon dioxide and carbonates, inorganic molecules do not contain carbon. Many inorganic ions are important biologically. These include **phosphate** (PO_4^{3-}), **nitrate** (NO_3^-), **carbonate** (CO_3^{2-}), **sulphate** (SO_4^{2-}), **sodium** (Na^+), **potassium** (K^+), **calcium** (Ca^{2+}), **iron** (Fe^{3+}) and **magnesium** (Mg^{2+}).

INSECTICIDES

Insecticides are chemical preparations that can be used to kill insect pests. They can be divided into three categories: inorganic insecticides, organic insecticides and artificial **growth** promoters and inhibitors, such as Juvenile Hormone Mimic, used against flies and mosquitoes.

Examples of inorganic insecticides are lead arsenate and mercuric chloride. Although these are cheap, they are no longer used much, because they are highly toxic to organisms other than insects and their heavy metal ions persist in the soil for many years.

► ORGANIC INSECTICIDES

The organic insecticides are the ones that have been used, and abused, most widely. There are several types.

Organic Plant Extracts (e.g. Pyrethrum)

Pyrethrum is very toxic to insects while being relatively harmless to other organisms, and it is readily biodegradable. Unfortunately, it is very expensive.

Chlorinated Hydrocarbons (e.g. DDT)

Many countries have now banned the use of DDT, though it is still used to kill mosquitoes in the control of malaria. Its advantages are that it is very cheap to produce, it is effective against most insects and it is persistent in crops and soil so does not need to be applied too often. Its persistence is also a disadvantage, however, because of food chain accumulation. DDT is applied to crops in concentrations too low to be harmful to animal life, but when **herbivores** eat the crops, the DDT is concentrated in their tissues by a factor of ten. With each succeeding trophic level, there is a further multiplication by ten, so that top **consumers** receive critical doses. In eagles and pelicans, for example, high levels of DDT cause thinning of their egg shells so that eggs are crushed before they can hatch. Other disadvantages of DDT are that many insect pests have developed resistance to it, and that it may worsen the pest problem by killing the natural predators of the pest.

Organophosphates (e.g. Malathion)

Malathion is an extremely toxic but non-persistent insecticide. Food chain accumulation does not occur, but even in low doses it is harmful to animals other than insects. Some insect pests have also developed resistance to it.
◀ Food chains, food webs, Heavy metals, Trophic levels ▶

INSECTS

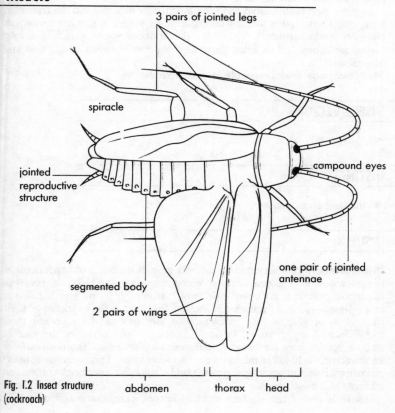

3 pairs of jointed legs

spiracle

jointed reproductive structure

compound eyes

one pair of jointed antennae

segmented body

2 pairs of wings

Fig. I.2 Insect structure (cockroach)   abdomen   thorax   head

Insects are a major class of the phylum Arthropoda. They are terrestrial animals and possess a **tracheal system** for **gaseous exchange**, and a malpighian tubules for **excretion**. The body of an insect is divided into three regions (see Fig. I.2):

- head, with compound **eyes**, jointed mouthparts and one pair of jointed antennae;
- thorax of three segments, bearing one pair of jointed legs per segment, and one or two pairs of wings in adults;
- an abdomen of eleven segments, with one pair of **spiracles** per segment and jointed reproductive structures on the last segment.

Because of their chitinous **exoskeleton**, all insects must grow and develop through a series of stages called instars, punctuated by **ecdysis** or moulting. In some insects, the immature instars lack wings but are otherwise similar in appearance to the adult, or imago. There is no pupa in the life cycle. These insects can be grouped together for convenience as exopterygotes, though this is not a taxonomic group. Examples include insects as diverse as earwigs, aphids, locusts and dragonflies.

In other insects, the **larva** and adult look totally different and the transition from one to the other occurs during a pupal stage, a process known as complete **metamorphosis**. These are the **Endopterygota**, which is a valid taxonomic group and includes butterflies and moths, bees, ants, flies and mosquitoes.

◀ Arthropods, Endopterygote insects, Spiracle ▶

INSECT VECTORS

◀ Vector ▶

INSTINCTS

◀ Innate behaviour ▶

INSULIN

Insulin is a **hormone** secreted by the beta cells of the islets of Langerhans in the **pancreas**, in response to raised **glucose** levels in the blood. It travels in the **blood plasma** to its target cells, which are mainly in the liver but also in other tissues such as muscle. It causes the liver cells to increase their conversion of glucose into **glycogen** for storage, and to decrease their metabolism of glycogen and fat into glucose. It also increases the rate of glucose uptake from the blood by muscle and other cells. The net result of insulin activity is to lower the blood glucose level again. This decrease in blood glucose inhibits further insulin production by **negative feedback** control, an example of homoeostasis.

Insulin is one of the smallest proteins known, being composed of just 51 amino acids. It is antagonistic to **glucagon**, a hormone secreted by the alpha-cells of the islets of Langerhans. Shortage of insulin results in diabetes mellitus, in which excess glucose is excreted in the urine. Effects include blindness, coma and even death.

INTELLIGENCE

Intelligence is the ability to learn, to reason and to communicate. There is a continuing debate as to whether it is primarily inherited or due to environmental influences.
◄ **Learned behaviour** ►

INTENSIVE FARMING

The aim of intensive farming is to reduce losses and costs, and to correspondingly increase the **productivity** of the land or livestock. **Selective breeding** is important, in order to develop strains with better disease and pest resistance, and to improve the quality or quantity of the **yield**. In arable farming improved water supply and control are required, and increased mechanisation is used in preparing the land, weed control and harvesting. Agricultural chemicals are used on a large scale, as fertilisers, insecticides and pesticides, and also synthetic growth hormones (e.g. BST – Bovine Somatotrophin). Intensive livestock farming may involve rather insanitary and cramped conditions for the animals, as in battery farming for the production of hens' eggs.

INTERACTIONS BETWEEN ORGANISMS

Interactions occur between organisms of the same and of different species, and they vary considerably from casual encounters to very close, obligate associations.

 FEEDING RELATIONSHIPS

All the organisms in a community are involved in feeding relationships. They belong to **trophic levels** and form part of a food web. Energy from the sun is harnessed by the green plant **producers** and passed on through **herbivores** to **carnivores**, and finally to **decomposers**. It is a balanced system, and the removal of one link in the chain will affect all the others.

 PREDATION

The relationship between a predator and its prey can be a close one, particularly if the predator **population** is limited mainly by its food supply. In these circumstances, a relatively stable situation is reached in which the two population sizes fluctuate together about a mean, representing the carrying capacity of the habitat for that species.

▶ COMPETITION

Interaction between members of the same species may involve **intraspecific competition**. This occurs mainly prior to reproduction, with competition among males for available females and competition for the space needed for nest sites. **Interspecific competition** occurs between individuals of different species that are on the same trophic level. The competition is greatest if the organisms occupy the same or a similar ecological niche.

▶ SOCIAL BEHAVIOUR

Intraspecific interaction may also take the form of social behaviour, though this occurs in relatively few species. Social organisation can be very complex, with distinct hierarchies and division of labour and involving elaborate systems of communication (e.g. honey bees).

▶ SYMBIOSIS

A close interspecific association in which one organism lives in or on the body of the other organism is called a **symbiosis** (literally 'living together'). There are three levels of symbiosis: commensalism, mutualism and parasitism.

Commensalism

This involves a host organism that neither loses nor gains and a commensal organism living on or in the host that receives some benefit. A good example is the colonial hydrozoan, *Hydractinia equina*, that attaches itself to whelk shells containing hermit crabs. This has no effect on the hermit crab, but the hydrozoan acquires a place to live and is able to feed on the scraps of food that the crab leaves. Many of the bacteria that inhabit the human gut can also be regarded as commensals.

Mutualism

This is a close relationship between two organisms that both benefit. An example of this is the mutualistic (or symbiotic), bacterium *Rhizobium* in the root nodules of leguminous plants. The bacterium receives shelter and the correct oxygen tension supplied by legume-haemoglobin and the legume receives fixed nitrogen. Other examples of mutualism include lichens, mycorrhizae and the gut flora of ruminants.

Parasitism

This is an association in which the parasite organism lives in or on the host organism, gaining both food and shelter and causing the host some degree of harm. Many parasites are highly adapted to their mode of life. Examples of parasites include the liver fluke in the liver of a sheep, the malarial parasite *Plasmodium* in the bloodstream of man and the potato blight fungus, *Phytophthora infestans*.

◀ Carrying capacity, Competition, Communities, Food chains, food webs, Mutualism, Parasitism, Predation, Social behaviour ▶

INTERCELLULAR FLUID

◀ Lymph ▶

INTERFERON

Interferon is a protein molecule that prevents the replication of viruses. Cells that are attacked by a virus can produce interferon much faster than they can synthesise the specific antibodies, partly because it is effective against all types of viruses. It is also effective against certain forms of cancer, so it has been the subject of a great deal of research. It appears that only human interferon gives **immunity** against human viral diseases, and since human interferon is scarce and expensive, **genetic engineering** is the only way to produce it commercially.

◀ Antibody ▶

INTERNODE ELONGATION

An internode is the distance between two nodes, or points of leaf attachment, on a plant stem (Fig. I.3). Increase in length of the internodal regions is brought about by the plant growth substance, **gibberellin**, which stimulates cell division and cell elongation.

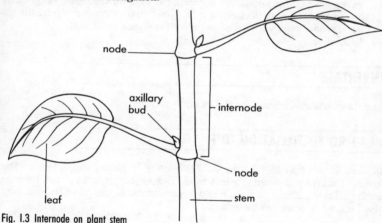

Fig. I.3 Internode on plant stem

INTERPHASE

Interphase describes the resting state during which cells grow and prepare for the next division. In actively dividing cells it can last between twelve and twenty-four hours, and is made up of three periods. These are a period of growth, followed by a period of DNA synthesis, when the chromosomes are duplicated, then a second period of growth. These three periods, together with mitosis comprise the cell cycle. During interphase the chromosomes are indistinct and the cell looks the same as a non-dividing cell.

INTERSPECIFIC COMPETITION

Interspecific competition occurs when organisms of two or more different species require the same resources, which are inadequate to supply the needs of all. They must therefore compete for these resources. Interspecific competition mainly occurs between organisms on the same trophic level competing for the same food supply. Plants compete for available light, water and soil nutrients, while animals compete for the same type of food plant or prey. Competition is particularly intense between organisms occupying the same ecological niche.

◀ Trophic levels ▶

INTRASPECIFIC COMPETITION

Intraspecific competition occurs when organisms of the same species compete for the same resources. It may be for nutritional needs, for mates or for nesting sites. If the population numbers increase rapidly, then competition for food may become particularly severe, which in turn imposes restraints on further reproduction by a kind of negative feedback mechanism.

◀ Population growth ▶

INVERTASE

Invertase is another name for the enzyme sucrase.

IN VITRO FERTILISATION (IVF)

In vitro fertilisation literally means 'fertilisation in glass', and refers to the fusion of sperm and ovum in a test tube. The zygote or embryo can then be implanted in the uterus. It is used as a treatment for human infertility, and may also be used in selective breeding.

INTEGRATED PEST MANAGEMENT

The control of pests may involve many different strategies and techniques. Different kinds of chemical pesticides may be used, at different times and in different concentrations, or biological control may be preferred. Other alternatives include cultural control, the development of pest-resistant varieties of crops and livestock, the use of physical barriers and repellants, and genetic control by the production and release of sterile males or the introduction of mutants with **lethal genes** into the pest population.

Integrated pest management is an approach based on a thorough understanding of the crop **ecosystem** and the wider environment. The ecology of all present or potential pest populations is studied and a management programme is developed, taking account of all the relevant factors and integrating the various pest-control measures that are available. This approach was used successfully in the management of cotton crop pests in Peru. After just four years of following the new programme, crop yields had more than doubled. Similar programmes have been successful for the alfalfa crop in the United States and for glasshouse crops in England.

IODINE

Iodine ions (I^-) are required in trace quantities by animals, because iodine is a consitituent of the **hormone thyroxine**, secreted by the **thyroid gland**. The main dietary sources for humans are drinking water and vegetables (if the soil contains iodine ions), and marine fish and shellfish. A shortage of iodine in the diet results in goitre, a condition characterised by a gross swelling of the neck due to enlargement of the thyroid gland.

ION

An ion is an electrically charged particle formed when an atom loses or gains electrons.

IONISING RADIATION

There are many kinds of radiation, but only radioactivity, cosmic rays and cathode-ray tubes produce radiation that is able to ionise, or remove electrons from, atoms. If the disrupted atoms form part of living tissue, then physiological and genetic damage may occur. There is a certain amount of natural background radioactivity everywhere on the Earth, but man-made ionising radiation poses greater hazards. This may stem from nuclear power stations, nuclear reprocessing plants, atomic weapons testing, X-ray machines and even television sets. Radioactive isotopes are particularly dangerous because they continue to emit radiation as they decay, and many have very long half-lives.

Physiological damage due to ionising radiation will vary depending on the dose received; high doses cause death. Leukaemia is common, as are other cancers, together with reduced growth rate and accelerated **senescence**.

Genetic damage involves an increase in the **mutation** rate, which introduces inheritable defects into the population. Some defects may be apparent immediately, but others may lie hidden for many generations.

◀ Radiation as pollutant ▶

ION UPTAKE

Mineral ions dissolved in the soil water can be absorbed into the plant through the root hairs. Some ions enter the root passively with the water, but their concentration in soil water is low, so active uptake is also required. This occurs against the concentration gradient, and involves the expenditure of adenosine triphosphate (ATP). There is evidence that ion uptake is also a selective process since some ions are taken up in preference to others, so it is possible that membrane carrier proteins may be involved.

Once in the root hair cells, most of the mineral ions are transported passively across the root through the apoplastic pathway of the cell walls to the endodermis. Here they are blocked by Casparian strips, and must pass through the plasma membrane and cytoplasm of an endodermal cell in order to reach the xylem.

◀ Apoplast, Apoplastic pathway, Water uptake in roots ▶

IQ TESTS

IQ stands for Intelligence Quotient, which is a ratio, commonly expressed as a percentage, of a person's mental age to his or her actual age. IQ tests consist of a variety of questions testing either spatial or verbal reasoning and are designed to determine a person's mental capacity or the age at which that capacity would be 'normal'

IQ tests can be useful but they do have limitations. The range of skills tested is small and the techniques for answering questions can be easily learned, in which case the test is reduced to a matter of 'jumping through hoops'. There are no universally agreed definitions as to what intelligence actually is and no set formula as to which skills must be acquired at which age. There are several 'higher' intelligence skills that are impossible to test within such a restricted framework.

IRON

Iron, in the form of Fe^{3+} ions, is an essential element for both plants and animals. It is a constituent of the electron carriers, ferredoxin and cytochromes, so it is needed for the electron transport system of cellular respiration, and for photophosphorylation. It activates catalase enzyme, which is important in both plant and animal tissues to speed up the breakdown of hydrogen peroxide.

In plants it is required for the synthesis of chlorophyll, hence a lack of iron in the soil results in chlorosis or leaf yellowing.

In animals, it is a constituent of haemoglobin in red blood cells and of myoglobin in muscle tissue. A lack of iron in the diet will result in anaemia. Good dietary sources of iron for humans include liver, kidneys, eggs and chocolate.

◀ Electron carrier, Electron transfer, ET systems ▶

IRRIGATION

Irrigation is the process of supplying agricultural land with water other than rainfall, and it is necessary wherever rainfall is inadequate or irregular. There are two types of irrigation: surface and overhead. In surface irrigation, canals or other watercourses are constructed to convey water to the crop from lakes, rivers or reservoirs. In overhead irrigation, water is piped from a mains water supply, or pumped from wells, and sprinkled over the whole plot. This latter method is more expensive so is used only for small areas or for occasional droughts. The main purpose of irrigation is to improve crop productivity, but other advantages include the increased range of crops that can be grown and the fact that farmers can be more independent of the weather.

ISOLATING MECHANISMS

An isolating mechanism describes anything that prevents succesful reproduction between individuals of the same species. If a group of individuals is reproductively isolated, gene flow with the rest of the population is prevented and intraspecific speciation becomes possible.

GEOGRAPHICAL ISOLATION

This occurs when a barrier such as a mountain range or waterway interrupts gene flow and so leads to reproductive isolation. If speciation takes place while the populations are geographically separated, then it is known as allopatric speciation. All other isolating mechanisms are effective when populations occupy the same geographical area, so may result in sympatric speciation. These isolating mechanisms can be divided into those that prevent fertilisation occurring and those that permit fertilisation but adversely affect the hybrids that are formed.

ISOLATION PREVENTING FERTILISATION

This could be:

- seasonal, where populations are sexually mature at different times of the year;
- ecological, where the two populations live in the same area but prefer different habitats;
- behavioural, in animals, where the two populations have different or incompatible courtship behaviour and mating rituals;
- mechanical or physiological, where cross-fertilisation is prevented because of physiological incompatibility (e.g. stigma – pollen interactions) or because genitalia differ so much mechanically that gamete transfer cannot occur (e.g. in spiders).

▶ ISOLATING MECHANISMS AFFECTING HYBRIDS

These could be:

- hybrid inviability, where hybrids are produced but fail to develop to maturity;
- hybrid sterility, where the hybrids fail to produce functional gametes due to a failure of meiosis and abnormal segregation of chromosomes and genes.

ISOLATION OF MICRO-ORGANISMS

◀ Microbiological techniques ▶

JACOB-MONOD MODEL OF GENE CONTROL

With the exception of a **gamete** every human **cell** contain twenty-three pairs of **chromosomes**. This means that all cells have a full genetic blueprint for human life, yet each type of cell develops differently and clearly uses only a tiny proportion of these genes. A mechanism must exist, therefore, that keeps most genes switched off but allows some genes to function, either continuously or intermittently, according to the requirements of the cell. In 1965 the French scientists Francois Jacob and Jacques Monod shared a Nobel Prize for their work explaining how genes may be controlled. Their research concerned **enzyme** synthesis in the bacterium *Escherichia coli*, but the model they proposed is applicable to higher plants and animals as well.

In *E. coli* some enzymes are produced all the time but the synthesis of others depends on environmental factors. Some enzymes are not produced at all unless their **substrate** is present; thus the substrate causes enzyme induction. Some enzymes are usually produced but synthesis ceases if excess end product is present; thus the end product causes enzyme repression.

Jacob and Monod proposed that chromosomes contain three types of **gene**, these being structural genes, that code for polypeptide and hence enzyme synthesis, operator genes and regulator genes. Each operator gene is linked

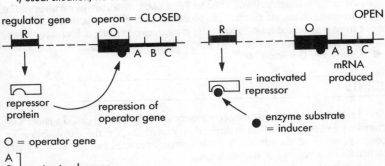

i) usual situation, no substrate:

ii) if substrate present:

regulator gene   operon = CLOSED

OPEN

= inactivated repressor

mRNA produced

repressor protein

repression of operator gene

enzyme substrate = inducer

O = operator gene

A
B   = structural genes
C

Fig. J.1 Diagrammatic representation of: a) for enzyme induction

i) usual situation, little end-product: ii) if excess end-product present:

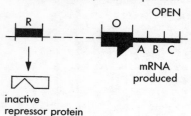

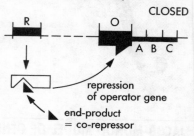

b) for enzyme repression

to a small group of structural genes, and together they form a unit called an operon. If the operator gene is 'open', all the structural genes in the operon become functional and start transcription of mRNA, but if the operator gene is 'closed', no mRNA can be transcribed. The operator gene is controlled by repressor proteins that are coded for by the regulator gene, and it is the repressor proteins that are affected by enzyme substrate or end product. For enzyme induction (Fig. J.1a), the repressor protein is inactivated by substrate molecules; for enzyme repression, (Fig. J.1b) the repressor protein is activated by end-product molecules.

◀ Bacteria, Substratum ▶

JAW ACTION

The jaw action of herbivorous mammals differs from that of carnivorous mammals because of the different problems associated with their food materials.

In **herbivores** the jaw movement is from side to side or backwards and forwards. This produces the grinding action that is required to mechanically break down the tough cellulose cell walls of plant material. In carnivores the jaw movement is up and down. This produces a scissor-like action to shear off meat from bones, and it also allows the jaws to close with much greater force, enabling the carnivore to seize its prey and to crush bones.

◀ Carnivore, Dentition ▶

JOINTS

The junction between two or more elements of a **skeleton** is called a joint. The chitinous **exoskeleton** of an arthropod is jointed, as are the cartilaginous or bony skeletons of **chordates**. In both systems muscles can act across joints to produce movement of the skeleton.

In mammalian skeletons, the joints can be divided into three categories depending on the amount of movement they permit.

■ Immovable joints, such as the suture joints between the bones of the skull and between the bones of the pelvic girdle. These are found where strength and rigidity are required, to give protection or to provide support.

■ Partly moveable joints (Fig. J.2a), such as the sliding joints between the **vertebrae**. Each joint permits a little movement, so that the vertebral column as a whole is quite flexible, while still providing protection for the **spinal cord**.

■ Freely movable or synovial joints (Fig. J.2b), such as the **hinge joint** at the elbow and the ball and socket joint at the shoulder. These are the

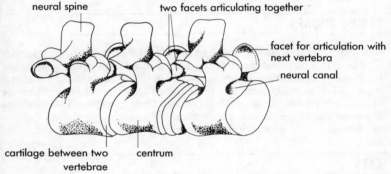

neural spine

two facets articulating together

facet for articulation with next vertebra

neural canal

cartilage between two vertebrae

centrum

Fig. J.2a) Sliding joint

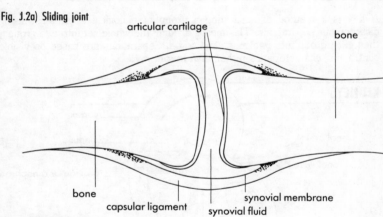

articular cartilage

bone

bone

capsular ligament

synovial fluid

synovial membrane

Fig. J.2b) Synovial joint

joints involved in **locomotion** and most body movements, so they are subject to the greatest stresses and potential wear. For this reason, the articulating surfaces of the bones are protected with a layer of **cartilage** to reduce friction and act as a shock absorber. Friction is also reduced by the synovial fluid, which effectively lubricates the joint, and the bones are held firmly in position by a number of ligaments.

◄ Hinge joint, Shoulder joint, Synovial joint ►

KETOSE SUGARS

In a monosaccharide all the carbon atoms except one have a hydroxyl group attached. This carbon atom may form part of an aldehyde group, making the monosaccharide an aldose sugar, or part of a ketone group, making it a ketose sugar. A ketone group comprises three carbon atoms in a chain, in which the central carbon atom forms a double bond with an oxygen atom. Two examples of ketose sugars are ribulose and fructose.

◀ Aldose sugars, Monosaccharides ▶

KEYS

A key is a method of separating a group of biological specimens, using dichotomous separations. This means dividing the whole set into two groups, then each group into two more and so on. Separations are based on visible contrasting characteristics rather than taxonomy.

KIDNEYS

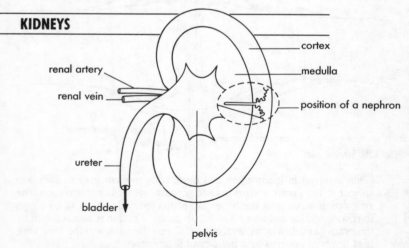

Fig. K.1 Transverse section of a mammalian kidney

The most important organ of **excretion** in **mammals** is the kidney, and it is also the mammalian organ of **osmoregualtion**. There are two kidneys, located one on either side of the vertebral column, and they receive their abundant blood supply through the right and left renal arteries. The gross structure of the kidney is shown in Fig. K.1).

A kidney is composed of millions of nephrons, which are the structural and functional units of the organ. Each **nephron** is a long coiled tube, open at one end and closed at the other, made up of four regions: a Bowman's capsule at the closed end, which surrounds a knot of **capillaries** called a glomerulus, then a proximal tubule, the loop of Henle, and a distal tubule, which leads into a collecting duct.

Nephron function involves three distinct processes: ultrafiltration, selective reabsorption and secretion of further excretory products.

▶ ULTRAFILTRATION

This means filtration under pressure. It describes the way in which every **molecule** with a molecular mass of less than 68,000 is filtered out of the blood of the glomerulus into the Bowman's capsule. The pressure for filtration comes mainly from the hydrostatic pressure of blood opposed by the **water potential** of the plasma proteins. The hydrostatic pressure in the glomerular capillaries is higher than might be expected because the glomerulus occurs between two arterioles and not between an arteriole and a venule.

▶ SELECTIVE REABSORPTION

The selective reabsorption of useful substances occurs in different parts of the tubule. The proximal tubule is well adapted for absorption, with a greatly increased internal surface area due to the brush border of **microvilli** on the epithelial cells. All the **glucose** and **amino acids** are reabsorbed here, together with 85 per cent of the **water** and dissolved **inorganic ions**. Absorption occurs by a combination of passive and active means. Water leaves by **osmosis**, but other molecules enter the epithelial cells by **diffusion** and then are actively transported into the capillaries around the tubule, so maintaining a concentration gradient for further diffusion.

Reabsorption of chloride ions occurs in the loop of Henle. A chloride pump actively removes chloride ions, followed passively by sodium ions, from the ascending limb of the loop into the interstitial fluid of the medulla. The increased ionic concentration of the medulla leads to the osmotic loss of water from the descending limb of the loop, which is permeable to water though not to solutes. These movements result in the loop acting as a counter-current exchange system and make possible the passive uptake of water from the distal tubule and collecting duct (Fig. K.2).

▶ SECRETION

The secretion of further substances not required by the body occurs mainly in the distal tubule. This is an active process and is particularly important in maintaining the **pH** of blood plasma at pH 7.4. If the plasma pH falls, hydrogen ions and ammonium ions are secreted into the tubule; if the plasma pH rises, hydrogencarbonate ions are secreted. Tubular secretion is also used to eliminate excess potassium ions (which are exchanged for sodium ions) and certain nitrogenous waste products such as creatinine.

▶ HORMONES

In order to maintain constant blood volume and constant ionic concentration in the plasma, variable amounts of water and chloride will need to be reabsorbed. This homoeostatic control is carried out by hormones. ADH is secreted by the posterior lobe of the **pituitary gland** if the water potential of the blood rises. It increases the permeability of the collecting duct to water so more water is reabsorbed into the blood. Aldosterone is secreted by the adrenal cortex if the ionic concentration of blood falls or if blood volume falls. It causes the active reabsorption of chloride ions, which is followed by the osmotic uptake of water.

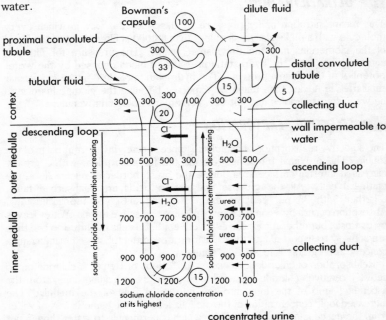

Fig. K.2 Changes in concentration of tubular fluid

◀ Adrenal glands, Arteries, Arterioles, Counter-current mechanisms, Excretion, Homoeostasis, Osmoregulation, Renal blood vessels, Vertebrae, Vertebral column ▶

KIN SELECTION

Kin selection is a form of **altruism** which puts the survival of kin, or relatives, at a higher priority than one's own survival. A good example of kin selection is the way worker bees will defend their relatives in the hive by stinging an intruder. The sting sticks fast in the intruder's body so if it struggles the gut of the bee will be pulled out and the bee dies.

KINESIS

Kinesis is a type of locomotory behaviour found in animals such as woodlice and water fleas. It involves non-directional changes in movement or position according to the type of **stimulus** or its intensity. The direction of the stimulus has no effect, unlike in **tactic responses**. Woodlice, for example, will move at varying speeds according to the humidity of their environment. Sudden dryness causes them to move faster and turn more quickly, thus increasing their chances of returning to damper conditions.
◀ Locomotion ▶

KINGDOMS

A kingdom is the largest taxonomic grouping used in the **classification** of organisms. Traditionally only two kingdoms were used, with all organisms being divided into plants or animals. This is not consistent with current scientific understanding, however, and it is now recommended that five kingdoms should be recognised.

▶ *PROKARYOTAE*

These are prokaryotic organisms, lacking a true nucleus. They are all **bacteria**, some non photosynthetic (e.g. *Escherichia coli*) and some photosynthetic (e.g. *Nostoc* – now called blue-green bacteria not blue-green algae).

▶ *PROTOCTISTA*

Eukaryotic organisms that are neither fungi, plants nor animals are now grouped as protoctistans. The kingdom includes all nucleated **algae**, all protozoa and the slime moulds. There are a total of nine phyla:

- Rhizopoda (rhizopods) – e.g. *Amoeba*;
- Zoomastigina (flagellates) – e.g. *Trypanosoma*;
- Apicomplexa (sporozoans) – e.g. *Plasmodium*;
- Ciliophora (ciliates) – e.g. *Paramecium*;
- Euglenophyta (euglenoid flagellates) – e.g. *Euglena*;
- Oomycota (oomycetes) – e.g. *Phytophthora*;
- Chlorophyta (green algae) – e.g. *Chlamydomonas*;
- Rhodophyta (red algae) – e.g. *Chondrus*;
- Phaeophyta (brown algae) – e.g. *Fucus*.

▶ FUNGI

In this classification system, fungi are elevated to kingdom status. They are non-photosynthetic organisms, organised into multi-nucleate hyphae. There are three phyla:

- Zygomycota (zygomycetes) – e.g. *Mucor*;
- Ascomycota (ascomycetes) – e.g *Neurospora*;
- Basidiomycota (basidiomycetes) – e.g. *Agaricus* (mushroom).

▶ PLANTAE

Plants are now limited just to those organisms that are multicellular, eukaryotic and photosynthetic, with a **cellulose cell wall**. Note that the **pteridophytes** have been sub-divided, as have the spermatophytes, so the kingdom now includes six phyla:

- **Bryophyta (moss and liverwort)** – e.g. *Pellia, Bryum*;
- **Lycopodophyta (club mosses)** – e.g. **Selaginella**;
- Sphenophyta (horsetails) – e.g. *Equisetum*;
- **Filicinophyta (ferns)** – e.g. *Pteridium* (bracken);
- Coniferophyta (conifers) – e.g. *Pinus* (Scots pine);
- **Angiospermophyta (flowering plants)** – e.g *Triticum* (wheat), *Ranunculus* (buttercup).

▶ ANIMALIA

Animals are non-photosynthetic multicllular organisms with nervous co-ordination. There are eight major phyla:

- Cnidaria (formerly **coelenterates**) – e.g. *Aurelia* (jellyfish);
- **Platyhelminthes (flatworms)** – e.g. *Fasciola* (liver fluke);
- Nematoda (roundworms) – e.g. *Ankylostoma* (hookworm);
- Annelida (segmented worms) – e.g. *Lumbricus* (earthworm);
- Mollusca (molluscs) – e.g. *Helix* (garden snail);
- Arthropoda (**arthropods**) – e.g. *Locusta* (locust);
- Echinodermata (echinoderms) – e.g. *Asterias* (starfish);
- Chordata (**chordates**) – e.g. *Homo* (man).

◀ Basidomycete, Flagellum, flagellates, Taxonomy, Zygomycete ▶

KREBS CYCLE

Krebs cycle is an important part of cellular **aerobic respiraion**. It is also known as the **tricarboxylic acid cycle**.
◀ Cellular respiration, TCA cycle ▶

KWASHIORKOR

Kwashiorkor is a widespread illness that results from protein shortage in the diet. It particularly affects children since their protein needs are so much greater than those of adults. Children suffering from kwashiorkor are physically weak and listless, show poor bone growth and may have a pot-bellied appearance, due to slackening of the abdominal muscles and swelling of the intestine. If the diet is not improved, the child will die, either from liver damage or from diseases such as measles, because of reduced disease resistance.

◄ Proteins ►

LACTATION

Lactation is the production and release of milk by the mammary glands. It is under the control of a variety of hormones, which all play a role in the formation and release of milk. The major **hormone** involved with the secretion of milk is **prolactin**, a hormone produced by the **pituitary gland**. During pregnancy, levels of prolactin start to increase, but lactation is initiated only when the levels of **oestrogens** and **progesterone** drop towards the end of pregnancy. High levels of oestrogen and progesterone inhibit the action of prolactin by causing the release of an inhibiting factor from the **hypothalamus**. Lowering levels of the ovarian hormones remove this inhibition and also cause the release of prolactin-releasing factor (PRF) from the hypothalamus, which regulates the prolactin levels. High levels of prolactin are maintained in the post-pregnant stage due to infant suckling, which sends impulses to the hypothalamus, increasing the release of PRF. Sucking by the infant also initiates the release of **oxytocin**, another hormone from the pituitary. Oxytocin causes the ejection of the milk from the mammary glands into the ducts, where it can be sucked by the infant. The first secretion from the mammary glands after birth is called colostrum and contains maternal antibodies which will protect the baby for the first few weeks of its life.

LACTIC ACID

Lactic acid is an intermediate product produced by anaerobically respiring muscle cells. Its molecular formula is $CH_3.CHOH.COOH$. During severe exercise, insufficient oxygen is provided to the rapidly respiring muscle cells for them to aerobically oxidise **glucose**. In order to maintain some ATP production, the muscle cells produce ATP solely from the glycolytic breakdown of glucose. For **glycolysis** to proceed, the two end products, **pyruvate** and reduced **NAD** ($NADH_2$) must not be allowed to accumulate in the cell. Reoxidation of $NADH_2$ is vital so that it can continue to accept hydrogens from the oxidation of glucose. Consequently the hydrogens from the reduced NAD are used to reduce pyruvic acid to lactic acid. Thus lactic acid acts as an alternative hydrogen store for the continued oxidation of glucose. The levels of lactic acid slowly build up in the **cytoplasm** of the cell and eventually inhibit further oxidation. Lactic acid is removed from the muscle cells by diffusing into the blood, where it is taken to the liver. In the hepatocytes it is oxidised back to pyruvic acid by a dehydrogenase enzyme called lactate dehydrogenase. The pyruvic acid can then either be completely oxidised in the **Krebs cycle** or converted back to glucose and **glycogen** in the liver.

If lactic acid is allowed to accumulate in muscle cells, then cramp occurs until the **oxygen debt** is repaid.

◀ Anaerobic respiration, Dehydrogenase enzymes ▶

LAMELLAE IN CHLOROPLASTS

Lamellae are the internal membranes in a **chloroplast**. They form flattened fluid-filled sacs in and between the grana in chloroplasts.

◀ Plastids ▶

LAMINA OF LEAF

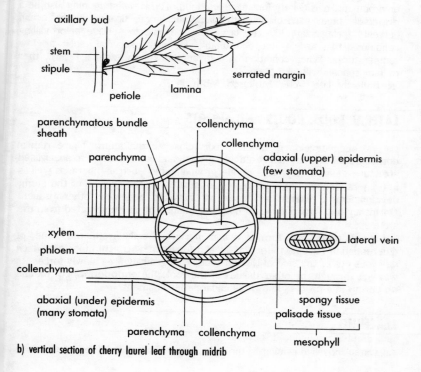

Fig. L.1 Dicotyledon leaf structure:
a) leaf of cherry laurel (underside)

main vein (midrib)
lateral veins
⎤ reticulate (net) venation

axillary bud
stem
stipule
petiole
lamina
serrated margin

parenchymatous bundle sheath
collenchyma
parenchyma
collenchyma
collenchyma
adaxial (upper) epidermis (few stomata)
xylem
phloem
collenchyma
lateral vein
abaxial (under) epidermis (many stomata)
spongy tissue
palisade tissue
parenchyma
collenchyma
mesophyll

b) vertical section of cherry laurel leaf through midrib

The lamina is the flat leaf blade which is connected to the stem by the **petiole**. In most plants the lamina is a thin structure in which the cells are arranged to maximise their ability to receive sunlight. In **dicotyledonous** plants (Fig. L.1) the lamina tends to be broad and supported by a branching network of **veins**. The upper surface which will receive the most light is different from the lower surface. **Monocotyledonous** plants have leaves differentiated into a blade and a sheath. The blade is narrow and the venation is parallel as opposed to forming a network. The upper and lower surfaces are not differentiated as the leaves tend to be borne vertically.

LARVA

A larva is a juvenile, sexually immature form of an animal which hatches from the egg and is anatomically distinct from the adult. It turns into the adult form by a process of **metamorphosis**, which is usually a rapid change. The larval form will usually have a different habitat and diet to the adult (e.g. tadpole larvae of **frogs, toads** and newts; caterpillars of butterflies and moths; planktonic trochophore larvae of polychaete worms and molluscs; and the bipinnaria larvae of **starfish**). The value of having larval forms is that the larva and adult are not in **competition** with each other for the resources of the environment, particularly for space and food. The larval stage may also be a **dispersal** stage, particularly with planktonic larvae floating in the ocean currents (pelagic larvae). The larva may be able to survive in prevailing conditions that would not be suitable for adult survival, such as low temperatures. When conditions are favourable for the adult's return, then metamorphosis will take place.

◀ Butterfly, Life cycles, Mollusca, Moth ▶

LATERAL BUDS, ROOTS AND SHOOTS

Lateral buds develop in the leaf axils close to the stem. These remain dormant until they are triggered into growth and can develop into specialised structures, such as flowers, or underground stems, such as tubers, as well as into lateral shoots. Because growth originates on the surface of the stem, development is exarch and does not have to penetrate other tissues. Dormancy of lateral buds is normally maintained by **auxin** secreted from the stem apex.

Lateral roots are formed when pericycle cells from the zone of differentiation become meristematic and form a new **apical meristem** which develops out of the side of the old root. This growing area slowly forces its way out through the other tissues of the root, the **endodermis, cortex** and **epidermis** in a process known as endarch development.

LEACHING

As water moves downwards through the **soil** and is then removed in the drainage system of streams, rivers, pools and lakes, it will take up soluble substances which are thus removed from the soil into the **aquatic habitats**. This is called leaching, and can lead to soil infertility as soluble nitrates are lost. If farmers use **nitrate** fertilisers, these nitrates might leach into pools and lakes and cause **eutrophication** and algal blooms. Industrial wastes dumped at rubbish sites may become leached and are then a hazard to humans who drink the water. High levels of aluminium leached into drinking water has been linked to the development of senile dementia.

LEAF AREA INDEX

The leaf area index (LAI) is a measure of crop **yield** or **productivity**.

$$LAI = \frac{\text{total leaf area of plant}}{\text{area of ground covered by plant}}$$

Plants having shoot systems with small surface areas can be expected to produce less dry matter than plants bearing shoot systems with large leaf surface areas. It is of advantage to breed crop plants which have high LAI values, since this improves crop yield. In the USA, sugar cane achieves LAI value of 7 and maize of 4. The leaves of these plants are erect and have little mutual shading.

LEAF FALL

Many perennial plants survive conditions of water unavailability by shedding their leaves, so reducing water loss by **transpiration**. This is also a mechanism by which plants get rid of toxic waste products such as tannins.

In most woody plants there is an abscission zone at the base of the petiole. This extends into the petiole and finally forms a plate of tissue in which meristematic divisions can occur. On the stem side of this plate the cells become corky to prevent water and sap loss from the stem. These changes are brought about by a drop-off in the levels of **auxin** in the leaf, which also triggers a number of degenerative changes in the leaf tissues. A fall in the **chlorophyll** content of the leaf allows the other pigments whose colours are usually masked by the chlorophyll to be seen as the typical autumn colours of the leaves. Vascular tissue is slowly blocked by the deposition of callose in the sieve plates and xylem, so the transport of water and solutes stops. The leaf dries out, the abscission layer becomes completely ruptured and the leaf is left hanging by its vascular bundle, ready to be blown off by the wind.
◀ Sieve plate ▶

LEAF STRUCTURE

Leaves are flattened structures adapted for **photosynthesis**. In gross structure the leaf consists of a thin broad lamina, a **petiole** that attaches the leaf to the stem and a system of **veins** or vascular tissue for removing the products of photosynthesis. Internally, it is composed of epidermal, vascular and ground tissues. Leaf structure is very variable, not only throughout the plant kingdom but within the different plant groups. A generalised leaf of a **dicotyledon** has distinctions between the upper and lower surfaces. The upper epidermal layer is composed of cuticularised cells, which are tightly bound together with no air spaces between them. Sometimes these cells contain pigments in their sap and also some contain outgrowths called hairs. The epidermis of the lower surface is usually less cuticularised and is perforated with stomata to allow **gaseous exchange**. With the exception of the stomatal guard cells the epidermal cells do not contain chloroplasts.

The ground tissue of the leaf is called the **mesophyll**. This tissue is composed of specialised **parenchyma** cells and is adapted for the process of photosynthesis. The upper layer is the palisade mesophyll, which is composed of vertical, closely packed cells, like columns, which are full of chloroplasts. The mesophyll tissue found in the lower layer is more irregular in shape, has fewer chloroplasts and there are numerous air spaces between the cells. For this reason it is known as spongy mesophyll. The air spaces connect up to the substomatal air spaces and are involved with the aeration of the leaf.

The vascular tissue of the leaf produces the characteristic vein network of dicotyledonous plants and the typical parallel venation of monocotyledonous plants. The vascular tissue consists of supporting **sclerenchyma** or **collenchyma** surrounding a quantity of **xylem** and **phloem**. The smaller and smaller branches of the veins of a dicotyledononous leaf eventually end openly in the mesophyll tissue.

Support for the leaf can be due to the development of collenchyma found just below the epidermis, near to the larger veins and sometimes around the edge of the blade. Most of the support however comes from the turgidity of the tissue cells.

◀ Dicotyledon, Lamina of leaf, Monocotyledon ▶

LEARNED BEHAVIOUR

Learned behaviour is adaptive and developed in response to past experiences. With some types of behaviour this takes the form of conditioning whereby a specific and predictable type of behaviour is triggered by a precise **stimulus**. For example, Pavlov's experiments in which he initiated the behavioural **response** of salivation by dogs when a bell was rung. In this example a stimulus was associated with a specific favourable outcome which initiated the response.

If the stimulus does not produce the expected outcome, then eventually the organism will ignore the stimulus and not respond. This is known as habituation and is important to many organisms, otherwise they would continue to waste energy on responding to obsolete stimuli.

Many organisms learn by **trial and error**, (i.e. a particular behavioural response is selected by trying out a series of responses and selecting the one that gives the desired result). For example, a rat in a maze, if given the choice of two corridors, will try them both out in turn quite randomly until it learns that food is to be had only at the terminus of one of the corridors. From then on the rat chooses only the one corridor. This type of learning often requires reinforcement, whereby the desired behaviour is elicited by continual repetition of the 'reward' or 'punishment'.

A more complex form of learning is known as insight learning or reasoning. This is the ability of an organism to respond correctly to a situation not previously encountered (i.e. past learning experiences can be applied to a novel situation without resorting to trial and error).

Imprinting is a type of behaviour much studied by Konrad Lorenz using ducks. Ducklings can be observed to always follow the mother duck as soon as they become mobile. This has obvious survival value to young organisms, who are at a vulnerable period of their development. Lorenz found through a series of famous experiments that the young ducks form attachments to the mother duck by being exposed to the female during a critical period of early life. This behavioural mechanism can be elicited using non-duck objects, such as Lorenz himself. If the ducklings were exposed to an object other than the mother, they would form attachments to that object in exactly the same way. Imprinting also has importance in later social and sexual development, especially among birds.

LEGUMINOUS PLANTS

Leguminous plants are dicotyledons that bear fruits which are pods or legumes (e.g. gorse, broom, lucerne, clover, vetches, peas, beans). The plants are biologically important because of their association with the mutualistic nitrogen-fixing bacterium **Rhizobium** in their root nodules. They thus improve soil fertility and are included in crop rotations.
◄ Mutualism, Nitrogen fixation ►

LENTICELS

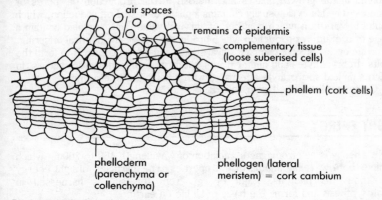

Fig. L.2 Vertical section of a lenticel

Lenticels are areas of loosely packed, dead suberised cells that occur on woody stems (Fig. L.2). They provide an efficient aeration system for **gaseous exchange** in trees, permitting the entry of **oxygen** for respiring cells and the exit of **carbon dioxide**. No **photosynthesis** occurs in woody stems, so gaseous exchange does not occur in the opposite direction.

LETHAL GENES

Lethal genes are often produced by **mutation** of a host **gene** so that it causes death of the organism in the pre-natal stage of development. Because the organism dies before it reaches reproductive age, lethal genes as such are not hereditary.

Oncogenes are genes thought to cause cancer. They are portions of viral genomes inserted into normal host DNA, causing the viral genome to be incorporated into the host genome. This then causes uncontrolled growth of the host cell and viral replication. It is now thought that oncogenes are not restricted to retroviruses but can also be found in normal animal cells and they have been isolated from cancerous cells that have arisen without any known viral invader.

◀ Virus, Viral replication ▶

LH

◀ Luteinising hormone ▶

LIFE CYCLES

The life cycle of an organism is the series of changes progressively undergone during its life time, from **fertilisation** to form the **zygote** until the death of the gamete-forming individual (Fig. L.3). In **diploid** organisms, **mitosis** will be involved in the growth phases and **meiosis** in the production of spores or gametes. The life cycle usually contains a phase of sexual reproduction, which results in **variation** which could be of survival value, and may also contain a phase of **asexual reproduction** which produces genetically identical offspring. Some life cycles involve complex larval stages and **metamorphosis** to form the adults. In bryophytes and higher plants **alternation of generations** occurs, in which a diploid **sporophyte** alternates with a haploid **gametophyte**.

◀ Gamete, Haploidy, Larva, Spore ▶

LIGHT ENERGY

Light **energy** is electromagnetic radiation of wavelength 400 to 700nm which exhibits both wavelike and particle properties. The 'particles' of light energy are known as photons. Light energy from the sun is harnessed in **photosynthesis** and forms the basis of all life on earth.

◀ Food chains, Food webs ▶

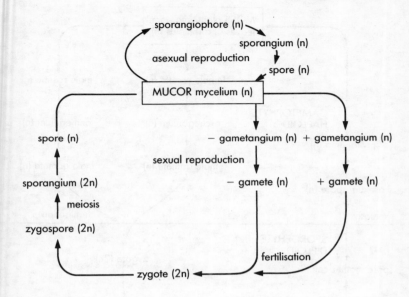

Fig. L.3 Life cycles
a) a fungus (*Mucor*)

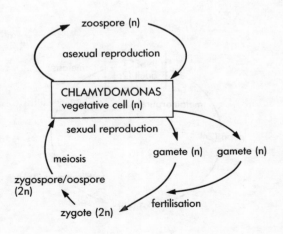

b) an alga (*Chlamydomonas*)

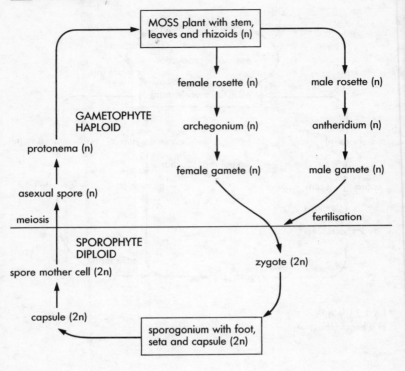

c) a moss

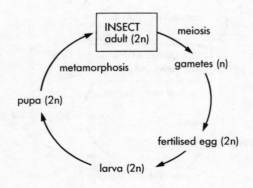

d) butterfly (complete metamorphosis)

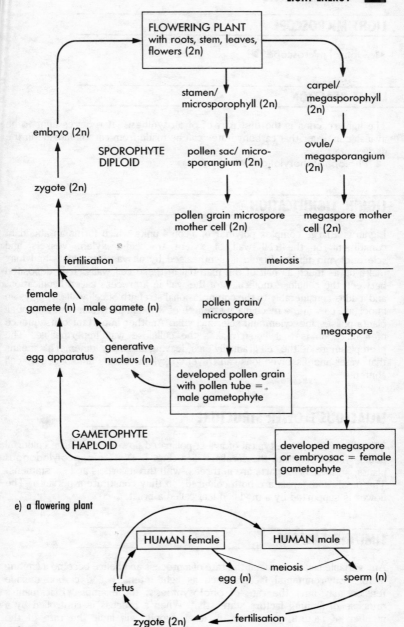

e) a flowering plant

f) Man

LIGHT MICROSCOPE

◄ Optical microscope ►

LIGHT REACTION

The light reaction is the first part of **photosynthesis**. It requires light to be available in order that carbohydrates can be made from carbon dioxide in the dark stage.

◄ Photophosphorylation ►

LIGNIN, LIGNIFICATION

Lignin is a large complex polymer of alcohol units which forms an abundant constituent of the cell wall of xylem tracheids, xylem vessels and **sclerenchyma** fibres. Lignin is synthesised by all vascular plants and may make up as much as half of the material in these cell walls. It is deposited between the cellulose molecules of the wall in a process called lignification, and it adds considerably to the compressional strength of cell walls. It plays an important part in the mechanical strength of wood in particular, but also of all plants possessing xylem and sclerenchyma. Another important consequence of lignification is that lignin makes the cellulose wall impermeable. The protoplasm inside the cell gradually dies, leaving an empty lumen. This means that water and dissolved ions can travel up xylem vessels unimpeded by cell contents.

LILIACEOUS FLOWER STRUCTURE

Liliaceous flowers are typical of insect-pollinated flowers with large colourful petals which constitute the corolla. Lilies (Fig. L.4) are **monocotyledonous** plants, so their floral parts are in threes, with three carpels and six stamens. The petals and sepals are both coloured, so they constitute a perianth. The flower is supported by a modified leaf called a bract.

LIMITING FACTORS

Any variable factor may limit the rate of a process and hence become a limiting factor. Environmental factors such as light intensity and carbon dioxide tension may limit the rate of **photosynthesis**, for example. Blackmann's principle of limiting factors states that 'When a process is controlled by a number of factors, the factor in least supply will limit the rate of the process'.

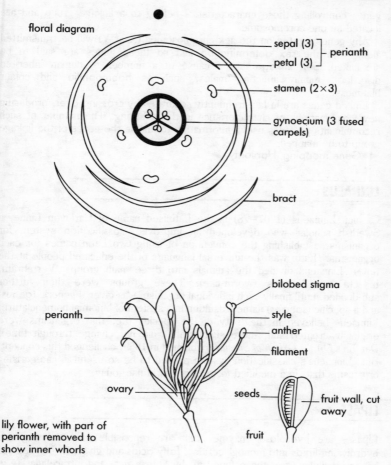

floral diagram

sepal (3)
petal (3)
} perianth

stamen (2×3)

gynoecium (3 fused carpels)

bract

bilobed stigma

perianth

style

anther

filament

ovary

seeds

fruit wall, cut away

fruit

lily flower, with part of
perianth removed to
show inner whorls

Fig. L.4 Lily flower

LINKAGE

Genes that lie on the same chromosome belong to a linkage group. This means that they cannot be separated during **meiosis** (except due to breakages) and therefore cannot be independently assorted, and will be inherited together as a group. In general the number of linkage groups is an indication of the haploid number of **chromosomes** in a particular species. For example, in maize there are ten linkage groups and there are ten pairs of chromosomes. If during a breeding experiment there is little independent assortment of two or more characteristics, it is a strong indication that the genes controlling those characteristics belong to a linkage group and are located on one chromosome.

Any genes located on the sex chromosomes (X or Y) will be transmitted along with the **sex determination** and so these genes are said to be sex-linked. **Sex linkage** is the cause of a number of human inherited disorders, mainly afflicting males, such as **haemophilia** and colour blindness.

Linked genes are in fact frequently separated by **crossing over**, producing new combinations of characteristics in the offspring. The number of such recombinants provides useful information to enable the genes of the linkage group to be mapped.

◀ Gene mapping, Haploidy ▶

LINNAEUS

Carolus Linnaeus (1707–78) is the Latinised name of Carl von Linne, a Swedish scholar who developed an improved **classification** system for organisms, establishing the convention of using two Latin names for each organisms. (Latin was the universal language of the educated people at the time). Linnaeus divided the animals into three main groups: Vertebrata, Insecta and Vermes (worm-like). These groups were then further sub-divided, until finally each individual organism was given a generic (**genus**) and a specific (**species**) name, resulting in a system of binomial nomenclature. Linnaeus believed in the fixity of the species (i.e. that organisms were originally created and, more significantly, did not change through time). Darwin's *On the Origin of Species*, published in 1859, challenged this concept. But, Linnaeus's classification system proved to be so useful in categorising organisms that, in a modified form, it is still in use today.

LIPASE

Lipases are **hydrolase** enzymes that are reponsible for catalysing and hydrolysing **lipids** into monoglycerides, **fatty acids** and glycerol. Lipases can be extracellular (e.g. those found in the human gut) and intracellular (e.g. those found especially in adipose cells). Gut lipases are produced as a constituent of pancreatic juice and are released into the duodenum during the digestion of food. These break down the lipids into glycerol and fatty acids in order for them to be absorbed by the small intestine. Intracellular lipases break down triglycerides into fatty acids and glycerol and are important for the mobilisation of the fat reserves as an energy source.

◀ Pancreas ▶

LIPIDS

Lipids are organic macromolecular compounds which consist of the elements carbon, hydrogen and oxygen. This is a large and diverse chemical group whose members have little in common, apart from their lack of solubility in polar solvents such as water. They are soluble, however, in non-polar organic solvents such as chloroform and ether. Types of lipid include triglycerides, phospholipids, steroids and steroid alcohols or sterols, terpenes and carotenoids, glycolipids and the prostaglandins. Fats are esters formed from fatty acids combined with alcohol by ester linkages (COO−). A triglyceride, for example, consists of three fatty acids linked to glycerol by condensation reactions. Fatty acids have long hydrocarbon chains, which may be either saturated or unsaturated. A fat which contains saturated fatty acids will be solid at room temperature (e.g. animal fats such as lard, suet and butter). Unsaturated fats tend to be liquid at room temperature, and are called oils (e.g. peanut oil, corn oil etc.). The presence of fats can be demonstrated using the grease-spot test for fats and using Sudan red.

◀ Condensation reactions, Food tests, Steroid ▶

LIVER, FUNCTIONS IN HOMEOSTASIS

The liver performs many vital processes, most of which have a role in homeostasis. For example:

- **deamination** of unwanted amino acids, resulting in the less toxic **urea**, which can be excreted via the urine;
- **detoxification** of poisons into forms which can be excreted;
- storage of **glucose** as **glycogen** (this is under the control of **insulin** and helps to regulate the **blood glucose level**);
- production of **bile** salts (partly as a result of detoxification), which can be used in the small intestine for the **emulsification** and **absorption** of fats;
- synthesis of **plasma** proteins, such as albumin and clotting factors;
- breakdown of aged **red blood cells**, degradation of **haemoglobin** to bile pigments for excretion and to iron, which is stored for reuse.

◀ Blood glucose level, Liver, structure, Ornithine cycle ▶

LIVER, STRUCTURE

The human liver weighs about 1.4 kg and is divided into four lobes, covered by dense connective tissue. It is drained by the bile duct which also receives bile stored in the gall bladder. Oxygenated blood enters the liver from the aorta via the **hepatic artery**, and deoxygenated blood, rich in absorbed food substances from the intestines, enters via the hepatic portal vein. The drainage of blood is via the hepatic vein to the posterior **vena cava**. (Fig. L.5).

The histological structure of the liver lobes is that they are made up of functional units called lobules. In transverse section these are hexagonal in shape and consist of plates and cords of hepatic cells arranged in radial fashion around a central vein, which is a branch of the hepatic vein (Fig. L.6).

◀ Liver, functions in homeostasis ▶

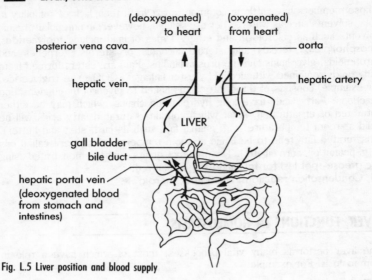

Fig. L.5 Liver position and blood supply

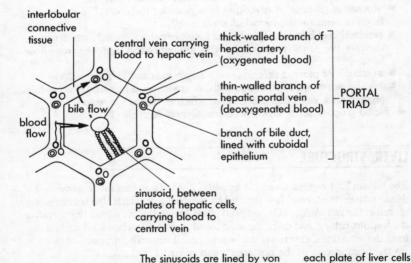

The sinusoids are lined by von Kuppfer cells, which are fixed macrophages. These engulf bacteria and debris from broken old red blood cells

each plate of liver cells is one cell thick, and twenty to thirty cells deep

Fig. L.6 Liver histology

LIVER FLUKE

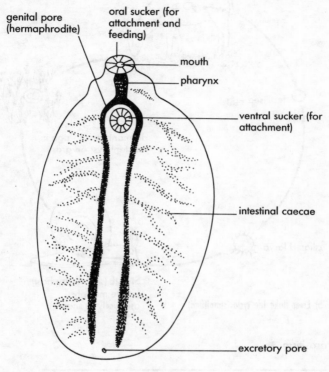

Fig. L.7a) Liver fluke structure   a) genital pore

The liver fluke is a member of the phylum **Platyhelminthes**, class *Trematoda*. It is an endoparasite of sheep, in which it resides in the liver, but it has a complicated life cycle. (Fig. L.7b)) involving several larval forms and a snail secondary host.

The larval forms and use of a secondary host are specific parasitic adaptations, enabling the fluke to disperse from one primary host, or sheep, to another. Additional advantages are that several of the larval forms are capable of multiplying asexually, to greatly increase the chances of reinfection, and that one of the larvae can form a dormant resistant cyst. Other parasitic adaptations of the liver fluke include the suckers, for attachment to host tissues and to allow feeding, and the fact that the adult fluke is hermaphrodite so can reproduce sexually inside the sheep's liver without needing to find a mate. The fertilised eggs leave the liver through the bile duct and are shed in the faeces.

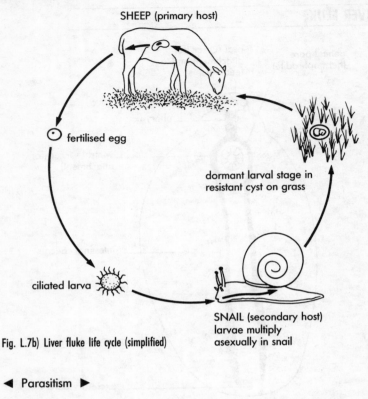

Fig. L.7b) Liver fluke life cycle (simplified)

◄ Parasitism ►

LIVERWORT

Liverworts belong to the phylum **Bryophyta**, along with the mosses. They show **alternation of generations** with a dominant **gametophyte** which is usually a flat thallus, or has leaves in three ranks. This has unicellular rhizoids and bears male antheridia and female archegonia. The **sporophyte** is borne on, and supported by, the photosynthetic gametophyte. It consists of a foot, seta and capsule and produces spores by **meiosis**. (e.g. *Marchantia*, *Pellia*, Fig. L.8)

◄ Life cycles, Moss ►

LIVING ORGANISMS

All living things exhibit seven characteristics of life: feeding (nutrition), respiration, excretion, growth, reproduction, movement and irritability. Non-living things do not show all of these characteristics.

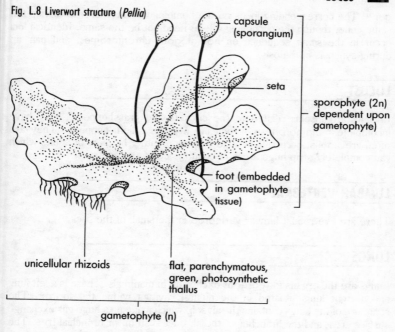

Fig. L.8 Liverwort structure (*Pellia*)

capsule (sporangium)

seta

sporophyte (2n) dependent upon gametophyte)

foot (embedded in gametophyte tissue)

unicellular rhizoids

flat, parenchymatous, green, photosynthetic thallus

gametophyte (n)

LIZARD

Lizards are terrestrial reptiles, well adapted for dry conditions. They have scaly skins and their eggs have leathery shells. They possess lungs and are ectothermic. They are tetrapods (four-legged) but the legs are at the side of the body and do not raise the body from the ground.

LOCOMOTION

Locomotion means movement of the whole organism from one place to another. In unicells such as *Euglena* and *Chlamydomonas*, it is achieved by flagella, in *Paramecium* by cilia, in *Amoeba* (Rhizopoda) by pseudopodia. In multicellular animals it involves muscles and the skeleton. Locomotion enables organisms to find food, to escape from predators or unpleasant conditions, to find a mate, and to *colonise* new areas.

◀ Colonisation, Flagellum, flagellates, Predation, Striated muscle ▶

LOCUS

A locus is the particular position on a chromosome occupied by a particular gene. The corresponding locus on the homologous chromosome carries the same gene, though the occupying **alleles** need not be the same. Identical loci occur in the same sequence on **homologous chromosomes**, and pair up during synapsis in **meiosis**.

LOCUST

Locusts are **insects** related to the crickets and grasshoppers. They have incomplete **metamorphosis**, producing nymphs called 'hoppers'. They are often gregarious, occurring in huge swarms of either hoppers or adults which can completely strip huge areas of countryside of all vegetation.

LUMBAR VERTEBRAE

There are five robust lumbar **vertebrae** in the small of the back.

LUNGS

Lungs are the organs for **gaseous exchange** in mammals. There is a left lung and a right lung situated in the pleural cavities within the **thorax**. The structure of the lungs contains the alveoli, which make up a huge gas exchange surface area, and the branches of the air duct system, or bronchial tree. The histology (Fig. L.9) is suited to withstand dimension changes during ventilation and to enable efficient gas transfer between air and blood.
◀ Ventilation mechanisms ▶

LUTEINISING HORMONE (LH)

LH is a gonadotrophic hormone released by the anterior **pituitary gland** which stimulates **ovulation**, the development of a corpus luteum and the secretion of progesterone.
◀ Menstrual cycle ▶

LYCOPODOPHYTA

◀ Selaginella ▶

LYMPH

Lymph is the fluid that leaves the **blood** at the arterial end of the capillary beds, exchanges metabolites with the tissues, and is taken back into the blood at the venous end of the capillary beds. Alternatively, it may be drained back to the **veins** via the system of **lymphatic vessels**. Lymph is blood plasma minus

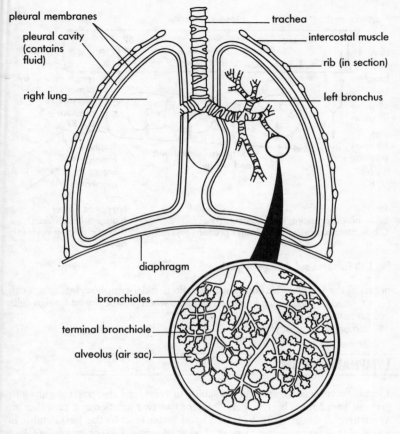

Fig. L.9 Human thorax and lung structure

the plasma **proteins** that are too large to escape through the capillary walls. It carries **nutrients, oxygen,** hormones and salts to the cells from the blood, and receives **waste substances,** such as CO_2 and urea in return (Fig. L.10). In the region of the cells, where the exchange of chemicals is occuring, the lymph is referred to as **tissue fluid.**

◀ Capillaries, capillary circulation, Hormone ▶

LYMPH NODES

Lymph nodes are small bodies situated in particular areas of the body on the lymphatic vessels. The lymph passes through sinusoids in the nodes, which contain fixed macrophages or phagocytes. These engulf bacteria or other

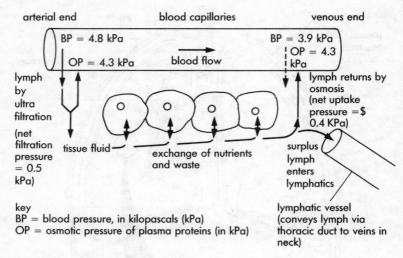

arterial end   blood capillaries   venous end

BP = 4.8 kPa

OP = 4.3 kPa   blood flow

BP = 3.9 kPa
OP = 4.3 kPa

lymph by ultra filtration

(net filtration pressure = 0.5 kPa)

tissue fluid

exchange of nutrients and waste

lymph returns by osmosis (net uptake pressure = $ 0.4 KPa)

surplus lymph enters lymphatics

key
BP = blood pressure, in kilopascals (kPa)
OP = osmotic pressure of plasma proteins (in kPa)

lymphatic vessel (conveys lymph via thoracic duct to veins in neck)

Fig. L.10 Formation and drainage of lymph

debris in the lymph. The nodes also contain B and T-lymphocytes, which can be activated to produce an immune response when phagocytosed foreign cells are presented to them.

◀ Immunity, Phagocytosis ▶

LYMPHATIC VESSELS

Lymphatic vessels are structurally similar to veins, and also possess valves to prevent backflow. The lymphatic system has two functions: it provides an alternative drainage route to return used tissue fluid to the blood and it is involved in defence against disease. The used tissue fluid, or lymph, is taken into the open ends of the smallest lymphatic vessels at the tissue level. It is then moved through the vessels by the movement of the surrounding organs and muscles, and passes through one or more lymph nodes before draining into the veins of the neck via the thoracic duct (Fig. L.11).

LYMPHOCYTES

Lymphocytes are white blood cells possessing large round nuclei and little cytoplasm. They are initially formed from lymphocyte stem cells in the red bone marrow of the fetus, but prior to birth they migrate from here to the thymus, where they become T-cells, or to the spleen and lymph nodes, where they become B-cells. When the thymus is reabsorbed during development, the T-cells migrate to the spleen and lymph nodes and are stored there with the B-cells. Lymphocytes are responsible for the immune response and when

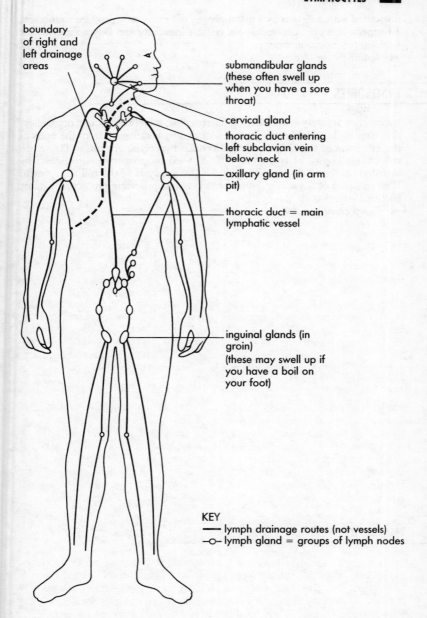

boundary of right and left drainage areas

submandibular glands (these often swell up when you have a sore throat)

cervical gland

thoracic duct entering left subclavian vein below neck

axillary gland (in arm pit)

thoracic duct = main lymphatic vessel

inguinal glands (in groin) (these may swell up if you have a boil on your foot)

KEY
—— lymph drainage routes (not vessels)
—o— lymph gland = groups of lymph nodes

Fig. L.11 Lymph vessel drainage system

presented with **antigens** by a macrophage, will eventually produce antibodies, T-lymphocytes are responsible for cellular **immunity** and B-lymphocytes for humoral (chemical) immunity.

◄ Antibody ►

LYSOSOMES

Lysosomes are very small electron microscopic, membrane-bound organelles, abundant in the cytoplasm. They are formed by budding off from the ends of the cisternae of the Golgi body and contain hydrolytic enzymes. These are collectively known as lysozyme. This is used by phagocytes to digest the ingested bacteria, and is responsible for the autolysis of the cell after death. High contents of lysozyme are present in tears, providing protection against bacterial infection via the eye.

◄ Golgi complex ►

MACROMOLECULE

Macromolecules are made up of thousands or millions of atoms and are compounds such as **proteins, polysaccharides** and **nucleic acids**.

MAGNESIUM

In plants magnesium is absorbed from the soil solution as magnesium ions (Mg^{2+}). It forms part of the **chlorophyll** molecule and may donate electrons in the light reactions of **photosynthesis**. Magnesium deficiency in plants results in chlorosis. In animals and plants magnesium ions act as cofactors for several enzymes (e.g. phosphohydrolases, phosphotransferases).
◀ Ion, Mineral nutrition ▶

MAGNIFICATION

Magnification is the diameter of the image divided by the diameter of the object. Hand lenses generally magnify about five or ten times, while the compound microscope is efficient up to about 1,000 times.
◀ Light microscope ▶

MALARIA

After malnutrition, malaria is the most common cause of death in humans. The disease is caused by a parasite, *Plasmodium*, which is a protozoan member of the phylum Apicomplexa, and which uses an *Anopheles* mosquito as a **vector** and secondary host. The sexual phase of the parasite's life cycle is initiated in man but is completed in the mosquito.

When the mosquito bites humans, it releases saliva into the human blood stream which contains an anticoagulant to stop the blood from clotting. The saliva may also contain *Plasmodium* cells at the sporozoite stage which are carried in the blood to the cells of the liver. Here they mature and multiply, producing large numbers of merozoites which are released into the bloodstream to invade **red blood cells**. They again reproduce asexually, producing further merozoites in the red cells, which burst at regular intervals, releasing toxins and merozoites to infect new red cells. It is the release of the toxins at regular intervals which causes the characteristic periodic fever of malaria.

Eventually merozoites develop into male and female gametocytes, but these form gametes only if ingested by a mosquito. The gametes can then fuse, forming a **zygote**, which encysts in the gut wall and divides many times to form sporozoites. The sporozoites migrate to the salivary glands, from where they can be introduced into a new victim, thus starting the life cycle again (Fig. M.1).

Malaria is best controlled by controlling the mosquito. The adults can be sprayed with DDT, but resistant strains have developed. The larvae, which

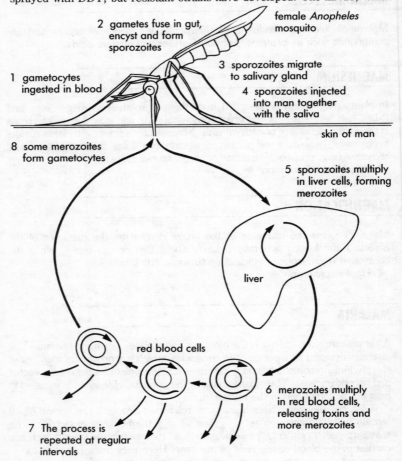

2 gametes fuse in gut, encyst and form sporozoites

female *Anopheles* mosquito

3 sporozoites migrate to salivary gland

1 gametocytes ingested in blood

4 sporozoites injected into man together with the saliva

skin of man

8 some merozoites form gametocytes

5 sporozoites multiply in liver cells, forming merozoites

liver

red blood cells

6 merozoites multiply in red blood cells, releasing toxins and more merozoites

7 The process is repeated at regular intervals

Fig. M.1 Life cycle of Plasmodium (malarial parasite)

are aquatic, can be controlled by draining swamps, by not allowing puddles or water to lie, by introducing fish into the water which eat the larvae and pupae, and by spreading oil on the water surface, which suffocates the larvae and pupae. The adults can be prevented from biting man by humans using mosquito nets when sleeping and over windows. Quinine and other drugs are effective in killing the parasites in the blood, although the parasites within the liver are difficult to kill and may remain dormant for years, eventually starting division again and causing a relapse in the sufferer.

◀ Parasitism, Toxicity, Toxins ▶

MALTOSE

Malt sugar is a disaccharide breakdown product of starch and glycogen, formed when these are hydrolysed using amylases, either in the alimentary canal or in germinating seeds. Maltose can be hydrolysed by maltase in the duodenum to yield two glucose molecules per maltose molecule. It is formed by the condensation of two molecules of alpha-D-glucose, which thus become joined by a I,4 glycosidic alpha link. Maltose is a reducing sugar.

◀ Amylase, Condensation reactions, Disaccharides, Reducing sugars ▶

MAMMALS

Mammals are chordates that are characterised by having skin with hair in follicles, milk secretion from mammary glands for suckling the young, a diaphragm used in ventilation, three middle-ear ossicles connecting the tympanic membrane with the inner ear, only the left systemic (aortic) arch, only one bone in each half lower jaw, and usually they are viviparous (young born alive after a pregnancy or gestation period, during which the young was housed in the mother's uterus). They are endothermic.

There are three sub-classes of mammals: the monotremata or egg-laying mammals, such as the duck-billed platypus and spiny anteater, which are the only living remnants of this group: the marsupials or pouched mammals, such as kangaroos and wallabies, which are endemic to Australasia; and the eutherian or true placental mammals, such as the rabbit, cow and human.

MARASMUS

Marasmus is a deficency disease similar to Kwashiorkor, caused by depleted amounts of both carbohydrate and protein in the diet. It affects inhabitants of famine-stricken areas.

MARINE ENVIRONMENT

Compared with fresh-water environments, the marine environment is very stable. With the exception of estuaries, chemical, physical and biological characteristics vary only slightly over huge areas of the sea, even though the seawaters are constantly moving about due to currents and tides.

The average salinity of seawater is around 35.5 per cent, but varies slightly according to a region's rainfall, average temperatures and estuarine inflow. Marine organisms from the open sea, especially **plankton**, cannot withstand large changes in salinity.

The **oxygen** content of surface waters is usually high, because of solution of the gas from the atmosphere, and its production by the photosynthetic **phytoplankton**. Because animals use up the oxygen, deeper waters below the photosynthesis areas may become deprived of oxygen and thus be relatively lifeless. However, the oceanic deeps are often supplied with water from the Arctic or Antarctic, and these are cold. Since oxygen is more soluble in cold water than in warm water, this does allow high enough oxygen tensions to maintain much animal life in the deeps. The middle layers of water in the oceans, however, tend to be 'oxygen minimum layers' (Fig. M.2).

The **carbon dioxide** level in the upper layers of the sea tends to be rather low, since it is used up by photosynthesising phytoplankton. Its main source is from respiration of the marine animals, especially zooplankton.

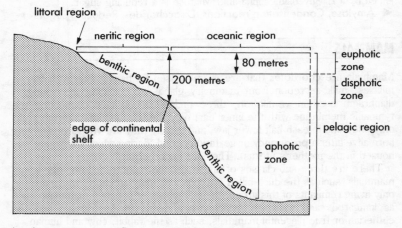

benthic region	=	sea floor, occupied by algae in lit areas
euphotic zone	=	well-lit areas with abundant phytoplankton
disphotic zone	=	poorly lit areas where phytoplankton live temporarily
aphotic zone	=	unlit, thus no plants
pelagic region	=	moving waters of the sea
neritic region	=	shallower waters over the continental shelf, turbulent, and receiving inflow from rivers
littoral region	=	seashore, subject to tidal action

Fig. M.2 Ecological regions of the oceans

The pH of the open sea is about 8.2, but varies inshore according to inflow from rivers and from the rocks (e.g. limestone) of the shore.

The temperature of the water varies with latitude and depth, obviously being coldest near the poles and warmest in the tropics. The great ocean currents, such as the gulf stream, do, however, cause local geographical variations in temperature. Sea water freezes at about $-2°C$, and as it cools its density increases. Thus the cold water sinks, meaning that the surface waters tend to be warmer than the deep waters.

Light penetrates to about 200 metres on average, depending on the latitude and incident angle of the sunlight, and also on the wavelength; blue light penetrates deepest. On the seashore (littoral zone) and in offshore regions, this affects the distribution of attached algae, the green algae occupying the higher zones, the brown algae the middle zones, and the red algae the lower zones.

◄ Filter feeding, Food chains, Food webs, Fresh-water ecosystems, Gills of fish, Nitrogenous excretion, Osmoregulation, Teleost ►

MASS FLOW

The mass flow hypothesis is an attempt to explain the **translocation** of **organic compounds** in the sieve tubes in the **phloem**. In the **sieve tube** elements next to the photosynthetic mesophyll cells, the sap is rich in organic solutes, and so has a reduced **water potential**. Thus water is absorbed into the sieve tube elements from surrounding tissues by **osmosis**. This region is called the source. A high pressure potential is thus established at the source, and the solution inside the sieve tubes is pushed towards a sink, along the pressure gradient. The sink could be the roots, or developing flowers, fruits and young leaves. Since the organic compounds in the sink (e.g. sugars) are being used up by respiration, or changed to osmotically inactive starch, the sink has a higher water potential and water flow is thus enhanced towards the sink.

MASTICATION

Mastication is the action of **teeth** in grinding and cutting up food, prior to swallowing.

◄ Dentition ►

MATRIX

The matrix is the space enclosed within the inner membrane of a **mitochondrion**, containing **Krebs cycle** enzymes and intermediates and **DNA**. The DNA codes for the mitochondrial proteins and is thus of importance when mitochondria replicate.

◄ Enzyme ►

MECHANICAL STRENGTHENING IN PLANTS

The main mechanical tissues in plants are **sclerenchyma** fibres, **xylem** vessels and tracheids and **collenchyma**. These tend to be concentrated in the stele or central part of the root, since this is mechanically advantageous in withstanding pulling forces. The vascular bundles and associated mechanical tissue in the stem are towards the outside, within the **cortex**. This is best for withstanding lateral forces (wind) which bend the stem.

◄ **Root systems, Secondary thickening, Stem structure, Vascular bundle** ►

MEDULLA OBLONGATA

The medulla oblongata, or just the medulla is the most posterior part of the vertebrate **brain**, joining to the **spinal cord**. The cranial nerves enter or leave it. The medulla contains centres for regulating **ventilation**, cardiac output and blood vessels.

MEIOSIS (REDUCTION DIVISION)

This type of cell division is used for **gamete** production and reduces the **diploid** state to **haploidy** thus compensating for the doubling effect of fertilisation. It also introduces **genetic variation** by the reshuffling of genes into new combinations. The process of meiosis is divided into two successive divisions, starting with a diploid cell (Fig. M.3). In Prophase 1 the **chromosomes** first appear as long, thin threads which then undergo **synapsis**, which is the exact pairing of **homologous chromosomes**, lying closely side by side as bivalent units. The **bivalents** become much shorter and fatter and can be seen to be double (replication actually occured in **interphase**). Thus each bivalent now consists of four chromatids, the chromatids derived from one chromosome attached at the centromere in each case. At certain places the chromatids of different but homologous paired chromosomes become held together by **chiasmata** or bridges. These are where cross-over of genes from one chromosome to its homologue occurs. In Metaphase I the bivalent units align up at the equator on the spindle attachments. At Anaphase I two of the four chromatids from each bivalent go to one pole of the spindle and the other two go to the other pole. The cross-over of genes at the chiasmata is completed at this time. It is a matter of chance as to which chromosome of each bivalent goes to which pole. There is a short Telophase and resting phase, or the second meiotic division may occur immediately. This is similar to **mitosis** but with only half the normal number of chromosomes, each already divided into chromatids. In Anaphase II these chromatids separate and go to separate poles of the spindle. In Telophase II, nuclear membranes reform around the four haploid nuclei, and division of the **cytoplasm** occurs. The

respiration, deamination, mobilisation of food reserves). Metabolic reactions are controlled by enzymes and involve **energy** loss or gain.

◀ Anabolism, Catabolism ▶

METAL COFACTORS

Metal cofactors are required for certain **enzyme** actions, the cofactor probably altering the shape of the enzyme to allow joining with the substrate. For example, Zn^{2+} is a cofactor for alcohol dehydrogenase and carbonic anhydrase; Fe^{2+} or Fe^{3+} are cofactors for the cytochromes, peroxidase, catalase and ferredoxin; Cu^{2+} is also a cofactor for cytochrome oxidase.

◀ Magnesium ▶

METAMORPHOSIS

Metamorphosis is a transition from a larval form to an adult form, usually

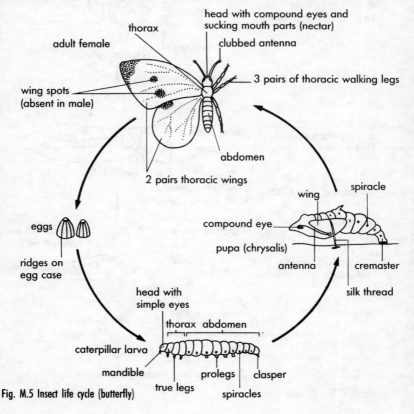

Fig. M.5 Insect life cycle (butterfly)

rapidly or suddenly. There is much breakdown of larval tissues by lysosome activity, and build up of adult tissues by **protein synthesis**. It is regulated by hormones (e.g. the transition of insect larvae to adults via the pupal stage, Fig. M.5; transition from tadpole larva to an adult amphibian — frog (Fig. M.6), newt, toad).

◀ Lysosomes ▶

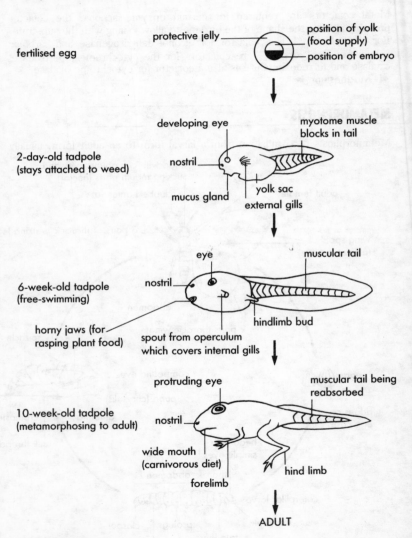

Fig. M.6 Frog life cycle

MICROANATOMY

Microanatomy refers to the microscopic or fine structure of both cells and tissues, including their **ultrastructure** and histology.

MICROBIOLOGY

Microbiology is the study of micro-organisms, such as unicellular, filamentous and colonial **algae, bacteria, fungi, protozoa** and viruses.
◀ Micro-organism, Virus, Viral replications, Yeasts ▶

MICROEVOLUTION

Species of organism often contain many variations in form within the population, and the different types can be referred to as microspecies. The species *Rubus fruticosus* (blackberry) could have as many as 300 microspecies in Britain alone, each of which could be selected and become a new species. This process of **speciation** is microevolution, and involves minute evolutionary changes.
◀ Variation ▶

MICROHABITATS

A microhabitat is a small part of a **habitat** with its own localised climate, which may be occupied by particular organisms (e.g. fallen trees and logs within a woodland habitat).

MICROMETRE

A unit of length for microscopic objects, being one thousandth of a millimetre, or 10^{-6} metre. The limit of resolution of the light microscope is about one fifth of a micrometer (written μm).

MICRONUTRIENTS

Micronutrients are substances which must be obtained by an organism from the environment, in small quantities, in order to maintain health. They are **vitamins** and **trace elements**.

MICRO-ORGANISM

Microscopic organisms are the **bacteria**, viruses and various protoctistans such as rhizopods, flagellates, sporozoans and ciliates (these used to be termed **protozoa**). Other protoctistans that are micro-organisms would be certain **algae**, such as Chlamydomonas.

◀ Cilia, Flagellum, Flagellates, Protoctista, Rhizopoda, Virus, Viral replication ▶

MICROSCOPE

◀ Electron microscope, Light microscope ▶

MICROTUBULES

Microtubules are fine protein filaments that appear in **cytoplasm**. They are hollow and cylindrical, and form the cytoskeleton and the spindles for cell division. They also occur in **undulipodia** (eukaryotic **cilia** and flagella). They are electron microscope features.

◀ Flagellum, Flagellates ▶

MICROVILLI

Microvilli are electron-microscopic, finger-shaped projections of **cell membranes**. Under the **light microscope** they appear as a striate border. They increase the cell surface area for exchange of materials, in or out of the cell. They occur, for instance, on the columnar epithelial cells lining the villi in the **small intestine** and on the cuboidal epithelia lining the kidney tubules.

◀ Villus ▶

MIGRATION

Migration is the regular movement of animals between alternate areas that they inhabit at different times of the year; generally the movement is between the breeding areas and the non-breeding areas. Migration is common amongst **birds,** such as geese and ducks, starlings, swallows, swifts and housemartins. Often the birds migrate in huge flocks. Many **fish** migrate: for example, salmon and eels. Since these migrate between salt and fresh water, they have to undergo changes in their kidney structure and physiology to cope with the changes in osmotic concentration of the water. Some **insects,** such as butterflies, migrate, and also some **mammals,** such as the great herds of caribou in North America.

Many animals migrate over thousands of miles, and it is unclear how they navigate and orientate so successfully. Some may use the positions of the sun, moon or stars; others may use magnetic lines of force due to the natural magnetism of the earth. Migratory behaviour is usually triggered by such things as **day length,** light intensity, temperature and **hormone** levels.

◀ Innate behaviour ▶

MINERAL NUTRITION

In plants the macronutrients (salts required in relatively large amounts) are nitrogen, phosphorus, potassium, calcium, magnesium, sulphur and iron. Nitrogen is taken up as **nitrate** to be used in synthesis of **amino acids, proteins, nucleic acids** and **chlorophyll**. Phosphorus is absorbed as dihydrogenphosphate ions, and is used to manufacture nucleic acids, **phospholipids** and **adenosine triphosphate** (ATP). Potassium, absorbed as K^+, is an important **cofactor** for many enzymes, and is required for translocation in sieve tubes. Calcium, absorbed as Ca^{2+}, is required in the middle lamella of plant cell walls. Magnesium, absorbed as Mg^{2+}, is a component of chlorophyll as a possible electron donor, and also an **enzyme** cofactor. Sulphur is taken up as sulphate ions and is required to manufacture the sulphur-containing amino acids cysteine and methionine which are incorporated into many proteins. Iron, absorbed as Fe^{2+}, is present in the **cytochromes** and important for electron transport. It is also needed for chlorophyll synthesis.

Micronutrients (required in trace amounts) in plants are manganese, which acts as a cofactor for carboxylase enzymes; zinc, a cofactor for carbonic anhydrase; copper, a cofactor for some oxidase enzymes; boron, required for **meristem** activity; molybdenum, required to activate nitrate reductase in **nitrogen fixation**; and chlorine, essential for the evolution of oxygen in **photosynthesis**.

Macronutrients in animals (e.g. man) include calcium. This is required in bones and **teeth**, for **blood clotting**, for normal nerve and muscle activity and for the synthesis and release of transmitter substances. Phosphorus is required also in bones and teeth, but is a component of nucleic acids, many proteins and ATP. Sodium is the main cation in extracellular fluid, whereas potassium is the main cation in intracellular fluid. Both these cations are important in maintaining membrane potentials and in nerve impulses. **Iodine** is a component of the thyroid growth hormones, and iron is a component of **haemoglobin, myoglobin** and the cytochromes.

Micronutrients in animals include zinc, a cofactor for carbonic anhydrase in red cells; fluorine, which hardens teeth; cobalt, required for the maturation of red cells; and manganese, a cofactor for various enzymes.

◀ Trace elements ▶

MINERAL UPTAKE

Mineral uptake occurs from the soil solution into the **root hairs** of the roots, or from the alimentary canal into the blood stream of the animal.

◀ Ion uptake ▶

MITOCHONDRION

A mitochondrion (Fig. M.7) is a cytoplasmic organelle in **eukaryotic cells**, usually rod-shaped, about 10 micrometres long and 0.5 micrometres in width. They are bounded by a double unit membrane, the inner membrane being folded into shelves or **cristae**. These are covered by elementary particles which contain components of oxidative enzyme systems. Inside the inner membrane is a matrix containing enzymes and DNA.

◀ Krebs cycle, Matrix, Oxidative phosphorylation ▶

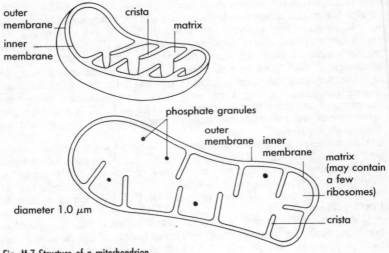

Fig. M.7 Structure of a mitochondrion

MITOSIS

In mitosis the chromosome number of the daughter cells is the same as the parent cell and the same cell **genome** is maintained. This type of cell division is important in **growth** and ensures that all cells formed (except gametes) have identical genomes to each other and to the original **zygote** of the organism (Fig. M.8).

In prophase, the **chromosomes** appear as long, thin threads, which shorten and thicken by coiling into a tight spiral. The chromosomes replicate except at their centromeres (central bodies or spindle attachments).

In metaphase the nuclear membrane dissolves and spindle threads appear from the poles to the equator, the microfilaments of the spindle coming from the centrioles in animal cells. The chromosomes lie at the equator, attached to the spindle ends by their spindle attachments. In anaphase the replicated chromosomes separate at the spindle attachments and are pulled towards the poles, one set of chromosomes going 'north' and a duplicate set 'south'. In telophase the chromosomes in the daughter nuclei uncoil, elongate and disappear, forming a chromatin pattern. Nuclear membranes reform around the daughter nuclei and the spindles disappear. The cytoplasm divides between the two nuclei, either by constriction in animals or by the formation

of a cell plate and new cell wall in plants.
◄ Meiosis ►

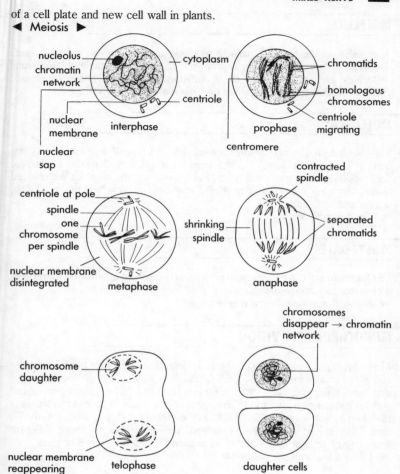

Fig. M.8 Stages of mitosis

MIXED NERVE

A mixed nerve consists of both sensory and motor neurones, which may be voluntary neurones, sympathetic or parasympathetic. Particular nerve fibres will be in particular nerve bundles within the nerve. For example, the sciatic nerve to the hind limb contains sensory neurones, voluntary motor neurones and autonomic motor neurones. Some neurones will be myelinated, others will be non- myelinated.
◄ Nervous system, Neurone ►

MOLECULE

A molecule is the smallest particle of a substance which can exist by itself. Atoms of sodium, magnesium or iron, for instance, are stable so atoms and molecules are the same for these substances. Molecules of oxygen and chlorine contain two atoms, since the single atoms are unstable.

MOLLUSCA

Mollusca is a phylum of unsegmented animals with a head, a foot and a visceral hump. They often have a calcareous shell. There are three classes: Gastropoda are the snails and slugs, Pelycopoda are the bivalves with hinged shells, such as oysters and mussels, and Cephalopoda are the cuttlefish, squids and octopus.
◄ Gastropods ►

MOLYBDATE

Molybdenum is a trace element in plants and is involved in nitrogen fixation as a cofactor for nitrate reductase.
◄ Mineral nutrition, Trace elements ►

MONOCHROMATIC VISION

Monochromatic vision involves the rods only. It is therefore black and white vision and occurs in dim light. The chemistry is similar to cone vision, except that the retinine combines with the protein scotopsin to form rhodopsin (visual purple) instead of with various photopsins as in cones. The rod rhodopsin is bleached by any wavelengths of light in the visible spectrum, from 400 to 700 nm. Thus colour cannot be perceived, unlike in cones, where different wavelengths of light bleach different proteins in different types of cone.
◄ Retina, Trichromatic vision ►

MONOCLONAL ANTIBODIES

Monoclonal antibodies are antibodies produced in tissue culture clones of B-lymphocytes, which have been hybridised with cancerous cells. An animal such as a mouse is first injected with a specific antigen (relating to the eventual antibody required). The mouse's immune system responds by rapid mitosis of the relevant B-lymphocytes so that after a time the spleen has a very high proportion of these cells. The spleen is removed and a preparation for tissue culture is made of suspended separated cells, which continue to produce the antibody. A cell culture is also grown of myeloma tumour cells. These are 'immortal' in the sense that they will continue growing and dividing 'in vitro' (tissue culture). The two cultures are mixed in the presence of polyethylene glycol, and some cells fuse together to form a B-cell/myeloma hybrid, known as a hybridoma. The cells are sub-cultured to a new medium where the uncombined spleen cells soon die, and unattached myeloma cells can be blocked. The hybridoma cells producing the antibody survive, and can be grown in fermenters, either on small scale or on a bulk scale. The monoclonal antibodies can be harvested and purified at regular intervals.

Monoclonal antibodies can be produced against cancer cells from a patient. When the monoclonal antibodies are injected into the patient they will target themselves on to the cancer cells, even if these are diffusely spread throughout the body. Drugs can also be attached to the molecules of antibody, and so carried directly to the cells they need to act on and eliminate them with greater efficiency. Monoclonal antibodies also have applications in tissue typing prior to transplantation, in the purification of drugs and in pregnancy diagnosis.

◀ Antigens, Biotechnology, Immunity ▶

MONOCOTYLEDON

Monocotyledonous plants are members of the phylum Angiospermophyta, class Monocotyledoneae. The embryos have only one seed leaf or cotyledon, the foliage leaves are iso-bilateral with parallel venation, the floral parts are in threes and they have a fibrous root system (e.g. rushes, sedges, grasses, irises, lilies, orchids).

◀ Dicotyledon, Floral morphology, Leaf structure, Root systems, Vascular bundle ▶

MONOESTROUS SPECIES

In monoestrous mammals there is only one oestrous cycle per breeding season. For example, the domestic dog has two breeding seasons per year, in early spring and autumn, but in each season there is only one time of oestrous. The breeding season of roe deer is July and August, but there is only one time of oestrous in this period.

◀ Polyoestrous ▶

MONOHYBRID INHERITANCE

Monohybrid inheritance is the Mendelian inheritance of one pair of **alleles**. In pea plants (*Pisum sativum*), which are normally self-pollinating, tallness (allele T) is dominant to shortness (allele t). Mendel artificially cross-pollinated pure strains of tall plants with pure strains of short plants (Fig. M.9).

The F2 phenotypic ratio is thus three tall to one short pea plants. These results led Mendel to formulate the Law of Segregation.

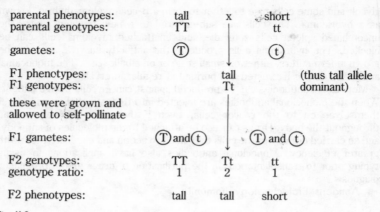

parental phenotypes: tall   x   short
parental genotypes: TT   tt

gametes: (T)   (t)

F1 phenotypes: tall   (thus tall allele
F1 genotypes: Tt   dominant)

these were grown and
allowed to self-pollinate

F1 gametes: (T) and (t)   (T) and (t)

F2 genotypes: TT   Tt   tt
genotype ratio: 1   2   1

F2 phenotypes: tall   tall   short

Fig. M.9

◀ Dihybrid inheritance, Genetics, Mendelian inheritance, principles of · ▶

MONOSACCHARIDES

Monosaccharides are the simplest sugars, consisting of single sugar molecules. If they are broken down further, they lose the properties of sugars. They are polyhydroxy aldehydes or ketones. Monosaccharides have the empirical formula $(CH_2O)_n$ where n = 3 or a larger number.

Trioses have three carbons in their molecules ($C_3H_6O_3$). There are two examples:

- Glyceraldehyde
  CHO

  HCOH

  CH$_2$OH

- Dihydroxyacetone
  CH$_2$OH

  C=O

  CH$_2$OH

Tetroses have four carbons in their molecules ($C_4H_8O_4$). There are three examples including Erythrose.

Pentoses have five carbons in their molecules ($C_5H_{10}O_5$). There are six examples including Ribose, Arabinose, Xylose, Ribulose. The aldehyde examples have ring structures to their molecules.

Hexoses have six carbons in their molecules. ($C_6H_{12}O_6$). There are sixteen examples including Glucose, Mannose, Galactose, Fructose and Sorbose. These all have ring formulae.

The most abundant monosaccharide is glucose, which is the major respiratory substrate of most organisms and also the most common building block of **polysaccharides**. Monosaccharides are white crystalline solids, soluble in water and with a sweet taste.

◀ Disaccharides, Glycogen, Starch ▶

MORPHOLOGICAL ISOLATION

Morphological isolation is where there are mechanical reasons preventing exchange of gametes, and therefore of genes between different demes of a population. This is supposed to occur in spiders, many insects, millipedes and certain snails, where the sexual organs have become so complex and modified that **copulation** is restricted to members of the same deme.

◀ Isolating mechanisms ▶

MOSS

Mosses are members of the phylum **Bryophyta**, class *Musci* (Fig. M.10). A moss gametophyte has a stem which bears simple green leaves in a spiral arrangement and has multicellular **rhizoids** at its base. The male antheridia and female archegonia are produced at the stem apices in male and female rosettes (of leaves). The spermatozoids swim in the surface water, or are aided by rain splash, to the archegonia, to which they are chemically attracted. **Fertilisation** occurs in the archegonial base and the **diploid sporophyte** grows, attached to the **gametophyte** by a foot. It obtains its nutrition from the gametophyte, and eventually bears a complex capsule which produces spores by **meiosis**. The spores are dispersed when the operculum of the capsule

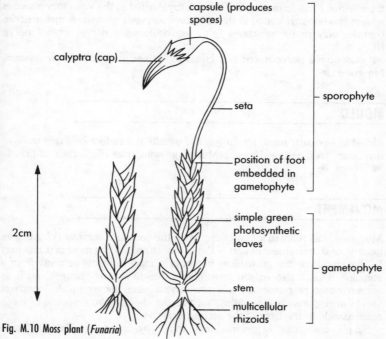

Fig. M.10 Moss plant (*Funaria*)

breaks away, and when they land on a suitable moist substratum they germinate into prostrate green branched threads called protonema. This produces buds from which the gametophyte stems develop.

◄ Germination, Life cycles, Sporangia ►

MOTH

Moths belong to the class *Insecta* and are members of the order *Lepidoptera* (butterflies and moths). They tend to fly at night and have complete metamorphosis of egg, caterpillar, pupa (chrysalis) and adult. The larvae feed on specific food plants and the adults feed on nectar from flowers. The larvae of some species are of economic importance: clothes moth caterpillars damage wool, cotton and linen garments, wax moth caterpillars damage honeycomb in beehives and silk moth caterpillars produce silk, which can be commercially harvested. Because moths fly at night, the flowers they pollinate are often highly scented and white or pale blue, to show up in the moonlight.

◄ Entomophilous flowers ►

MOTOR NEURONE, MOTOR NERVE

Motor neurones conduct impulses away from the central nervous system to the effector (muscle or gland). They are myelinated in the voluntary nervous system and non-myelinated in the autonomic nervous system. A motor nerve contains only motor neurones (e.g. the oculomotor nerve, cranial nerve III).

◄ Autonomic nervous control, Effectors, Mixed nerve, Nervous system, Neurone ►

MOULD

Mould is a popular name for fungus and usually refers to a covering mass of mycelium, such as bread mould (Mucor) growing over the surface of bread.

◄ Fungi ►

MOVEMENT

Movement can refer to locomotion, when the complete organism changes its locality, or to movement of part of the organism only. Movement in plants may be due to differential growth, as in tropisms made towards or away from a stimulus. Plants also exhibit movements due to turgor changes, such as certain nastic responses. Taxes are shown when the complete organism moves in response to a stimulus, such as the chemotactic response of moss antherozoids to the base of the archegonium.

Simple unicellular organisms may move by means of flagella (some bacteria), **undulipodia** (*Chlamydomonas, Euglena, Paramecium*) or by pseudopodia (*Amoeba*). Higher animals move using muscles which operate with a **skeleton** (hydrostatic, **exoskeleton** or **endoskeleton**).

◀ Flagellum, Flagellates, Tactic responses, Taxes ▶

mRNA

◀ Messenger RNA ▶

MUCUS

Mucus is a glycoprotein (combination of **carbohydrate** and protein), synthesised in the Golgi bodies of cells and secreted as mucin. Mucin dissolved in water forms mucus, which is used as a lubricant and protectant. For example, it is released into synovial fluid at **joints** in order to reduce friction, it coats the stomach and intestine linings to prevent attack by the digestive juices and it coats much of the inner surface of respiratory ducts to trap dust and bacteria and allow ciliary action. Cells which secrete mucus are usually of the **goblet cell** type.

Plants secrete mucilage, which is used as a lubricant or anti-drying agent (e.g. around spores and gametes in sporangia and gametangia, within and on seaweeds).

◀ Golgi complex, Proteins ▶

MULTICELLULAR ORGANISATION

In multicellular organisms, each cell of the organism is dependant on other cells of the organism, and there is division of labour, so that certain cells and tissues become specialised to perform particular jobs for the benefit of the complete organism. In Porifera or sponges, the individual cells remain largely independent, and this can really be considered a colonial type of organisation rather than an integrated multicellular one. The beginnings of multicellular organisation in one line of plants is well illustrated by the Volvocine series in the phylum **Chlorophyta**. *Chlamydomonas* is the starting organism and is a unicell. Chlamydomonad type cells can become associated together to form other organisms (e.g. *Gonium*, sixteen cells; *Pandorina*, sixteen or thirty-two cells; *Eudorina*, thirty-two or sixty-four cells; *Volvox* 500 to 10,000 cells). Division of labour occurs in these organisms, with outer cells bearing **undulipodia** for **locomotion**, other cells being specialised for **sexual reproduction**. Parenchymatous tissue develops in the higher **algae** and in the bryophytes, and vascular tissue (**xylem** and **phloem**) develops in the clubmosses, horsetails, ferns, conifers and **flowering plants**.

In animals a diploblastic (two germ layers) organisation appears in the **Cnidaria** (Hydra, Obelia, sea anemone, jelly fish). The outer ectoderm tends to develop into musculo-epithelial cells concerned with movements and the endoderm becomes the digestive lining of the emteron. In triploblastic animals a third germ layer forms between the ectoderm and endoderm. This is the mesoderm, and will form various connective-type tissues. In the Platyhelminthes (planaria, flukes, tapeworms) the mesoderm remains a solid mass of mesenchyme cells, but in Annelids and above, a coelom is developed in the mesoderm. This enables complex organs to form (e.g. heart, lungs, intestines).

◄ Acoelomate organisation, Bryophyta, Cell, Coelomate organisation, Conifer, Fern, Parenchyma, Tissue, Triploblastic organisation ►

MULTIPLE ALLELES

Multiple alleles occur where a **gene** has more than two **alleles**. For example, the blood groups of the ABO system are controlled by a single gene which has three alleles. If the gene is designated I the alleles are I^A, I^B, and I^O. I^A produces antigen A, I^B produces antigen B, I^O does not produce an antigen. I^A and I^B are codominant, and both are dominant over I^O.

There are six possible allelic combinations in the human population, giving four possible phenotypes or blood groups, as shown in the table.

Genotypes	Antigens produced	Blood group phenotype
$I^A I^A$ or $I^A I^O$	A	A
$I^B I^B$ or $I^B I^O$	B	B
$I^A I^B$	A and B	AB
$I^O I^O$	none	O

Other examples of multiple alleles are those controlling MN blood groups in man, coat colour in rabbits and coat colour in cattle.

◄ ABO blood groups, Antigens, Codominance, Phenotype ►

MUSCLE CONTRACTION

Within the sarcomeres of **striated muscle** are thick filaments of **myosin** and thin filaments of **actin** (their arrangement relative to each other can be seen in Fig. S.3). In each thin filament are many actin molecules forming long threads that spiral around each other in pairs. Along each thread are many sites where myosin molecules can become attached (myosin-binding sites) and these are covered by another protein called tropomyosin. A thick filament consists of about 200 myosin molecules which each have a rounded head and a filamentous tail. They are arranged so that the heads project from the sides and ends of the filaments. On the ends of these heads are sites which will bind them to the thin filaments, and molecules of ATPase enzyme (Fig. M.12).

In the relaxed state the myosin-binding sites are covered by tropomyosin. When the muscle fibre is depolarised by a **nerve impulse**, **calcium** ions leak from the sarcoplasmic reticulum into the sarcoplasm. These displace the tropomyosin, thus exposing the myosin-binding sites. This enables the myosin heads to attach to the binding sites on the actin, drawing the thin filaments into the myosin region and thus shortening the **sarcomere**. As the muscle repolarises and calcium ions are pumped back to the sarcoplasmic reticulum (using adenosine triphosphate–ATP), the myosin heads uncouple and the tropmyosin moves back to cover the myosin-binding sites. The ATP also provides energy for the bonding between the myosin heads and the binding sites.

Cardiac muscle is myogenic, the contraction is initiated by the muscle itself and does not require a nerve impulse.

◄ Smooth muscle ►

MUSCLE STRUCTURE

Muscles consist of contractile cells or fibres and the associated connective tissue, blood and nerve supplies.

◄ Cardiac muscle, Sarcomere, Smooth muscle, Striated muscle ►

MUTAGENS

Mutagens are agents which cause mutation. They may be physical, such as ultra-violet radiation, alpha (helium nuclei), beta (electrons), gamma (electro-magnetic radiation) rays, and X-rays. Alternatively, they may be chemical, such as colchicine, mustard gas and methanal.

◄ Ionising radiation, Ultraviolet light ►

MUTATION

A mutation is a sudden change in the genotype or chromosomal DNA of an organism, resulting in discontinuous variation.

◄ Chromosome mutation, Gene (point) mutation, Polyploidy ►

MUTUALISM

Mutualism is an association or symbiosis between two dissimilar organisms, from which both derive benefit: for example, the relationship between herbivores such as ruminants and the cellulose-fermenting bacteria in their rumens; the relationship between the leguminous plant and the nitrogen-fixing bacteria (Rhizobium) in their root nodules; and lichens which are associations between an alga and a fungus.

◄ Nitrogen fixation ►

MYELIN SHEATH

Myelin is a fatty mixture of phospholipid and cholesterol which forms a sheath around voluntary motor neurones and sensory neurones. It is formed in blocks by the Schwann cells. The blocks are termed the internodes, separated by the nodes of Ranvier, which have no myelin. Myelin speeds up the impulse velocity, since the impulses jump from one internode to the next (saltatory conduction).

◀ Neurone ▶

MYOGENIC

Myogenic refers to the ability of **cardiac muscle** to initiate contractions of its own accord, rather than requiring a **nerve impulse**.

MYOGLOBIN

Myoglobin is a variety of **haemoglobin** found in muscle sarcoplasm and gives muscle its red colour. It binds oxygen, which it accepts from the unloading of oxygen from the haemoglobin in the red cells, and the oxygen is then available for use in the muscle.

◀ Haemoglobin ▶

MYOSIN

Myosin is one of the contractile **proteins** of muscle, making up the thick filaments of the sarcomeres of **striated muscle**. Each filament has about 200 molecules of myosin, each with a rounded head containing a binding site and ATPase enzyme, and a filamentous tail.

◀ Muscle contraction, Sarcomere ▶

MYRIAPOD

Myriapods (Fig. M.11) are members of the phylum Arthropoda, belonging to two classes: Chilopoda, which are centipedes, and Diplopoda, which are millipedes. Chilopods are terrestrial carnivores, with a distinct head bearing a pair of poison jaws, and similar legs along the body length with one pair per segment (e.g. *Lithobius*). Diplopods are terrestrial herbivores with two pairs of legs per body segment (e.g. *Iulus*).

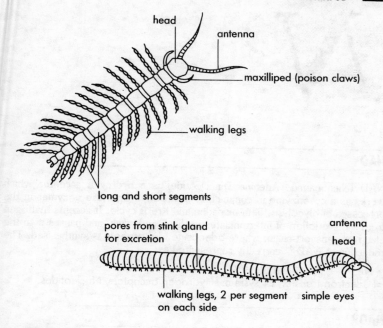

head

antenna

maxilliped (poison claws)

walking legs

long and short segments

pores from stink gland
for excretion

antenna

head

walking legs, 2 per segment
on each side

simple eyes

Fig. M.11 Myriapods

NAD

NAD (Nicotinamide Adenine Dinucleotide) is a hydrogen acceptor which works as a co-enzyme in conjunction with dehydrogenase enzymes in the processes of glycolysis, beta-oxidation and Krebs cycle. It accepts hydrogen from the oxidation of intermediates in these pathways, and passes it to the electron transport chain, where adenosine triphosphate is synthesised. The reduction of NAD is correctly represented as:

$$NAD^+ + 2H \rightarrow NADH + H^+$$

◀ Electron transfer, ET systems, Hydrogen acceptors, Nucleotides ▶

NADP

NADP (Nicotinamide Adenine Dinucleotide Phosphate) is also a hydrogen acceptor, but unlike NAD it is used in photosynthesis. It is reduced to $NADPH + H^+$ in the light reaction for use in the dark reaction. It is also used in the pentose-phosphate shunt of respiration.

◀ Hydrogen acceptors, Nucleotides ▶

NANOMETRE

One nanometre (nm) is 10^{-9} metre. It is used for measuring wavelengths of radiation. Visible light is from 400 (violet) to 700 (red) nanometres in wavelength. 1 nm is 10 Angstrom units.

NASTIC RESPONSES, NASTY

Nastys are plant movements made in response to a diffuse stimulus, such as the opening and closing of flowers in response to temperature or light intensity. Some nastic responses involve differential changes in growth rate, while others are due to turgor changes. Thermonasty occurs in the flowers of crocus and tulip, where if the temperature rises a few degrees, the closed flowers open, due to a more rapid growth rate on the inner surface of the perianth parts. A fall in temperature speeds up growth on the outer surface.

Photonastic movements occur in daisy flowers, which open on exposure to light, and in *Oenothera* (evening primrose), whose flowers open at night. The tendrils of *Bryonia dioica* (white bryony) respond to touch by curling around other stems or supports, and *Mimosa* (sensitive plant) droops sharply when touched, due to a sudden loss of turgor in cells at the base of the **petiole**. These last two examples are called haptonastic responses.

NATIONAL NATURE RESERVES (NNRs)

Like **Sites of Special Scientific Interest** (SSSIs), these are sites which contain habitats and **communities** which are of scientific importance and which require **conservation** and protection. Man's activities within such areas are limited by law and restricted to those that will not disrupt the reserve adversely.
◄ Habitat ►

NATIONAL PARKS

National Parks are governed by a National Parks Committee. They are large areas of the countryside in which human activities are curtailed to the extent that the natural habitats and **communities** are not adversely disrupted, and the natural beauty of the landscape is preserved. Access to the public is allowed for leisure pursuits which are harmless to the environment, and for study or aesthetic enjoyment of the environment. Examples include Snowdonia, Dartmoor, Pembrokeshire National Parks.
◄ Conservation, Habitat ►

NATURAL SELECTION

Natural selection was proposed by **Darwin** and by Wallace as being the mechanism by which new species arise from pre-existing species. They observed that the number of individuals within a **population** remains more or less constant. Most organisms have tremendous reproductive potential, however, and produce far more offspring than actually survive to adulthood, so there must be a 'struggle for existence' within the population. The mechanism depends on the fact that individuals within a population show many phenotypic variations, some of which give advantage in this 'struggle for existence'. Thus those individuals best suited to the prevailing conditions will survive better and have a reproductive advantage, producing more offspring than the less favoured organisms. (Darwin called this 'survival of the fittest'). Their advantageous variations are passed on to their progeny, resulting in a shift in gene frequencies when compared to the parent generation. If natural selection operates together with isolation then **speciation** may follow eventually.
◄ 'Fitness', Isolating mechanisms, Phenotype, Selection pressure, Variation ►

NECROTROPHIC DISEASE

A necrotrophic disease causes necrosis, or death, of a cell or group of cells. In bone, for instance, necrosis can be caused by blockage of the blood supply due to fracture, by the uptake of radioactive materials, or as a result of diseases such as yaws. Gangrene is a particularly serious necrotrophic disease caused by Clostridium bacteria in which large areas of tissue die and then rot. Frostbite is also necrotrophic.

NEGATIVE FEEDBACK

In physiology negative feedback is the most common method of control. If a physiological value deviates from the mean, the deviation is sensed and control mechanisms are stimulated which return the deviating value to the mean. The control mechanism is then curtailed or damped. For example, osmoreceptors in the hypothalamus sense that the water content of the blood is too low (blood too concentrated). The hypothalamus then stimulates the nerve endings in the posterior pituitary to release anti-diuretic hormone (ADH) to the blood. This targets on to the cells of the nephron collecting ducts making them more permeable to water, so water is absorbed from the urine back to the blood along the concentration gradient. As the blood concentration falls to the mean value, the osmoreceptors are no longer stimulated, and the release of ADH is suppressed.

◀ Homoeostasis, Kidneys, Osmoregulation ▶

NEO-DARWINISM

Darwin's theories were proposed before Mendelian genetics were discovered. Neo-Darwinism is the name given to modern evolutionary theory, which embraces Darwin's work but also the principles of Mendelian genetics, and information from contemporary studies in molecular biology, genetics, palaeontology, ethology and ecology.

◀ Darwin, Evolution, Gene mutation, Mendelian inheritance, principles of, Natural selection, Polyploidy, Selection pressure, Variation ▶

NEPHRON

The nephron is the functional unit of the kidney, regulating blood composition and urine formation. Each nephron starts as a double walled cup, the Bowman's or renal capsule, which lies in the cortex of the kidney. It surrounds a capillary network called the glomerulus. The inner wall of the capsule is made of podocytes and is in close contact with the endothelium of the glomerular capillaries. This endothelial-capsular surface is where glomerular filtration occurs. The capsule opens into the first part of the renal tubule, known as the first convoluted tubule, which also lies in the cortex. This descends into the medulla as the descending limb of the loop of Henle, and then ascends towards the cortex as the ascending limb of the loop of Henle. It continues as the distal convoluted tubule, which joins a collecting duct.

◀ Excretion, Kidneys, Osmoregulation ▶

NEREIS

Nereis diversicolor (Fig. N.1) is the most common European ragworm, and is a member of the phylum **Annelida**, class Polychaeta. They are confined to seawater, have a distinct head, are metamerically segmented and have numerous chaetae, borne on parapodia (projections). *Nereis diversicolor* lives in U-shaped burrows around the mid-tide level on muddy shores. Since it can tolerate a lowered salinity, it is common in estuaries.

◀ Polychaete ▶

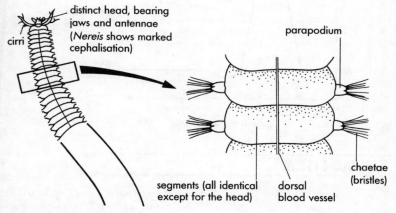

distinct head, bearing jaws and antennae (*Nereis* shows marked cephalisation)

cirri

parapodium

segments (all identical except for the head)

dorsal blood vessel

chaetae (bristles)

Fig. N.1 External features of Nereis

NERVE IMPULSE

The **neurone** at rest has a resting membrane potential, the outside being positive with respect to the inside, to the extent of 65–95 mV. At rest the neurone membrane is impermeable to **sodium** ions. Stimuli such as heat, pressure, pain, cold, light, sound and electric currents may initiate a nerve impulse. The effect of the **stimulus** is to make the neurone membrane permeable to sodium ions for a few ten-thousandths of a second, and since sodium ions are in high concentration outside the cell, they rush in along the concentration gradient. There are now more positive ions inside the neurone, and thus the polarity is reversed. The value of the reversal potential is about 35 mV. The membrane is said to be depolarised. The repolarisation or restoration of the resting potential, is initially caused by the loss of **potassium** ions along the concentration and electrical gradients to the outside of the neurone. The sodium pump restores the true resting potential only when impulses have ceased to pass (Fig. N.2a).

The **depolarisation** of one bit of the neurone membrane results in an adjacent bit of membrane being depolarised, due to the flow of local currents across the margins of depolarisation. Thus the wave of depolarisation and repolarisation (the **action potential** or impulse) passes along the neurone (Fig. N.2b)). An impulse can pass either way along a neurone, but only one way across a synapse.

◄ Refractory period, Resting potential ►

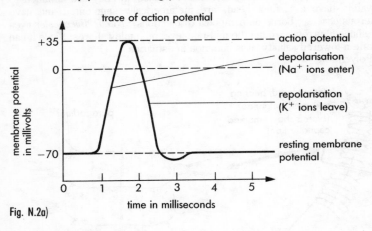

trace of action potential

action potential

depolarisation (Na⁺ ions enter)

repolarisation (K⁺ ions leave)

resting membrane potential

membrane potential in millivolts

time in milliseconds

Fig. N.2a)

NERVOUS SYSTEM

A nervous system is present in all multicellular animals except sponges. It co-ordinates the various activities of the animal with each other and with changes in the internal and external environment (i.e. it is concerned with sensitivity). Information is passed through the nervous system by means of electrical nerve impulses, transmitted by neurones, and by chemical transmission across synapses between neurones. Simple animals, such as Cnidarians (coelenterates such as **Hydra**, sea anemones, jelly fish), have a simple nerve net as nervous system. In annelids, a ventral double nerve cord has developed, with ganglia in each segment and a cerebral ganglion (simple brain) in the head. This is the basic plan in most invertebrate coelomate phyla, although increases in complexity occur in the more advanced groups. In vertebrates the nerve cord is dorsal, hollow and single, and there is a well-developed **brain**, protected by the cranium.

In mammals the **central nervous system** (CNS) consists of the brain and **spinal cord**, and the peripheral nervous system of sensory and motor nerves. The motor nerves run from the CNS to the effector (muscle or gland) while the sensory nerves relay impulses from the sense organs or **receptors** to the CNS. Functionally the system is divided into the **voluntary nervous system**,

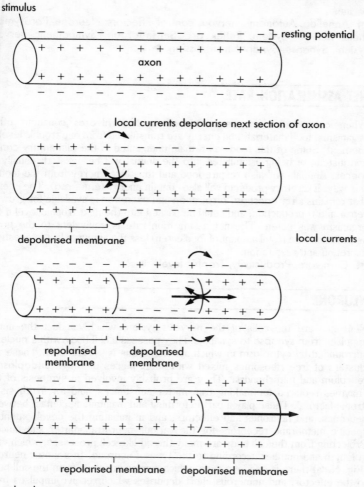

stimulus

− − − − − − − − − − − −]- resting potential

+ + + + + + + + + + + +   axon

+ + + + + + + + + + + +

− − − − − − − − − − − − −

local currents depolarise next section of axon

+ + + + + − − − − − − − − −

− − − − − +\ + + + + + + + +

− − − − − +/ + + + + + + + +

+ + + + + − − − − − − − − −

depolarised membrane   local currents

− − − − − + + + + + − − − −

+ + + + + − − − − − +\ + + +

+ + + + + − − − − − +/ + + +

− − − − − + + + + + − − − −

repolarised   depolarised
membrane   membrane

− − − − − − − − − − − + + + +

+ + + + + + + + + + +− − − −

+ + + + + + + + + + +− − − −

− − − − − − − − − − − + + + +

repolarised membrane   depolarised membrane

no local currents occur here,
since membrane super-
permeable to K^+ and very
impermeable to Na^+ at this
point.

Fig. N.2b) Nerve impulse transmission

which controls voluntary activities, and the autonomic nervous system, which controls involuntary functions such as the control of breathing and of gut peristalsis. The autonomic nervous has sympathetic and parasympathetic divisions, in which the 'sympathetic stimulates while the parasympathetic pacifies'.

◀ Annelida, Autonomic nervous control, Effectors, Neurone, Parasympathetic nervous system, Reflex arc, Sense organ, Sympathetic nervous system, Synapse, Synaptic transmission ▶

NET ASSIMILATION RATE

When consumers such as herbivores and carnivores consume other organisms, food materials and energy are transferred from one trophic level to the next. Some of this food will remain undigested in the alimentary canal, and instead of being assimilated into the animal will be egested, usually as faeces. Animals will also respire food and thus lose energy from the food in this way. Excretory products will also contain energy (e.g. urea). The energy that remains after egestion, respiration and excretion is available for growth, repair and reproduction, and could be passed into the next trophic level if the organism was eaten. The net assimilation rate is equivalent to the gross assimilation rate (total amount of food eaten) less the amounts lost in egestion, excretion and respiration.

◀ Carnivore, Productivity, Trophic levels ▶

NEURONE

Neurones are the cells of the nervous system which conduct the nerve impulses from synapse to synapse. They possess a cell body with a nucleus, surrounded by cytoplasm in which are numerous Nissl granules. These are clusters of free ribosomes mixed with short pieces of rough endoplasmic reticulum and mitochondria. They are probably involved in synthesis of the enzymes required for making transmitter substances, and for synthesis of 'tropic factors'. These play a part in forming and maintaining contact between neurones, and neurones and effectors, and in initiating the development of specific membrane receptors for the various neurotransmitter substances. Projecting from the cell body are many thread-like cell processes, which vary in length and number according to the type of neurone. In a motor neurone (Fig. N.3a) there is one long axon, which carries impulses from the cell body to the effector, and numerous short dendrites which receive impulses from the axons of other neurons, via synapses. The axons may be coated with blocks of myelin secreted by Schwann cells, with thin areas called nodes of Ranvier between the blocks. These help to speed up the impulse passage where rapid relay is required because the impulse effectively 'jumps' from one node to the next. Sensory neurones (Fig. N.3b), motor neurones in the voluntary nervous system and relay neurones in the white matter of the central nervous system (CNS) all have myelinated fibres (Fig. N.4). Other fibres are non-myelinated and conduct more slowly: for example, some sensory neurones in the ANS (autonomic nervous system), motor neurones in the ANS, relay neurones in the grey matter of the CNS.

◀ Enzyme, Mitochondrion, Nerve impulse, Reflex arc, Ribosome ▶

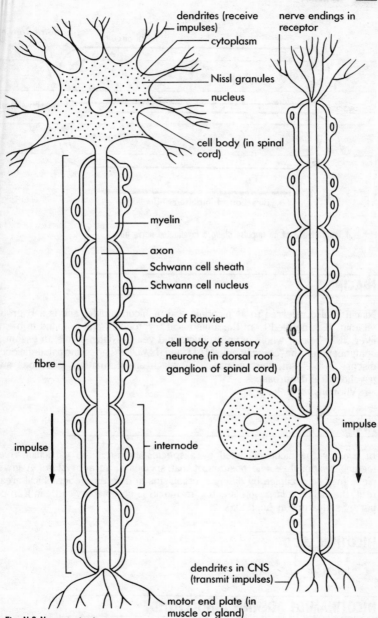

Fig. N.3 Neurone structure:
a) motor neurone   b) sensory neurone

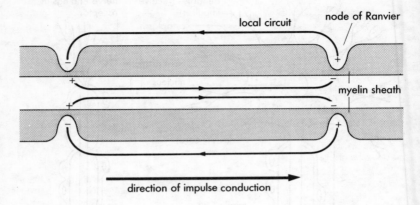

Fig. N.4 Transmission of an impulse along a myelinated nerve fibre

NIACIN

Niacin is also referred to as nicotinic acid or nicotinamide, and is a B group vitamin. It is derived from the amino acid tryptophan, and is found in meat, liver, fish, beans, whole grain products and yeast. Niacin forms an essential component of the co-enzymes NAD and NADP. The principal deficiency disease is pellagra, the symptoms of which are dermatitis, diarrhoea and psychological disturbances.

◄ Vitamins ►

NICHE

In ecology the niche occupied by a species indicates the particular role, feeding relationships and position of that species in an ecosystem. A given niche may be occupied by different organisms in different geographical areas (e.g. the niche for large grass-eating mammals is occupied by cattle in Europe but by kangaroos in Australia).

NICOTINIC ACID

◄ Niacin ►

NICOTINAMIDE ADENINE DINUCLEOTIDE

◄ NAD ►

NICOTINAMIDE ADENINE DINUCLEOTIDE PHOSPHATE

◀ NADP ▶

NITRATE

Plants obtain their nitrogen by absorbing it in the form of nitrate ions from the soil solution, via their **root hairs**. The nitrogen is then incorporated into plant protein which can then enter the food chain to become animal protein. The absorbed nitrate ions in the plant are initially reduced to nitrite by the **enzyme** nitrate reductase, and then to ammonia using nitrite reductase. The ammonia is then used to aminate alpha-keto-glutaric acid to alpha-amino-glutaric acid. This can be used to synthesise other **amino acids** by transamination, and the amino acids can then be used in **protein synthesis**. Alpha-keto-glutaric acid is an intermediate compound in Krebs cycle.

◀ Food chains, Food webs, Nitrate pollution, Nitrogen cycle ▶

NITRATE POLLUTION

Nitrate pollution may occur where sewage is added to water or, increasingly common nowadays, where inorganic nitrogenous fertilisers run off the land in the drainage water and enter ponds, lakes and streams. The increased nutrient level in the water leads to an algal bloom (overgrowth of **algae**), more algae being produced than are eaten. The algae on the surface shade water plants and algae lower down from light, thus curtailing **photosynthesis**. As large quantities of algae die, they are decayed by aerobic micro-organisms, which multiply greatly in number and decrease the amount of available oxygen in the water. Most aquatic animals die, particularly the fish, and the lake rapidly becomes devoid of life. This process is called **eutrophication**.

Some algae in the blooms may produce toxins which kill aquatic life, and are also dangerous to animals, such as cattle or humans who drink the water. Blue-green bacteria are implicated in this. Where algal blooms occur in the sea, the toxins may be concentrated by shellfish and can lead to paralytic shellfish poisoning in man if the shellfish are eaten.

◀ Nitrogen cycle ▶

NITROGEN CYCLE

The nitrogen cycle (Fig. N.5) ensures that nitrogen which is bound up within **proteins** and other compounds in the biosphere is constantly recycled, so that it may be reused, and continually available. The main processes going on in the **soil** concerned with the nitrogen cycle are nitrification, **nitrogen fixation** and denitrification. In nitrification, **amino acids** in the soil organic matter are deaminated by various micro-organisms, including saprophytic **fungi** and **bacteria**, resulting in ammonia formation. This is then oxidised to nitrite by chemoautotrophic bacteria, such as *Nitrosomonas*, and then to nitrates by *Nitrobacter*. These processes are aerobic and oxygen is required as an electron acceptor. If the soil is waterlogged and anaerobic conditions occur, denitrification may take place. This converts ammonia, nitrite and nitrate to nitrogen, which is released into the atmosphere. The bacteria *Pseudomonas denitrificans* and *Thiobacillus denitrificans* are responsible for this.

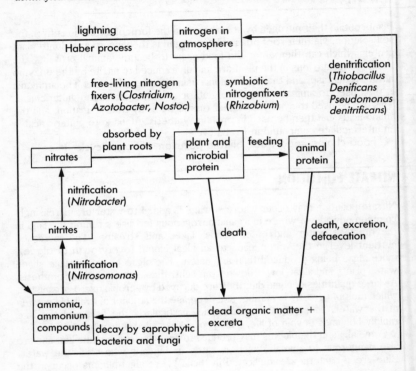

Fig. N.5 Nitrogen cycle

◀ Nitrate, Protein synthesis, Saprophyte, Saprophytism ▶

NITROGEN FIXATION

This is the only way in which nitrogen can be made directly available to organisms, but it is an ability confined to prokaryotic organisms only. The process is energy-consuming since the two nitrogen atoms of the nitrogen molecule must be separated. This is done using 'nitrogenase' **enzyme** and **adenosine triphosphate** (ATP) as energy source. Nitrogen fixation results in the formation of ammonia (*not* nitrate – a common error at A-level). The ammonia can then be changed to nitrate in the soil and absorbed into plants.

The free-living nitrogen fixers in the soil are blue-green bacteria, such as *Nostoc*, and colourless bacteria, such as *Clostridium* and *Azotobacter*. There are also symbiotic nitrogen-fixers, such as the bacterium Rhizobium that lives in the root nodules of leguminous plants.

Some nitrogen is fixed in the soil by the action of electrical discharge (lightning) on atmospheric nitrogen and oxygen, the nitrogen oxides formed being washed into the soil by rain.

Huge amounts of ammonia are produced commercially in the Haber process, and these are used for making nitrogenous fertilisers, which are added to the soils to increase fertility.

◀ Leguminous plants, Nitrogen cycle, Prokaryotae, Prokaryotic cells ▶

NITROGENOUS EXCRETION

Nitrogenous excretory products are formed by catabolism of proteins, amino acids and nucleic acids. Animals generally take in more protein than they require and, since protein cannot be stored, the surplus must be broken down and removed. Amino acids are also toxic and can thus be kept as amino acids in the body only in very low concentrations. The toxic amine groups are removed from the amino acids by the process of deamination. The highly toxic ammonia is very soluble and in aquatic organisms, such as protozoa, coelenterates, turbellarians, enchinoderms, freshwater teleost fishes and amphibian tadpole larvae, can be removed in the available water, which is abundant. In other organisms the ammonia may be altered to the less toxic urea by the ornithine cycle, and though it is less soluble than ammonia, the necessary amounts can still be removed in the available water. It is the main nitrogenous excretory end product in elasmobranch fish, some marine teleost fish, adult amphibia and mammals. In animals that have shelled eggs (i.e. reptiles and birds), the nitrogenous end product is uric acid. Since this has low solubility, it also has low toxicity and thus can be stored without harm to the embryo in the closed environment of the egg. In the adults a minimum amount of water is required for lubrication, since the urine is semi-solid in consistency.

NON-CELLULAR ORGANISATION

Viruses have non-cellular organisation since they do not possess cells, but consist of virions containing a core of nucleic acid and a capsid of protein.

◀ Virus, Viral replication ▶

NON-COMPETITIVE INHIBITION

In non-competitive enzyme inhibition, the inhibitor has no structural similarity to the substrate, and forms a complex with the enzyme which does not involve the **active site**. In this complex, however, the shape of the active site is modified, due to the inhibitor changing the 3D configuration of the protein. Thus the enzyme can no longer interact with the substrate. The inhibition can be often reversed if the inhibitor is removed, an example being cyanide, which reacts with the metallic prosthetic groups of some enzymes, such as the copper ions of cytochrome oxidase, acting as a reversible inhibitor.

Some non-competitive inhibitors form permanent links with the enzyme, however, and such inhibition is irreversible (e.g. mercury ions, lead ions and arsenic ions all combine permanently with sulphydryl (-SH) groups of enymes). Another example is DFP, which is a nerve gas that combines with the active sites of the enzyme acetylcholine esterase. Synaptic transmission is thus prevented, resulting in paralysis and death.

◄ Competitive inhibition, Cytochromes, Prosthetic group, Synapse, Synaptic transmission ►

NON-CYCLIC PHOTOPHOSPHORYLATION

Non-cyclic **photophosphorylation** occurs in the light dependent stages of photosynthesis.

◄ Photoactivation of chlorophyll ►

NON-REDUCING SUGARS

An example of a non-reducing sugar is **sucrose** (cane sugar). This is a disaccharide formed by condensation between **fructose** and **glucose**. The glycosidic link formed between the glucose and fructose involves the reducing groups of both sugars, thus sucrose is without a remaining reducing group.

◄ Condensation reactions, Disaccharides, Food tests, Monosaccharides, Reducing sugars ►

NON-SEXUAL REPRODUCTION

Non-sexual reproduction does not involve sex. It depends on **mitosis** and produces no genetic variability because **meiosis** and **fertilisation** are not involved. **Asexual reproduction** and **vegetative reproduction** are methods of non-sexual reproduction.

◄ Sporangia, Spore, Sporulation ►

NON-VERBAL COMMUNICATION IN MAN

Non-verbal communication (NVC) involves passing information to others, consciously or unconsciously, without using language. The sense of sight may be involved, where facial expressions and shapes, bodily stances or movements of hands and arms provide the stimuli; or the sense of smell may be involved, where stimuli are transmitted by bodily odours or pheromones;

and the sense of touch may be involved, tactile stimuli being transmitted by bodily contact. NVC is particularly important in forming bonds between babies and their parents.

◄ Stimulus, Parental care ►

NUCLEIC ACIDS

Examples of nucleic acids are ribonucleic acid (RNA) and deoxyribonucleic acid (DNA). They are polymers of nucleotides and occur in all living organisms. DNA is the main constituent of chromosomes and is concerned with inheritance, while RNA is concerned with the expression of the genetic code in polypeptide synthesis. DNA and RNA are also found in viruses.

NUCLEOLUS

The nucleolus is a conspicuous round structure in a nucleus, and some nuclei may have more than one. It is the site of synthesis of ribosomal RNA, and since it contains large quantities of DNA and RNA it stains intensely with basic stains. Portions of several chromosomes meet in the nucleolus. Such regions on a chromosome are known as the 'nucleolar organisers', and contain many genes all for the coding of ribosomal RNA. This is an example of 'gene amplification', where one gene alone could not produce the amounts of the substance required, so many genes occur, giving greater manufacturing power. The actual assembly of ribosomes is completed in the cytoplasm. Nucleoli disappear during prophase of cell division, but are reorganised during telophase.

◄ Gene, Meiosis, Mitosis, Ribosome ►

NUCLEOTIDES

Nucleotides (Fig. N.6) are equivalent to nucleoside monophosphates. Nucleosides are formed by a combination of a pentose (5C) sugar, which could be ribose or deoxyribose, and a nitrogenous base. The base can be pyrimidine, such as cytosine, uracil or thymine, or purine, such as adenine or guanine. The nucleosides of these bases are called adenosine, guanosine, cytidine, uridine and thymidine. Nucleoside triphosphates are energy-rich co-enzymes adenosine triphosphate (ATP), GTP, CTP, TTP, UTP.

Two nucleotides can join together by condensation to form a dinucleotide (Fig. N.6b). Important dinucleotides include NAD and NADP, hydrogen-accepting co-enzymes in respiration and photosynthesis respectively. Nucleotides may also be polymerised to form the nucleic acids RNA or DNA, depending on whether they contain ribose or deoxyribose.

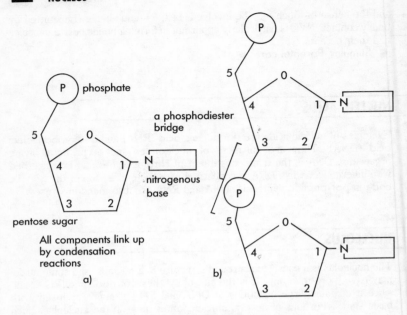

Fig. N.6 Outline structure of a) a mononucleotide b) a dinucleotide

NUCLEUS

The nucleus is the largest **organelle** in the **cell** in eukaryotes. It is separated from the rest of the cell by a double nuclear membrane with pores to allow transport in or out of the nucleus, in particular to permit the exit of **mRNA** for protein synthesis. Nuclei may be round or ovoid, and may contain one or more nucleoli. The nucleus contains the threads of protein and **DNA** known as **chromosomes**, which are visible during **cell division** but in **interphase** form a mass known as **chromatin**.

◄ Eukarytic cells, Mitosis, Meiosis, Nucleolus ►

NUTRIENTS

For **heterotrophs**, nutrients are mainly organic food substances that can be used in **metabolism** as either sources of **energy** or as building blocks (e.g. sugars, **fatty acids, amino acids**). For autotrophs, they are inorganic substances, which may be used for food manufacture (e.g. mineral ions, carbon dioxide).

◄ Autotrophic nutrition, Carbohydrates, Fats, Mineral nutrition, Proteins ►

NUTRITION

Nutrition is the way in which organisms obtain food. **Green plants** are self-feeding or autotrophic, since they manufacture their carbohydrates by **photosynthesis**, and then make their own **lipids** and **proteins** from the carbohydrates and various absorbed salts. Animals are heterotrophic, feeding on ready-made sources of food, such as plants and other animals, from which they digest and absorb the sugars, **amino acids** and lipids they require. **Bacteria** and **fungi** are also heterotrophic, being either saprophytes or parasites.

◀ Absorption, Carbohydrate, Digestion, Heterotrophs, Mineral nutrition, Parasitism, Saprophyte ▶

OBESITY

Obesity is defined as a condition resulting in a body weight 10–20 per cent above a desirable standard, as a result of an excessive accumulation of fat. It occurs only in humans and overfed domesticated animals who may eat out of habit, or addiction, rather than from necessity. It is unhealthy to be obese, since the added weight strains the heart, muscles, joints and internal organs.

OESTROGENS

Oestrogens are female sex hormones produced at the onset of puberty by the ovaries. They are derivatives of the **steroid** alcohol cholesterol and are responsible for the regulation of the **menstrual cycle**, maintenance of **pregnancy** and development of the female secondary sexual characteristics, such as breasts, wider hips and pubic and underarm hair.

◄ Hormone, Ovary ►

OLIGOCHAETE

Oligochaetes are annelids that possess only few chaetae. The class includes terrestrial oligochaetes such as the common **earthworm**, *Lumbricus terrestris*, and aquatic oligochaetes such as *Tubifex sp*. This group is very widely spread but not very diverse.

◄ Annelida ►

OOSPHERE

An oosphere is a female **gamete** or sex cell produced by certain groups of plants (e.g. **Chlorophyta**) which tend to be large, round and non-motile. When fertilized it develops into an oospore.

OPSONINS

Opsonins are substances which coat bacterial cells and other **antigens** in order to promote or enhance phagocytosis by neutrophils and tissue macrophages. Such substances include antibodies and the Complement proteins. Opsonisation results in a massive increase in the number of bacteria that can be destroyed.

◀ Antibody, Immunity ▶

OPTICAL MICROSCOPE

An optical microscope is a system of magnifying lenses that use light in order to view small objects. Early microscopes, known as simple microscopes, used only one lens system and had limited magnification properties. Modern microscopes are known as compound microscopes and consist of several lens systems, often split into objective lenses and eye-piece lenses. The object is therefore magnified in two stages. There are usually four objective lenses that are housed in a revolving turret, each having a different magnification power ranging from low (×4, ×10) to high (×40), and a lens designed for use with an immersion oil, which has a magnifying power of ×100. The eye-piece lens can range from ×4 to ×15, but ×10 is usual. The total magnifying power of the microscope is calculated by multiplying the objective lens power by the eye-piece lens power.

More important than the magnifying power of the lenses is their resolving power. This is the ability of the lens system to distinguish two points in an object as two separate points. This ability is ultimately limited by the wavelength of the illuminating medium (in this case light). The average wavelength of white light is approximately 500 nm and therefore the theoretical limits of resolution are about half of this figure – that is, 250 nm, which means that two objects which lie closer together than 250 nm cannot be distinguished separately. The wavelength of light gives a theoretical magnifying power of approximately ×1,500, but there are further limitations due to the optics and quality of the lenses. Thus in practice the uppermost magnification is ×1,200, though as new technology improves lens quality, the theoretical limits of resolution are being reached.

A third lens system found on most compound microscopes is the condenser lens. This is located under the stage and is used to focus the light emitting from the light source on to the specimen, allowing the whole field of view to be evenly illuminated.

Focusing of the lenses is achieved using both coarse and fine adjustment controls. These can be separate or concentrically mounted, allowing either the stage or the vertical eye-piece mounting to move.

ORAL THRUSH

Oral thrush is a disease of the buccal cavity or mouth caused by the yeast-like fungus *Candida albicans*. This organism exists as part of the normal flora of the mucous membranes but under certain conditions may become pathogenic causing disease.

ORGAN

An organ is a structure produced as a result of increasing specialisation in multicellular organisms. An organ consists of several different types of tissues coordinated to produce a structural and functional unit (e.g. the liver).

ORGANELLE

An organelle is a small structure found within the cytoplasm of a cell which has a specific function in the cell. Most organelles are separated from the rest of the cell contents by one or two surrounding membranes, so that their chemical reactions are also enclosed. Examples of organelles include the mitochondria, chloroplasts and ribosomes.

ORGANIC COMPOUNDS

Organic compounds always contain covalently bonded carbon and hydrogen. In biological systems organic molecules are usually very large (i.e. have a high molecular weight) and are responsible for structural, functional and morphological features of living organisms (e.g. proteins, carbohydrates, fats).

ORGANISM

An organism is an individual that is capable of reproducing itself and existing as a separate entity.

ORNITHINE CYCLE

The ornithine cycle (Fig. O.1) is a biochemical pathway that occurs in the liver. Deamination of unwanted amino acids produces the highly toxic nitrogenous waste product ammonia, which requires a large volume of water in order to dilute its toxicity. Ammonia is therefore converted to a less toxic waste product called urea, which requires less water for its safe elimination. This occurs through a cyclical system of enzyme reactions called the ornithine cycle, in which the substance ornithine acts as a carrier molecule. Ornithine reacts with carbon dioxide from respiration and one molecule of ammonia to give an intermediate which reacts with a second molecule of ammonia forming the amino acid arginine. The nitrogenous part of arginine is split off as urea by hydrolysis, regenerating ornithine which can react with further ammonia and carbon dioxide.

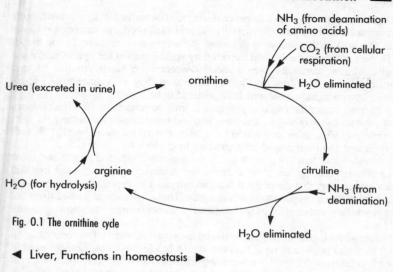

NH$_3$ (from deamination
of amino acids)

CO$_2$ (from cellular
respiration)

ornithine

H$_2$O eliminated

Urea (excreted in urine)

arginine

citrulline

H$_2$O (for hydrolysis)

NH$_3$ (from
deamination)

Fig. 0.1 The ornithine cycle

H$_2$O eliminated

◀ Liver, Functions in homeostasis ▶

OSMOREGULATION

Osmoregulation is the maintenance of the internal osmotic pressure of an organism's body fluids in order for it to maintain a constant osmotic equilibrium with its surroundings. Some animals cannot regulate their osmotic pressure at all (they are called osmoconformers), while others can control their body fluid composition so that it is independent of external fluctuations (these are osmoregulators). Most marine invertebrates are osmoconformers and their body fluids are isotonic to the sea water. Since the sea is extremely stable in its salt content, they are not usually faced with regulatory problems. If under experimental conditions they are placed in external media of higher or lower solute concentration than normal, they lose or gain water according to the physical laws of osmosis, and if the loss or gain is too great the organism dies. Examples of such conformers include starfish, sea anemones, some marine molluscs and spider crabs.

One of the disadvantages of osmoconformation is that the organism is restricted to a particular habitat because it is unable to adapt to changing environmental conditions. For this reason, more evolutionarily advanced organisms have developed mechanisms to regulate their internal fluid composition. Marine fish, for example, require a body fluid composition which is slightly hypotonic to the external environment. The skin of marine fish is impermeable but the gills and mouth are not, so osmotic water loss is a problem. Cartilaginous fish like the shark and the dogfish deal with the problem by concentrating urea in their blood so that they become isotonic with sea water. Bony fish cannot do this, however, and lose water to the sea continuously due to the hypotonic nature of their plasma. (This feature of marine bony fish suggests that they evolved from fresh-water ancestors and then migrated to the sea). In order to replace the water lost by osmosis, bony fish drink sea water in some quantity. This in itself produces osmotic problems as the salts in the sea water increase the solute concentration of the blood. These salts are removed and excreted by special cells in the epithelium of the gills. Marine mammals have a blood concentration similar to that of land mammals (i.e. hypotonic to the sea water), so they actively excrete excess salts by producing an extremely hypertonic urine.

In fresh water the osmotic pressure is low, so organisms face the problem of osmotic influx of water, and have evolved mechanisms for getting rid of it. Some protozoa, such as *Amoeba* have large contractile vacuoles that fill with water and can then periodically contract to excrete it.

Fresh-water fish will absorb water through their gills and mouth and must excrete large quantities of hypotonic urine. Unfortunately, some salt loss will also accompany this water excretion, so salt must be replaced by the action of special chloride secretory cells in the gills. These salts are absorbed from the surrounding water and moved against a concentration gradient into the blood.

Special problems will be encountered in estuaries, where the concentration of the water is liable to rapid fluctuations. Only a few osmoconformers exist in such conditions, either by possessing tissues that tolerate a wide range of salinities (e.g. the lugworm, *Arenicola sp.*) or by burrowing deep into the mud to prevent direct contact with the external medium. In one species of flatworm, excess water is stored in vacuoles in special gut cells, preventing other body cells becoming diluted. When the surrounding water becomes hypertonic again as the tide comes in, the stored water is released.

The problems facing terrestrial organisms is one of water conservation as opposed to water loss. Water tends to be lost as a result of evaporation and the excretion of toxic nitrogenous waste, which requires water for its safe elimination. Osmoregulation can be achieved in a variety of ways. Water retention is important, so many animals possess waterproof outer coverings, and water loss is minimised by the development of a nitrogenous waste product that does not require too much water in its elimination (i.e. urea in mammals and uric acid in reptiles and birds). The kidneys are able to reabsorb varying amounts of water and salts to counteract the effects of diet and water intake, and of evaporation for temperature regulation. In the mammalian kidney, the nephron possesses a loop which is designed to reabsorb differing amounts of water and salts depending on physiological conditions at the time. Thus a urine of varying concentration can be produced under the control of anti-diuretic hormone and aldosterone. This renal loop can vary in length as a special adaptation to extreme environments. Desert mammals like the kangaroo rat for example, can produce an extremely hypertonic urine due to the possession of a very long renal loop.

In the case of birds and reptiles uric acid, which requires very little water for its removal, is excreted. The excretory products are emptied into a common passage known as the cloaca, along with the faeces, and water is reabsorbed from both through the cloacal walls. The result is a black and white semi-solid sludge.

◀ Salt balance, Terrestrial life, adaptations for, Water conservation ▶

OSMOSIS

Osmosis is the movement of water molecules from a low-solute concentration to a high-solute concentration through a partially permeable membrane.

OSTEICHTHYES

Osteichthyes is a class of the Phylum Chordata. They are commonly known as the bony fish. The fins are supported by rays, and the gills covered by an operculum, or bony flap, (e.g. the herring, *Clupea*).
◄ Fish ►

OUT-BREEDING

Out-breeding means the mating of individuals that are not closely related. It increases genetic variation, which may be of selective advantage in evolution.
◄ Hybrids, Hybridisation, In-breeding ►

OVARY

The ovaries are the female gonads, concerned with the production of the female gamete. In the flowering plants the ovary forms part of the gynoecium and takes the form of a hollow structure at the base of the carpel which forms from the megasporophyll. Inside the ovary, one or more ovules form from placental tissue attached to the ovary wall. The ovary develops into the fruit after the egg nucleus within the ovule is fertilised.

In animals the ovary is the site of ova production and in the vertebrates it is also responsible for the production of a number of hormones.
◄ Fertilisation, Floral morphology, Hormones, Menstrual cycle ►

OVULATION

Ovulation is the release of a female gamete or sex cell into the oviduct ready for fertilisation by the male gamete. It is preceded by the gradual development of the ovum within primary follicles, under the control of follicle stimulating hormone (FSH) released from the pituitary gland.

In humans, ovulation occurs on day fourteen of a twenty-eight-day cycle due to the secretion of luteinising hormone (LH) from the pituitary. After ovulation has occured, LH causes the now empty follicle to develop into a corpus luteum, which then secretes progesterone.
◄ Menstrual cycle ►

OVULE DEVELOPMENT

An ovule is a structure found within the **ovary** of seed-producing plants which develops into a seed after the egg cell that it contains is fertilised. The ovule arises from placental tissue within the ovary, to which it is attached by a stalk known as the funicle. It consists of a mass of cells known as the nucellus, surrounded by one or two protective layers called the integuments. These all but meet over the top of the nucellus, leaving a small channel or opening called the micropyle. Within the nucellus, the megaspore divides by **meiosis** to produce four haploid, of which three degenerate and one develops into the embryosac. The nucleus of the embryosac divides three times by *mitosis* to produce eight haploid nuclei. Of the three nuclei at the micropyle cells end of the ovule, one develops into an ovum (functional egg cell) and the other two become supporting cells, or synergids.

◀ Fertilisation, Haploidy ▶

OVUM

An ovum (plural ova) is a female sex cell or **gamete** that contains the haploid number of **chromosomes**.

◀ Haploidy ▶

OXIDATION

Oxidation is the addition of oxygen to a molecule or, more commonly, the removal of hydrogen from a molecule or loss of an electron.

OXIDATIVE DECARBOXYLATION

Oxidative decarboxylation means the removal of **carbon dioxide** from a molecule, coupled with the **oxidation** of the molecule by the removal of hydrogen (a process known as dehydrogenation). This is an important process in some of the metabolic oxidation steps of **glucose** breakdown in **cellular respiration**. The intermediate compound pyruvate, for example, produced by the glycolytic degradation of glucose, is oxidatively decarboxylated to acetyl Co-A. The decarboxylation is catalysed by a decarboxylase **enzyme** and the dehydrogenation is achieved by pyruvate dehydrogenase. The hydrogen molecules removed from the pyruvate are accepted by the **co-enzyme** NAD^+, which becomes reduced as a consequence. This process is also responsible for two of the **Krebs cycle** reactions in which a six-carbon compound is decarboxylated twice to give a four-carbon compound with a subsequent release of energy.

◀ Glycolysis ▶

OXIDATIVE PHOSPHORYLATION

Oxidative phosphorylation involves oxidation coupled to adenosine diphosphate (ADP) phosphorylation. It is the last step in catabolism, and the point at which the major portion of metabolic energy is released. In this process, molecules of NADH + H^+ and FADH + H^+ transfer the electrons they have gained from the oxidation of food molecules eventually to molecular oxygen. The energy thus liberated is used to phosphorylate ADP to adenosine triphosphate (ATP). The pathway involved in the phosphorylation is known as the electron transport chain or the respiratory chain, which consists of a series of carrier molecules arranged in sequence on the inner mitochondrial membrane. Some of the carrier molecules are co-enzymes which work with dehydrogenase enzymes associated with glycolysis and Krebs cycle. NAD, the first acceptor in the chain, is a co-enzyme that is associated with a variety of dehydrogenases, like malate dehydrogenase. This enzyme catalyses the removal of hydrogen atoms from the intermediate substrate malate and these are then accepted by the NAD^+, which becomes reduced to $NADH+H^+$. The hydrogen atoms are then donated to the next acceptor in the chain, FAD^+, which becomes reduced to $FADH+H^+$, allowing the NADH to become reoxidised. The FAD^+ acceptor is at a lower energy level than the NAD^+ amd so in the transference of the hydrogen atoms enough free energy is released to phosphorylate one molecule of ATP. The hydrogen atoms are now donated to another co-enzyme, reducing it and oxidising the FADH back to FAD^+. This co-enzyme, known as co-enzyme Q, accepts only the electrons of the hydrogen atoms, so the protons escape into the intermembrane matrix of the mitochondrion. The reduced co-enzyme Q then passes the electrons to a series of protein pigments known as cytochromes. These contain an iron group, Fe^{3+}, which can accept electrons and thus become reduced to Fe^{2+}. At some point, as the electrons are passed from one cytochrome to another, enough free energy is released to phosphorylate two more molecules of ADP. The ultimate cytochrome in the chain is an enzyme known as cytochrome oxidase. It is at this stage that the uncoupled hydrogen ions (protons) are recombined with the electrons to form hydrogen atoms again. The final acceptor of the hydrogen atoms is molecular oxygen, which becomes reduced to water (H_2O) or in some pathways to hydrogen peroxide (H_2O_2). Thus for every two hydrogen atoms that travel along the chain, three molecules of ATP are formed. Each carrier alternates between being in an oxidised state and in a reduced state and so these series of reactions are known as redox reactions. The only acceptor molecule that does not act as a donator molecule as well and so is not regenerated for subsequent reductions is the final acceptor in the chain, oxygen. Therefore, the oxygen needs constant replenishment in order for the electron transport chain to proceed. Without oxygen as the final acceptor, the preceding carriers could not be reoxidised and so the chain (and therefore ATP production) would grind to a halt.

◀ Electron, Proton pumping, Respiration ▶

OXIDO-REDUCTASE ENZYMES

Oxido-reductase enzymes are involved in the **oxidation** of a substrate by catalysing the transfer of hydrogen from the substrate to an acceptor which becomes reduced as a consequence. There are two oxido-reductase enzymes :

▶ OXIDASES

These catalyse the removal of hydrogen and donate it to molecular oxygen, which becomes reduced to water (H_2O) or hydrogen peroxide (H_2O_2). For example, the enzyme cytochrome oxidase transfers electrons from one of the respiratory chain cytochromes (a protein pigment) to molecular oxygen to form water, thus oxidising the cytochromes and reducing the oxygen.

- cytochrome. Fe^{2+} + $\frac{1}{2}O_2$ $\xrightarrow{\text{(cytochrome oxidase)}}$ cytochrome Fe^{3+} + H_2O
  (reduced   (oxygen)   (oxidised   (water)
  substrate)   substrate)

▶ DEHYDROGENASES

These catalyse the transfer of hydrogen from a substrate to an acceptor molecule that is not oxygen. Thus the substrate is oxidised and the acceptor molecule becomes reduced. The acceptor molecule in many cases is a co-enzyme. For example, the enzyme malate dehydrogenase removes hydrogen atoms from the substrate malate as part of its conversion into oxaloacetate, an important component of Krebs cycle. The hydrogens are donated to the co-enzyme NAD, which becomes reduced as a consequence.

- malate + NAD^+ $\xrightarrow{\text{malic dehydrogenase}}$ oxaloacetate + $NADH + H^+$

(substrate)   (co-enzyme)   (product)   (reduced co-enzyme

OXYGEN

Oxygen is a naturally occurring element with an atomic weight of 16 which exists in the gaseous state and is an important component of biological systems.

OXYGEN DEBT

An 'oxygen debt' is an oxygen deficit due to cellular **adenosine triphosphate** (ATP) production in the absence of oxygen. During severe muscular activity, **oxygen** becomes insufficient for the complete oxidation of **glucose** but energy can still be made available via the glycolytic breakdown of glucose to pyruvate because these reactions do not require oxygen. As **glycolysis** proceeds there is a gradual build-up of $NADH_2$ and pyruvic acid. These must be removed so that end-product inhibition does not halt glycolysis and stop ATP production. An alternative end-product 'sink' is therefore required, to allow continuation of glycolysis, and this alternative is **lactic acid**, formed by the reduction of pyruvate using hydrogen from $NADH_2$. The net result of this is the regeneration of the NAD and the continuance of glycolysis to produce ATP. This energy production is extremely inefficient (about 2 per cent efficiency) and cannot proceed indefinitely as the build-up of lactic acid is toxic to the further metabolism of glucose. Eventually the lactic acid must be converted back to **pyruvate** (i.e. oxidised) and either then completely oxidised in the Krebs cycle reactions or else converted to glycogen in the liver. This obviously requires oxygen and so oxygen utilisation remains high even after the cells' apparent need for it has ceased. In effect, energy production has occurred without the oxygen to 'pay' for it, and this 'debt' needs to be 'repaid' after the cessation of the work.

OXYTOCIN

Oxytocin is a **hormone** produced in the **hypothalamus** and stored and released by the neurohypophysis of the **pituitary gland**. Oxytocin is a small protein (eight amino acid residues) whose release is triggered by distension as a result of the baby's head engaging in the cervical canal close to term. This sends impulses to the hypothalamus and pituitary, increasing the production and secretion of the oxytocin. The hormone causes contraction of the uterine smooth muscle, forcing the head of the baby further through the cervix and so increasing the distension and subsequent impulses to the brain. Thus more oxytocin is released and the uterine contractions increase in strength and severity. Hence the control of the release and action of oxytocin is by a positive feedback mechanism and the cycle is broken by the birth of the infant. Oxytocin is also involved in the ejection of milk by breasts that have already been primed by other hormones. Suckling by the infant initiates the release of oxytocin, which stimulates the **smooth muscle** of the glands to eject milk.
◄ Birth, Lactation, Pregnancy ►

OZONE LAYER

Ozone (O_3) forms a thin film around the Earth which is of extreme importance to life as it filters out large amounts of harmful ultra-violet radiation. Ultra-violet light causes both proteins and, more importantly, nucleic acids to denature. The UV affects the bases of DNA responsible for the genetic code and nuclear control of cellular activity. Such changes can cause mutation and can switch on genes responsible for cell growth and replication resulting in cancer. Without the ozone layer to protect living organisms from the severe mutagenic activity of UV, it is thought that many organisms would cease to exist. A number of chemicals used by man may deplete the ozone layer, causing thinning and actual holes to appear, especially above the polar regions. These chemicals include the chlorofluorocarbons (CFCs) commonly used as propellants in aerosol dispensers and as coolants in refrigerators.
◄ CFCs, Stratosphere ►

PANCREAS

The pancreas is a glandular organ situated just below the stomach that produces both ducted and endocrine secretions. It secretes pancreatic juice into the duodenum via the pancreatic duct, and also secretes hormones into the blood.

Pancreatic juice consists of water, salts, including **hydrogencarbonate** ions, which neutralise the acidic contents of the stomach, and a number of digestive enzymes. These enzymes are pancreatic **amylase**, which digests starch into **maltose**; pancreatic **lipase**, which hydrolyses **fats** into monoglycerides, glycerol and **fatty acids**; nucleases, which break down **necleic acids** into their constituent **nucleotides**; and two proteases which digest **proteins** into polypeptides. The proteases are released as inactive precursors chymotrypsinogen and trypsinogen, in order to prevent the destruction of the secretory cells that produce them. Trypsinogen is activated to trypsin by a hormone called enterokinase, produced from the intestinal mucosa, and then trypsin activates chymotrypsinogen to give chymotrypsin. The release of pancreatic juice is under both hormonal and nervous control. Two hormones are involved secretin and cholecystokinin, which are both released by the intestinal mucosa, and nervous control is effected by impulses passing along the vagus nerve during gastric secretion.

The endocrine portion of the pancreas consists of small islands of cells known as the islets of Langerhans, which contain alpha- and beta-cells. The alpha-cells secrete the hormone **glucagon**, which raises **blood glucose** levels, while the beta-cells secrete **insulin**, which has the opposite effect.

Diabetes mellitus is a group of disorders resulting in a raised blood sugar level (hyperglycaemia) and the presence of sugar in the urine. It can be due to an inability to produce and secrete insulin.

◀ Blood glucose level, Polypeptide ▶

PARASITISM

Parasitism is a type of **interspecific association** where one **species**, the parasite, obtains an advantage, while the host species is harmed. This harm is due directly or indirectly to the fact that the parasite is feeding heterotrophically on its host's tissues, body fluids or gut contents.

The parasitic mode of life is a gradation between commensalism and predation, and a parasite need not live all its life in this condition. Some parasites, for instance, have free-living larval forms for dispersal (e.g. hookworm).

Parasites can be grouped as either ectoparasites, which live on the external surface or in the external tissues of the host, such as the scabies mite, or as endoparasites, which live within the host or its tissues, such as *Plasmodium* (the malarial parasite), liver fluke and tapeworms.

In order to be successful, a parasite must be able to obtain all its nutritional requirements from the host and to form a permanent attachment to the host, which will be attempting to dislodge it by both behavioural and physiological means. Many parasites have hooks and/or suckers for mechanical attachment, and devices to protect against the enzymes or immune system of the host. The parasite must have a greatly increased reproductive capacity to ensure that sufficient offspring are produced to spread to new hosts, and many parasites spend part of their life cycle in an intermediate host, which may act as a vector (e.g. *Plasmodium* makes use of *Anopheles* mosquitoes).

◀ Life cycles, Liver fluke, Malaria ▶

PARASYMPATHETIC NERVOUS SYSTEM

The parasympathetic nervous system is the part of the autonomic nervous system concerned with decelerating or suppressing physiological events. Effects of parasympathetic stimulation include decrease in ventilation rate, constriction of the pupils and decrease in cardiac output. Acetylcholine is the transmitter substance throughout the parasympathetic system.

◀ Autonomic nervous control, Sympathetic nervous system ▶

PARENCHYMA

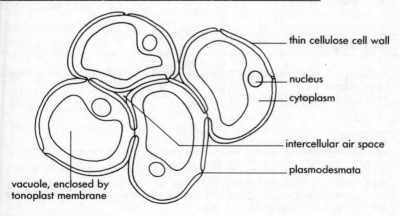

thin cellulose cell wall

nucleus

cytoplasm

intercellular air space

plasmodesmata

vacuole, enclosed by tonoplast membrane

Fig. P.1 Parenchyma cells

Parenchyma cells (Fig. P.1) are the basic packing cells of plant organs and make up ground tissue of the cortex and pith in stems and roots. They have thin **cellulose** cell walls and their turgidity helps to support the aerial parts of the plant. They remain living and can be modified to store **starch**, particularly in the wide root cortex, or to contain chloroplasts and thus become photosynthetic chlorenchyma in green stems.

◀ Root systems, Stem structure ▶

PARENTAL CARE

Parental care is a type of parental behaviour, elicited by the young offspring of the parent, to increase the chances of survival. The highest degree of parental care is shown by **birds** and **mammals**, who not only feed and protect their young but also instruct them in forms of behaviour. This increases the chances of survival by the young, but imposes a burden on the parents, in terms of time and energy. Animals that show parental care tend to produce far fewer offspring at a time and take longer to reach reproductive maturity than those not showing parental care. This is more likely to result in stable population numbers and such species are sometimes called 'K' population strategists, where K represents the **carrying capacity** of the environment for that species.

PASSIVE UPTAKE

Passive uptake means the uptake of molecules into cells without using energy. The molecules move along **diffusion** gradients, pressure gradients or gradients of electrical charge.

◀ Osmosis ▶

PATHOGENS

Pathogens are disease-causing organisms, commonly **bacteria**, viruses, **fungi** or **protozoa**.

◀ Disease transmission ▶

PENTOSE

A pentose is a five-carbon sugar. Examples include **ribose**, which is an aldose type (contains aldehyde group) and ribulose which is its ketose isomer (contains ketone group). Ribose and 2-deoxyribose are found in **nucleotides** and the nucleic acids, RNA and DNA.

◀ Monosaccharides ▶

PEP

◀ Phosphoenol pyruvate ▶

PEPSIN

Pepsin is a protein-splitting **enzyme** secreted into the gastric juice by the chief cells of the tubular glands in the stomach. It is secreted as an inactive precursor, pepsinogen, to avoid self-digestion of the secreting cells, and becomes active only when its active sites are exposed by the action of hydrochloric acid. The HCl is secreted into the gastric juice by the oxyntic cells of the gastric glands. The enzyme then hydrolyses the peptide bonds of ingested **proteins**, breaking them to shorter **polypeptide** fragments. Its optimum pH is about 1.5.

◀ Active site ▶

PEPTIDE LINKAGE

A peptide linkage is a covalent bond formed by condensation between the amine group of one amino acid and the acid carboxyl group of another amino acid. In this way **amino acids** can be linked to form long chains or polypeptides. Enzymes which hydrolyse peptide links are called peptidases.

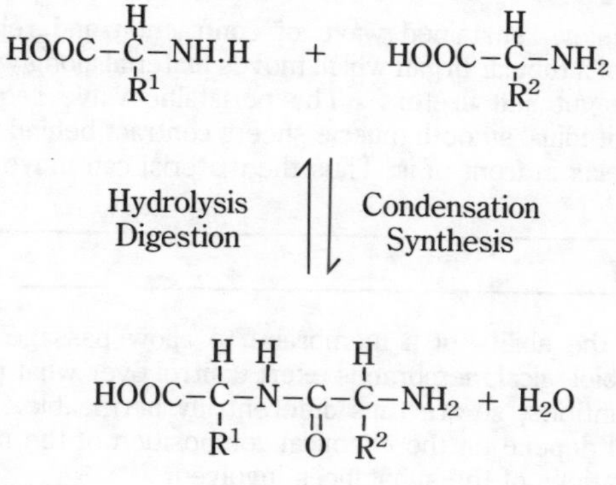

$$\text{HOOC}-\underset{R^1}{\overset{H}{\text{C}}}-\text{NH.H} \quad + \quad \text{HOOC}-\underset{R^2}{\overset{H}{\text{C}}}-\text{NH}_2$$

Hydrolysis   ⇅   Condensation
Digestion   Synthesis

$$\text{HOOC}-\underset{R^1}{\overset{H}{\text{C}}}-\underset{}{\overset{H}{\text{N}}}-\underset{O}{\overset{H}{\text{C}}}-\underset{R^2}{\overset{H}{\text{C}}}-\text{NH}_2 \quad + \quad \text{H}_2\text{O}$$

◀ Condensation reactions, Enzymes, Polypeptide ▶

PERENNATION

Perennation is the ability of a plant to survive unfavourable environmental conditions, particularly over winter, by producing a storage or perennating organ. During favourable growth periods, soluble photosynthetic products such as sugars are translocated to a specific part of the plant, which develops into the perennating organ. The sugars are usually converted to an insoluble storage polymer such as starch.

Perennating organs vary in size, shape and origin. For example: potatoes use stem tubers, which are swollen branch stems; crocuses use corms, which are swollen vertical main stems, irises use rhizomes, which are swollen horizontal main stems; and onions use bulbs, which consist of small disc-shaped stems and swollen leaf bases. A perennating organ always contains buds, however, which are dormant during the winter but become active and produce new plants on the return of suitable growing conditions. A single perennating organ can have several buds, so it can produce several new plants. This is vegetative reproduction and is a form of asexual reproduction since mitosis is the only cell division involved.

PERICARP

The pericarp is the fruit wall, and it develops from the ovary wall after the ovules have been fertilised. It may become hard and dry, as in hazel nuts, where it forms a protective covering, or become succulent, as in plums to attract animals to eat the fruit.

◄ Fruit development ►

PERISTALSIS

Peristalsis is a slow, sustained wave of contraction and relaxation in the smooth muscle of a tubular organ which moves material along within the organ (e.g. within the gut and ureters). The peristaltic wave requires that the circular and longitudinal smooth muscle sheets contract behind the material to be moved but relax in front of it. Thus the material can move forward.

PERMEABILITY

Permeability is the ability of a membrane to allow passage of substances across it. Most biological membranes exert control over what passes through and in what quantities, so are thus differentially permeable. The degree of permeability will depend on the chemical composition of the membrane, and on the concentrations of the substances involved.

◄ Active transport, Cell membranes, Diffusion, Osmosis ►

PETIOLE

A petiole is a leaf stalk in dicotyledonous plants. It attaches the leaf to the stem at the leaf base, and supports the lamina in a suitable position for photosynthesis. Histologically it is similar to the stem, though the vascular tissue of bundles tends to form an inverted C-shape rather than a ring to give better mechanical support to the lamina as it twists in the air currents. Collenchyma and sclerenchyma are also found in the petioles of many species. Monocotyledons usually have sheathing leaf bases, so do not require a leaf stalk.

◀ Dicotyledon, Lamina of leaf, Leaf structure, Monocotyledon ▶

PGA (phosphoglyceric acid)

◀ Glycerate 3-phosphate (GP) ▶

pH

This is a numerical scale indicating the acidity or alkalinity of a solution. The scale is a logarithmic measure of the concentration of hydrogen ions in a solution. It is a physical constant, that at 25°C in any aqueous solution the product of the concentrations of the hydrogen ions and the hydroxide ions is 10^{-14} gramme ions per litre. That is,

■ at 25°C $[H^+] \times [OH^-] = 10^{-14}$ g. ions. dm^{-3}
■ at neutrality H^+ concentration = OH^- concentration = 10^{-7} g. ions. dm^{-3}
■ in an acid solution H^+ concentration is raised to say $10^{-7+\times}$ g. ions. dm^{-3}
■ in an alkaline solution H^+ concentration is lowered to say $10^{-7-\times}$ g. ions. dm^{-3}

If these concentration are expressed as logarithms, it removes the need to use indices: $pH = -\log_{10}(H^+)$. Thus a neutral pH is 7, an acid pH is $7-\times$ and an alkaline pH is $7+\times$. The scale runs from 0 to 14.

The pH of a medium can be measured accurately using sophisticated pH meters or measured approximately using indicator dyes which alter colour according to H^+ concentration (e.g. litmus and universal indicator). The pH value has a marked effect on **enzyme action** so **buffers** are present in the **blood** and in **cytoplasm**. Most intracellular enzymes require a neutral pH, while digestive enzymes vary from **pepsin**, which requires pH 1.5, to pancreatic **lipase**, which requires pH 9.0. The pH of **soil** will determine to a large extent what plants can grow in it: few plants can tolerate very acidic soils, for example.

◀ Enzyme inhibition ▶

PHAEOPHYTA

Phaeophyta is phylum of the kingdom Protoctista commonly known as **brown algae**. They are photosynthetic but appear brown, because in addition to chlorophylls, their plastids contain brown pigments such as fucoxanthin. Examples include many seaweeds of the seashore, such as *Fucus*, *Ascophyllum* and *Laminaria*.

PHAGOCYTOSIS

Phagocytosis is an active process in which material is engulfed by amoebae, or by specially adapted cells called phagocytes or macrophages (from the Greek *phagos*, to eat). Phagocytosis is the means by which amoebae acquire their nutrients and it forms an important defence mechanism in animals, because phagocytes can engulf foreign material such as pathogenic bacteria. Fixed macrophages are attached in the body and cannot move around (e.g. the Von Kuppfer cells in the liver sinusoids, or the fixed macrophages lining the sinusoids of lymph nodes). These engulf bacteria and cellular debris (such as broken red cells) from the blood or lymph passing by. Other macrophages are mobile and can leave the blood and migrate by amoeboid action through the tissues (e.g. certain white blood cells). Phagocytes must recognise normal body cells and foreign or waste cells so that they do not engulf normal tissue. Cellular debris normally has a rough or sticky surface, which allows it to fuse with the phagocyte cell membrane, while the surfaces of pathogens may be coated with antibodies known as opsonins to make them more recognisable. Once the pathogen or debris is recognised, it is engulfed into a phagocytic vesicle. Lysosomes fuse with this and secrete hydrolytic lysozyme over the engulfed cell, which is thus digested. Some engulfed pathogens are presented to the B- and T-lymphocytes so that the immune response can be provoked.

◀ Amoeba, Amoeboid movement, Antibody, Immunity, Opsonins ▶

PHENOTYPE

The phenotype is the characteristics of an individual, usually resulting from the interaction between the organism's genotype and the environment in which development occurs. The same phenotype can be produced in organisms of two different genotypes (e.g. in pea plants, where tallness is imparted by allele T (dominant) and shortness by allele t (recessive), then the genotypes Tt and TT will both give tall plants). The phenotype is a physical expression of a genetic trait, but the expression may be modified by environmental influences.

◀ Dominant alleles, Gene expression, Mendelian inheritance, principles of, Recessive alleles ▶

PHENYLKETONURIA (PKU)

Phenylketonuria means phenyl ketone bodies appearing in the urine in abnormally excessive amounts. It is a symptom of a group of genetic diseases affecting the metabolism of the amino acids phenylalanine and tyrosine. The first recognised and most common of these diseases is *phenylpyruvica imbecilitus*, but the term phenylketonuria has become loosely synonymous with this and is often used to refer to this disease. In this disease an inherited

gene (point) mutation means that the baby cannot make the enzyme which converts dietary phenylalanine into the amino acid tyrosine. Toxic phenylalanine accumulates in the tissues and is metabolised in the liver to give phenylpyruvate, which impairs normal brain development. Such children characteristically have fair hair and blue eyes, because their tyrosine deficiency means that they cannot make adequate amounts of the pigment melanin, of which tyrosine is a precursor. The disease affects one in 10,000 babies and must be detected within a few days of birth by screening, using a simple blood or urine strip test (Phenistix). If the PKU baby is then fed on a phenylalanine-regulated diet throughout life, the disease can be avoided.
◀ Genetic counselling, Genetic screening ▶

PHEROMONES

Pheromones are chemical substances, secreted into the external environment in minute amounts, that produce behavioural changes in other animals of the same species. They play an important role in the production and maintenance of the social structure of many insects, such as bees and ants, and they act as attractants for the male to the female in the reproductive behaviour of moths. In mammals they are often produced by modified sebaceous glands in the skin, or they may be released in urine or sweat. For example, the musk deer of Tibet marks its territory with a secretion from abdominal glands which contains a pheromone that acts as a sexual attractant.

PHLOEM

Phloem is the plant vascular tissue concerned with the transport of soluble organic molecules such as sugars and amino acids.
◀ Sieve tube, Translocation, Vascular bundle ▶

PHOSPHATE

The phosphate ion, PO_4^-, is an important component of nucleotides and nucleic acids. The phosphate bond conserves chemical energy, which can later be utilised to do biological work. Such bonds are found in energy rich co-enzymes such as adenosine triphosphate (ATP) and creatine phosphate (in skeletal muscle). Phosphate is also found in bones and teeth as part of calcium hydroxyapatite, which hardens the tissue.
◀ Bone ▶

PHOSPHOENOL PYRUVATE (PEP)

PEP is a three-carbon intermediate compound of **glycolysis** that is converted to **pyruvate**, the reaction yielding enough free energy to phosphorylate a molecule of **adenosine diphosphate** (ADP) to **adenosine triphosphate** (ATP).

In **C_4 plants** such as maize and sugar cane, instead of **ribulose bisphosphate** being the only CO_2 acceptor, phosphoenol pyruvate is also used. CO_2 from the atmosphere is used to carboxylate PEP, using PEP carboxylase enzyme, yielding 4C malate. This moves into the bundle sheath cells of the leaf (by the malate shunt), where it is decarboxylated to pyruvate, the CO_2 moving into the chloroplasts to pass into the **Calvin cycle**. Pyruvate is phosphorylated back to PEP for reuse (Fig. P.2).

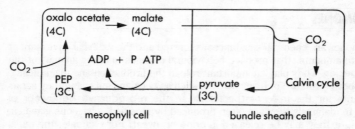

PEP = phosphoenol pyruvate
3C acceptor molecule

Fig. P.2 Outline of C_4 fixation using PEP

Ribulose biphosphate carboxylase can be inhibited by high oxygen tensions in the mesophyll, but PEP carboxylase is insensitive to oxygen tension, so this is a valuable method of CO_2 fixation in such conditions. The process is known as C_4 fixation or as the Hatch-Slack pathway.

◀ Photosynthesis ▶

PHOSPHOGLYCERIC ACID (PGA)

◀ Glycerate 3-phosphate (GP) ▶

PHOSPHOLIPIDS

Phospholipids (Fig. P.3) form major components of **cell membranes**. In phospholipids, two -OH groups of the glycerol are linked to **fatty acids** by ester/condensation reactions, while the third is linked to phosphoric acid. The phosphate group makes that part of the molecule polar and therefore soluble in water, while the long fatty acid chains are insoluble and hydrophobic.

◀ Fluid-mosaic model of cell-membrane structure ▶

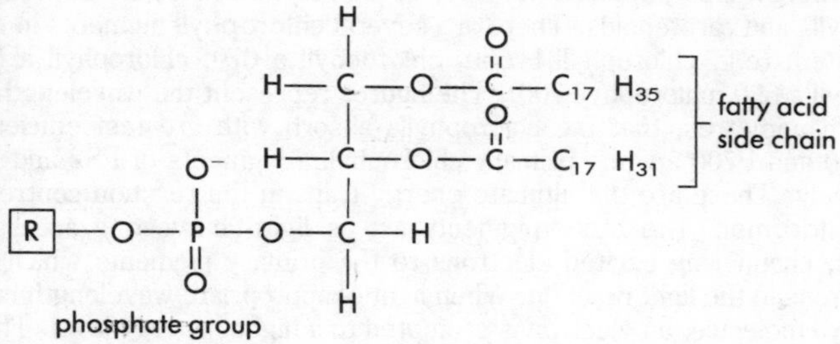

Fig. P.3 Structure of a phospholipid

PHOSPHORUS CYCLE

The phosphorus cycle involves absorption, utilisation and ultimate return of phosphate within the biosphere. Phosphate is absorbed from soil by plants in ionic form, and quickly becomes incorporated into a range of plant substances, including nucleic acids, nucleotides and proteins. These then pass through the food chain. Phosphate is excreted or returned to the environment by death and decay of the organisms, and it may also be released into the soil solution from phosphate-bearing rocks, but it is much less soluble than nitrate. It is now being increased in the aqueous parts of the phosphorus cycle by the activities of man, such as mining, sewage disposal, and the use of detergents and fertilisers, and it is frequently responsible for algal blooms.
◀ Food chains, Food webs, Nitrate pollution ▶

PHOSPHORYLASE ENZYMES

Phosphorylase enzymes add phosphate groups to biochemical substances. Examples include starch phosphorylase in plants and glycogen phosphorylase in animals, which result in the breakdown of starch or glycogen to glucose-1-phosphate for glycolysis. Glucokinase will phosphorylate glucose to glucose-6-phosphate, which isomerises to glucose-1-phosphate and undergoes glycolysis or starch/glycogen synthesis. The phosphorylation is supposed to 'capture' the sugar and prevent it from leaving the cell, and also make it more reactive.

PHOTOACTIVATION OF CHLOROPHYLL

Chlorophyll is photoactivated during the light stages of photosynthesis in order to allow the harnessing of light energy in photosystem I (PSI) and photosystem II (PSII). The harnessed energy will be used to synthesise adenosine triphosphate (ATP) and NADPH $+H^+$, both of which will be used in the dark reaction to fix CO_2 into carbohydrates.

Light energy absorption is a property of photosynthetic pigments, such as chlorophylls and carotenoids. There are several **chlorophyll** pigments in each photosystem (e.g. chlorophyll b 650, chlorophyll a 670, chlorophyll a 680, chlorophyll a 690, chlorophyll 700). The figures represent the wavelengths of light, in nanometres, that the chlorophylls absorb with greatest efficiency. The P690 and P700 are the primary chlorophyll a pigments of PS2 and PS1 respectively. These are the ultimate energy traps in the reaction centres of the **quantasomes**. The other pigments act as light- harvesting accessory pigments, channelling excited electrons to the primary pigments which use the electrons in the light reaction. When light of appropriate wavelength hits a chlorophyll molecule, an electron is promoted to a higher energy level. These electrons are shunted to the primary pigments and passed to the appropriate acceptors in the light reactions.

◀ Photolysis, Photophosphorylation ▶

PHOTOLYSIS

Light energy trapped in the **photoactivation of chlorophyll** is used to split water to H^+ and OH^-. The H^+ (protons) combine with the excited electrons from photosystem I, forming hydrogen (2H), which is then coupled on to $NADP^+$, yielding $NADPH + H^+$. This can be used in the dark reaction. The chlorophyll a (P690) of photosystem II is in an unstable state since it has lost an electron, so the OH^- donates its electron to chlorophyll, restoring stability and allowing oxygen to be evolved.

$$2OH^- \rightarrow 2e^- \text{ (to chlorophyll)} + H_2O + \tfrac{1}{2}O_2$$

◀ Photophosphorylation, Photosynthesis ▶

PHOTOPERIODISM

Photoperiodism is an organism's response to the relative times of exposure to periods of light and dark. Flowering is a response that in many plants depends upon **day length**, and it was first investigated by Garner and Allard in 1920, who coined the term 'photoperiodism'. They identified three types of plants in relation to their response to daylength:

- Short-day plants (SDP), such as cocklebur, chrysanthemum, soya bean, strawberry and tobacco, in which flowering is induced by dark periods in excess of 8½ hours for cocklebur or 10 hours for tobacco. (This is equivalent to short days of less than 15½ hours for cocklebur, 13 hours for tobacco).
- Long-day plants (LDP), such as henbane, snapdragon, cabbage, spring wheat and barley, in which flowering is induced by dark periods shorter than a critical length, which is 13 hours for henbane. (This is equivalent to long days of more than 11 hours).
- Day-neutral plants, such as tomato, cucumber, garden pea, maize and cotton, in which flowering is unaffected by the photoperiod.

The mechanisms involved in photoperiodic control of flowering are incompletely understood. They involve phytochromes in the leaves, which in some way perceive the stimulus, and a proposed **hormone** 'florigen', which transmits the stimulus from the leaves to the buds, switching them to flower formation rather than vegetative growth or dormancy. Florigen has not yet been identified or isolated.

Day length also influences other aspects of plant development. For example, long days promote **bulb** formation in onions and general vegetative growth, short days promote leaf **abscission** and dormancy in trees and other perennials, including the development of perennating organs such as corms, **bulbs** and tubers.

Photoperiodism plays a role in the geographical distribution of plants due to the different day lengths which occur at different latitudes. From the equator to the poles the days become progressively longer in summer and shorter in winter. In equatorial regions, the day length is 12 hours throughout the year, so plants which require less that 12 hours of darkness to induce flowering (LDPs) cannot reproduce sexually in equatorial zones. Similarly SDPs cannot reproduce sexually in far northern or southern latitudes because short nights prevail through the warm growing seasons.

Photoperiodism is also implicated in a variety of seasonal phenomena and **biorhythms** in animals. The mechanisms are physiological and probably involve both nervous and endocrine factors (e.g. photoperiod influences preparation for **hibernation** in mammals such as bears and hedgehogs, **migration** in birds, egg-laying in birds, diapause and pupation in insects, moulting in birds and mammals, and maturation in fish eggs).
◄ Phytochrome ►

PHOTOPHOSPHORYLATION

Photophosphorylation occurs in **photosynthesis** and is the phosphorylation of **adenosine diphosphate** (ADP) to **adenosine triphosphate** (ATP) using energy obtained from sunlight through the photosystems, rather than from the oxidation of energy rich substrates as in **oxidative phosphorylation**. It occurs during the light stage of photosynthesis and can be split into cyclic and non-cyclic photophosphorylation.

$$\text{Chlorophyll a (reduced)} \xrightarrow[\text{photoactivation}]{\text{light energy}} \text{Chlorophyll a}^+ \text{ (oxidised)} + \text{excited e}^-$$

In the cyclic mechanism the high energy-electrons from photoactivation of photosystem 1 (PS1 or P700) are passed to a substance X, which is a strong electron acceptor, and from this to a series of acceptor molecules, including, in order, plastoquinone, **cytochromes** and plastocyanin. As the electrons fall down the energy gradient, released energy is conserved in ATP as ADP + P forms ATP. The electron eventually returns to P700 to restore its neutrality (PS1).

In the non-cyclic mechanism (Fig. P.4a)) excited electrons are obtained from the photoactivation of both photosystem II (P690 or PS2) and P700

(PS1) and they reduce electron acceptors Y and X respectively. P700 is restored to neutrality by the electrons descending through a series of acceptors while coupling the energy yield to ATP production as in the cyclic process (Fig. P.4b)). P690 is neutralised by the electron yield from the **photolysis of water.** Electrons from X combine with protons from the photolysis of water and produce hydrogen forming NADPH $+H^+$ from $NADP^+$.

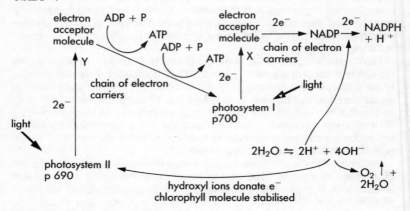

Fig. P.4a) Cyclic photophosphorylation

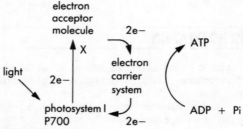

Fig. P.4b) Non-cyclic photophosphorylation

◀ Photoactivation of chlorophyll ▶

PHOTOSYNTHESIS

In this process light energy is trapped by photosynthetic **pigments** and used to manufacture **carbohydrate** by the **fixation** of CO_2, according to the overall reaction,

$$CO_2 + H_2O \xrightarrow[\text{chlorophyll}]{\text{sunlight}} C_n(H_2O)_n + O_2 \uparrow$$

Photosynthesis occurs in two stages, known as the light stage and the dark stage. The light stage produces **adenosine triphosphate** (ATP) and reduced **NADP** as its end products, in the reactions known as **photoactivation of chlorophyll, photolysis** and **photophosphorylation**. These steps require the promotion of electrons to high energy levels by the action of sunlight. The second stage, or dark reaction, though not directly dependent upon light, requires the ATP and reduced NADP produced by the light reaction. In this stage the CO_2 is reduced to carbohydrate. There are two pathways of CO_2 fixation, the **Calvin cycle** and the Hatch-Slack pathway, plants showing this last pathway are called C_4 **plants** (e.g. sugar cane).

Plants which use the only Calvin pathway are called C_3 plants, since the first stable compound of CO_2 fixation is the three-carbon compound glyceraldehyde 3-phosphate (GALP). Ribulose biphosphate (RuBP), a 5C compound accepts CO_2 to form an unstable 6C compound that immediately splits to give two molecules of glycerate 3-phosphate (GP), a 3C compound. This is at once reduced, using ATP and NADPH $+H^+$ from the light reaction to give GALP, a 3C sugar. The RuBP is regenerated by a series of reactions involving some of the synthesised GALP and using ATP from the light reaction. The remaining GALP is used to synthesise a number of hexose phosphate sugars, which also requires the use of ATP. The Hatch-Slack cycle uses phosphoenol pyruvate (**PEP**) as CO_2 acceptor and produces a 4C compound, malate. When this is decarboxylated it yields CO_2 that can enter the Calvin cycle in the bundle sheath cells of the C_4 plants (Fig. P.5).

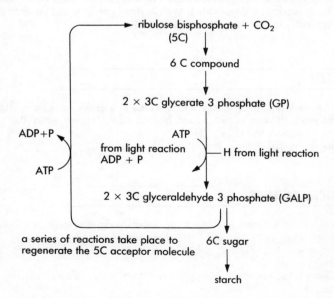

Fig. P.5 Events in the Calvin cycle of photosynthesis

PHOTOTROPISM

Stems and coleoptiles show positive phototropism in that they grow towards undirectional light or a light source of higher intensity. Roots show negative phototropism since they grow away from light. The curvature is caused by greater cell elongation in the zone of elongation behind the meristem, with the greatest elongation in the stem occurring on the side away from light. This causes the tip to grow towards the light. The stimulus is perceived by the tip, possibly by a mechanism involving beta-carotene or riboflavin, but this is uncertain. Auxin, produced in the tip diffuses down the elongation zone, but appears to be inhibited on the light side of the stem. The greater auxin concentration on the dark side stimulates greater cell elongation.

◀ Tropisms ▶

PHYLOGENETIC APPROACH TO TAXONOMY

A phylogenetic approach to a natural classification system of organisms reflects the evolutionary relationships between them. It is assumed that all organisms arose from a common ancestor or group of ancestors and that the different types of organism represent divergence from this common 'trunk'. Thus they can be grouped using natural characters and information on natural affinities to produce a classification system that is orderly and predictive.

◀ Kingdoms, Taxonomy ▶

PHYLUM

A phylum is a taxon, or group, found within a scientific ranking system of classification. Phylum is the second highest rank, coming under the taxon known as kingdom and above 'class'.

◀ Kingdoms, Taxonomy ▶

PHYSICAL FACTORS

Physical factors influence the types and distributions of organisms within the biosphere. They can be grouped into three categories.

- Physiographic factors which relate to the location and area topography.
- Climatic factors which include temperature, wind, salinity, humidity and rainfall.
- Edaphic factors which refer to the physical and chemical properties of the soil.

PHYTOCHROME

Phytochrome is a pale-blue plant pigment which is important in plant growth and development. It exists in two interconvertible forms. P_R has a maximum light absorption peak in the red end at 660 nm, whereas P_{FR} absorbs maximally in the far red at 730 nm. When P_R is exposed to light at 660 nm, it is converted to P_{FR}. When P_{FR} is exposed to light at 730 nm, it is converted to P_R, and it slowly decays to P_R in the absence of light.

Thus during daylight the plant accumulates P_{FR} due to the fact that daylight contains more red light. P_{FR} is believed to be enzymatically active and influences a number of light-related processes, including photoperiodism, leaf lamina unfolding and seed germination. During the night the P_{FR} slowly converts back to P_R, which is then ready to respond to the daylight again.
◀ Lamina of leaf ▶

PHYTOHORMONES

Phytohormones (plant hormones) are internally produced organic substances that are biologically effective at very low concentrations and play an important role in the co-ordination of plant growth and development. They include auxins, gibberellins, cytokinins, abscisic acid and ethene (ethylene).

Auxin has been most extensively studied. It is indole-3-acetic acid and promotes growth by stimulating cell elongation and cell differentiation.

Gibberellins are involved in stem elongation, abscisic acid in leaf fall and dormancy, cytokinins in differentiation, and ethene in fruit ripening.
◀ Gibberellin, Tropisms ▶

PHYTOPLANKTON

Phytoplankton consists of small plants that float passively or move slowly in the surface layers of natural waters, both fresh water and marine. It is largely photosynthetic and consists of unicellular algae of which diatoms are a major constituent. Phytoplankton is of ecological importance as the main primary producer in aquatic habitats.
◀ Plankton ▶

PIGMENTS

Pigments are coloured substances which serve a variety of purposes in all kinds of organism. Cytochromes and haemochromes are porphyrin derivatives which contain iron or copper. The cytochromes are ubiquitous in all living cells and are associated with electron transport. Haemochromes include haemoglobin, the red pigment of vertebrate blood, green chlorocruorin in polychaetes and blue haemocyanin in molluscs. All these act as oxygen carriers in the body.

Pigments found as waste products include bilirubin and biliverdin, which are derived from the breakdown of haemoglobin and are excreted from the body in the bile. Chlorophylls are porphyrin-derivatives which contain magnesium and are the green photosynthetic pigments of plants. Other photosynthetic pigments are the carotenoids, such as beta-carotene, and xanthophylls, which act as accessory pigments in some plants. Carotene is also found in animals as provitamin A.

Melanins are black-yellow pigments synthesised from the amino acid tyrosine, which are found behind the **retina** and in the **skin** for example. These pigments absorb light and confer protection from excessive **ultra-violet light** irradiation. They also aid some species (e.g. frogs) in camouflage.

◀ Chlorophylls, Electron transfer, ET systems, Vitamins ▶

PINOCYTOSIS

Pinocytosis is an active process whereby small amounts of liquid are taken into the cell by invagination of the plasma membrane to form a pinocytic **vesicle**. In this way small amounts of extracellular fluid together with any small suspended particles, can be incorporated into the cell. Pinocytosis is particularly associated with amoebae and with amoeboid cells such as macrophages, and it is one of the methods by which the early mammalian embryo absorbs nutrients from the **uterus** before the **placenta** forms. The process can also occur in plant cells.

◀ Amoeba, Amoeboid movement ▶

PITUITARY GLAND

The pituitary gland is an important endocrine gland, situated on the ventral side of the midbrain. It is attached to the **hypothalamus** by a stalk known as the infundibulum, though which the larger anterior lobe receives an excellent **blood** supply, and the posterior lobe receives nerve fibres. The adenohypophysis, or anterior lobe, secretes seven hormones when stimulated by chemical releasing factors received through the blood vessels from the hypothalamus. These are:

■ **Growth hormone (GH)**, which controls general body growth.
■ **Prolactin**, which stimulates milk production by the mammary glands.
■ **Thyroid stimulating hormone (TSH)**, which controls the growth and secretions of the **thyroid gland**.
■ **Follicle stimulating hormone (FSH)**, which controls the development of Graafian follicles and eggs in the **ovary** and spermatogenesis in the testis.
■ **Luteinising hormone (LH)**, which controls the development of the corpus luteum in the ovary after **ovulation** and the secretion of **progesterone**.
■ Adrenocorticotropic hormone (ACTH), which controls the growth and secretions of the adrenal cortex.

- Melanocyte stimulating hormone (MSH), which controls skin pigmentation and melanin synthesis.

With the exception of GH, prolactin and MSH, all these hormones are known as tropic hormones, since they stimulate the growth and activity of other **endocrine glands**. It is because of this that the pituitary is sometimes called a 'master gland'.

The neurohypophysis, or posterior lobe, does not consist of endocrine cells but of axon nerve endings from neurones that have their cell bodies in the hypothalamus. These cell bodies produce two hormones, which are transported down the axons to the axon endings by carrier proteins. When the hypothalamus receives suitable stimulation, it sends nerve impulses down the axons which trigger the release of the hormones to blood capillaries in the posterior lobe. This process is called neurosecretion, and the two hormones involved are oxytocin and ADH.

- **Oxytocin** stimulates contraction of **smooth muscle** cells in the **uterus** during **birth**, and contraction of smooth muscle cells around the milk reservoirs of the mammary glands during suckling.
- **ADH** (anti-diuretic hormone) increases the permeability of the **nephron** collecting ducts to water so that water may be reabsorbed from **urine** back to the blood.

◀ Adrenal glands, Menstrual cycle, Neurone ▶

PKU

◀ Phenylketonuria ▶

PLACENTA

The placenta develops from the **fetal membranes**, the chorion and the allantois, and becomes intimately attached to the endometrium of the mother's **uterus**. Two umbilical arteries connect the fetus to the placenta via the umbilical cord and form a profuse network of **capillaries** in the placenta in intimate contact with the uterine capillaries. Although maternal and fetal blood do not mix exchange occurs by a variety of active and passive methods, the fetal blood acquiring **oxygen** and **nutrients**, and giving up **carbon dioxide** and **urea**. The blood is then returned to the fetus by one umbilical vein, which shunts it directly to the fetal liver.

The placenta also manufactures fetal **red blood cells** and several hormones. Fetal **haemoglobin** has a slightly higher oxygen-loading capacity than maternal haemoglobin so that it can take oxygen from the maternal red cells. The main hormones secreted are chorionic gonadotrophin, oestrogen, and **progesterone**.

- Chorionic gonadotrophin (CG) is secreted for the first ten weeks or so after conception. It maintains the corpus luteum, which is secreting progesterone, and hence maintains the pregnancy. When CG concentration falls the corpus luteum regresses, but by then the placenta can itself produce oestrogen and progesterone.

- Oestrogen continues to maintain the pregnancy by stimulating further uterine development, and it also causes the mammary glands of the mother to develop for milk production.
- Progesterone causes further uterine development, but also suppresses contractions of the uterine smooth muscle so that spontaneous abortion does not occur. Just before birth progesterone secretion stops and this allows contractions to begin.

After delivery of the baby the placenta is ejected as the 'afterbirth'.
◀ Oestrogens, Rhesus blood groups ▶

PLANARIA

Planaria is a genus of the class Turbellaria of the phylum Platyhelminthes. They are free-living flatworms found in fresh water, and they have a ciliated body surface, a distinct head-end, bearing two simple eyes on the upper surface, and a single gut opening on the ventral surface (Fig. P.6).

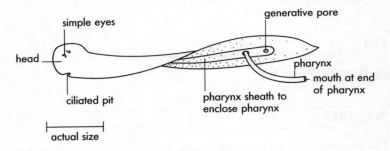

Fig. P.6 Planarian structure

PLANKTON

Plankton consists of tiny animals and plants (zooplankton and phytoplankton respectively), which have a relative density similar to that of the fresh water or sea water in which they are found, so they tend to float near the surface. The phytoplankton photosynthesises and is of vital importance to aquatic food webs, being the major primary producer. They are fed upon by zooplankton and by other herbivores, which are predated upon in turn. Levels of plankton in water are cyclical, increasing in the warmer seasons, as water temperature rises and day length increases, and falling in cooler seasons, as water temperature falls and day length shortens. Levels may fall due to grazing by developing animals such as fish during their growing season.
◀ Chains, food, Food webs ▶

PLANTAE

Plantae is one of the five **kingdoms** in the natural classification of organisms. They are multicellular, eukaryotic and photosynthetic. Their cell walls contain cellulose.

PLANT GROWTH SUBSTANCES, PLANT HORMONES

◄ Phytohormones ►

PLASMA

Plasma is a straw-coloured fluid which makes up around 55 per cent of the total **blood** volume. It is about 95 per cent water and contains various dissolved solutes:

- Inorganic ions, such as Na^+ and Cl^-, which contribute to the osmolarity of the blood, Ca^{2+}, which is required as a clotting factor, and H^+ and HCO_3^-, which are excretory products but also affect blood pH.
- Plasma **proteins**, such as albumin which is responsible for much of the osmolarity and viscosity of the blood, globulins, which include antibodies, and fibrinogen for **blood clotting**.
- Transported organic nutrients, such as glucose and amino acids.
- Transported waste products, such as **urea** from **deamination**, **uric acid** and creatinine, and dissolved CO_2 from respiration.
- Hormones and **vitamins**.

Plasma that has clotted, and is thus minus the clotting factors, is known as serum. Plasma that leaves the capillaries to bathe the cells, and is thus minus the proteins, is known as **tissue fluid**.

◄ Antibody, Hormone ►

PLASMIDS

Plasmids are small circular molecules of DNA found in bacteria and yeasts, replicating independently as the cell replicates. They contain various vital genes, such as those conferring resistance to antibiotics, and are of great importance as **vectors** in **recombinant DNA** technology.

◄ Genetic engineering ►

PLASMODESMATA

Plasmodesmata are very fine threads of **cytoplasm** which pass through pores in the cell walls of adjacent plant cells, thus joining their cytoplasm together. This continuous cytoplasmic system is called the symplast system and is involved in the transport of water and dissolved solutes across the plant tissues, avoiding the need to cross cell walls.

◀ Symplastic pathway ▶

PLASMOLYSIS

Plasmolysis is the loss of contact between the cell wall and the protoplast in plant cells. The cell wall is completely permeable to both water and solutes and so does not act as an osmotic barrier. However, the cytoplasm and tonoplast around the **vacuole** are both partially permeable and act as an osmotic unit. If the cell is placed in a solution of more negative **water potential** than the cell sap, then water will leave the cell sap and the cell contents will shrink away from the wall. The process can be reversed if the cells are placed in a solution of less negative water potential than the cell sap, in which case water moves into the cell sap. Plasmolysis of cells in nature will result in wilting of the plant, which may be a valuable response to curtail water loss by transpiration.

◀ Incipient plasmolysis, Turgor, Turgidity ▶

PLASTIDS

Plastids are organelles characteristic of plant cells. They have a double limiting membrane or **envelope** and a complicated internal pattern of membranes. They are generally classed according to the types of pigment they contain, and thus their colour. Leucoplasts contain no **pigments**, so are colourless. Their main function is to store **starch**, oils and protein granules, particularly in the cells of plant storage organs.

Chromoplasts store the fat soluble pigments carotenoids and are thus yellowy-orange. They have a diverse range of shapes and are found in cells colouring flowers, ripe fruits and senescent (ageing) leaves.

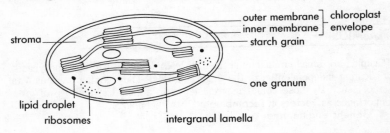

Fig. P.7 Ultra-structure of a chloroplast

Chloroplasts (Fig. P.7) contain the green **chlorophyll** pigments for **photosynthesis**, as well as accessory pigments such as carotenoids. The chloroplast has many membranes or lamellae, which form intergranal lamellae where they run through the stroma, and grana lamellae where they are

stacked like coins, each disc like 'coin' being known as a thylakoid. The lamellae contain the pigments housed in small bodies called quantosomes.
◄ Organelle ►

PLATYHELMINTHES

Platyhelminthes is a phylum of the animal kingdom, being the flatworms. They are flat animals, without metameric segmentation, have a mouth (except cestodes) but no anus, and are usually hermaphrodite with a complex reproductive system. There are three classes:

- Class **Turbellaria** – free-living planarian worms.
- Class **Trematoda** – endoparasites with a non-ciliated outer surface and one or more suckers (e.g. *Fasciola hepatica*, the liver fluke).
- Class **Cestoda** – endoparasites with flat, elongated bodies, usually divided into sections called proglottids, each of which is a sexually reproducing unit. They have a head or scolex bearing hooks and suckers for attachment to the host gut wall (e.g. *Taenia* species – tapeworms of sheep and cattle and other vertebrates).

POINT MUTATION

◄ Gene (point) mutation ►

POLLINATION

Pollination is the transfer of pollen grains from the anthers to the stigmas so that fertilisation can occur. Self-pollination occurs if the pollen falls on to stigmas of the same plant, and this results in in-breeding. Cross-pollination is the transfer of pollen to the stigmas of a different plant of the same species, and it results in out-breeding, which is genetically advantageous. Cross-pollination is usually achieved by the use of wind or by insect vectors. A plant that is insect-pollinated (entomophilous) generally develops brightly coloured flowers which are often scented, and secretes nectar, a sweet sugary solution. These features attract insects such as bees, which transfer pollen on their hairy bodies from flower to flower. In some flowers, humming birds are used as vectors for pollen. A plant that is wind-pollinated (anemophilous) has reduced petals, which are green and not attractive to insects. Stamens and stigmas are generally exposed and hanging (pendulous), and are thus easily able to release pollen into the air currents or to receive it. The stigmas are also feathery, to increase surface area for pollen capture. Large quantities of minute 'dusty' pollen grains are produced in order to increase the chances of cross-pollination, so the process is a wasteful one.
◄ Anemophilous flowers, Bee, Entomophilous flowers, Floral morphology, Vector ►

POLLUTION

Pollution occurs when the environment is contaminated, either with an excess of natural substances or with even small amounts of toxic, non-biodegradable material. It results in biological imbalance, as natural cycles and relationships are disrupted. There are many types of pollution. In thermal pollution hot water is discharged into river systems from power stations. The increased temperature of the water reduces the amount of dissolved **oxygen**, causing death to many organisms. Radiation pollution is usually due to accidental leakage from nuclear power stations, or due to increase in the amounts of **ultra-violet light** reaching the Earth's surface because of ozone depletion. Chemical pollutants include **CFCs** from fridges and aerosol cans, which are depleting the **ozone layer**; nitrogenous fertilisers, which run off the land into water systems, causing **eutrophication** of lakes; oil spillages which disrupt the **ecosystem**, killing many species; **heavy metals**, such as mercury and lead, which accumulate through the **food chains** and cause harm to **carnivores**; CO_2 from the excessive burning of fossil fuels, which causes an increase in atmospheric temperature via the **greenhouse effect**; SO_2 from industrial processes, which can dissolve in the rain and fall as **acid rain**.
◄ Nitrate pollution, Radiation as pollutant, Stratosphere, Sulphur dioxide ►

POLYCHAETE

The polychaetes are a class of the phylum **Annelida**. They are metamerically segmented marine worms, with a distinct head and numerous chaetae borne on parapodia (e.g. **Nereis**, ragworm, *Arenicola*, lugworm).

POLYGENES, POLYGENIC INHERITANCE

Polygenes are multiple genes (three or more) which exert small cumulative effects to control characters showing **continuous variation**, such as height in humans. Polygenic inheritance is the inheritance of characters whose expression is controlled by several genes, each with slight individual effects upon the **phenotype**. A feature of polygenic inheritance is the effect that environment plays in **gene expression**. An individual possessing many 'tall' genes may not reach their full height potential if **diet** has not been adequate.

POLYMER

A polymer is a long chain molecule produced by chemically linking together individual units known as monomers, in a process called polymerisation. The monomers are usually joined by **condensation reactions**. Examples of polymers include **starch** and **glycogen**, which are polymers of **glucose** and used as storage compounds, **cellulose**, which is a structural polymer of glucose in plant cell walls, polypeptides, which are polymers of **amino acids**, and **nucleic acids** which are polymers of **nucleotides**.

◀ Carbohydrate, Fat, Polypeptide, Proteins ▶

POLYMERASE ENZYMES

Polymerase enzymes catalyse the linking together of monomers into polymers. For example, peptide synthetase catalyses the formation of peptide links during **polypeptide** synthesis in the ribosomes, RNA polymerase catalyses the **transcription** of the **genetic code** of DNA on to RNA, DNA polymerase catalyses the replication of DNA into 'daughter DNA'.

◀ Peptide linkage, Protein synthesis, Ribosome ▶

POLYMORPH BLOOD CELLS

Polymorph white blood cells are produced by the red bone marrow and characterised by having several lobes in their nuclei. They have cytoplasmic granules so are also known as granulocytes.

POLYMORPHISM

Polymorphism is the occurrence of several distinct phenotypes of a **species** within a **population** at the same time, in such frequencies that the presence of the rarest form cannot be explained by **mutation** alone. Examples include the peppered moth, *Biston betularia*, with its normal light form and dark melanic form, and the land snail, *Cepaea nemoralis*, which shows variation in the colours and banding patterns of its shell, related to camouflage needs.

◀ Banding in Cepaea nemoralis, Industrial melanism ▶

POLYOESTROUS

Polyoestrous means having more than one oestrous cycle in a breeding season. Humans are continually polyoestrous, menstrual cycles follow each other without pause throughout reproductive life, unless suppressed by **pregnancy**. Other **mammals** are seasonally polyoestrous, exhibiting several successive oestrous cycles at a particular time of year – the breeding season (e.g. cows, deer).

◀ Menstrual cycle, Monoestrous species ▶

POLYPEPTIDE

A polypeptide is a unit of a protein that is synthesised according to the DNA genetic code that is transcribed on to mRNA. It consists of a sequence of amino acids, determined by the codon sequence of a DNA cistron, and joined together by peptide bonds. Protamines contain twenty to thirty amino acids in their polypeptides, albumin about 550. The amino acid sequence is the primary structure of the protein.

A polypeptide is folded into a betapleated sheet or into an alpha-helix, to give the secondary structure of the protein, characteristic of fibrous proteins. Alternatively, the polypeptides may fold further into a globular shape, giving the tertiary structure of the protein, characteristic of globular proteins like enzymes.

◄ Globular proteins, Protein synthesis ►

POLYPETALOUS

In a polypetalous flower the petals remain separated from each other, rather than fusing to form a corolla tube (e.g. buttercup).

◄ Floral morphology, Sympetalous ►

POLYPLOIDY

Polyploidy is a state in which the organism has more than the normal diploid number of chromosomes. In polysomy or aneupolyploidy (not true polyploidy) there may be only one extra chromosome, but it is always harmful. For example, in Down's syndrome there is an extra chromosome, number 21, in the human baby (trisomy 21), while in Klinefelter's syndrome there is an extra X-chromosome in the male (XXY). These conditions are due to non-disjunction in anaphase of meiosis, when the pairs of chromosomes fail to segregate accurately to the gametes.

Eupolyploidy (true polyploidy) involves an increase in the total number of sets of chromosomes. It is very common in plants and has been of great evolutionary value. There are two types: autopolyploidy and allopolyploidy.

Autopolyploidy (self-polyploidy) is where the chromosome number doubles because chromosomes fail to segregate to the poles, so the nuclear membrane reforms around a double lot of chromosomes (known as a restitution nucleus). If this occurs during mitosis in the plant meristem, then the tetraploid (4n) cell can still undergo mitosis and will produce a sector of the plant that is 4n instead of 2n (known as a chimaera). If this sector of the plant reproduces vegetatively, the offspring will be 4n. Any gametes they produce would be 2n and if these were to fuse with normal haploid (n) gametes, triploid (3n) plants could be produced. As the degree of ploidy rises, the plants tend to become sterile, since meiosis is difficult to achieve due to the mechanics of synapsis requiring 3, 4, 5, 6, etc. groupings of homologous chromosomes to be made.

Thus the plants rely more and more on vegetative propagation (e.g. *Ranunculus ficaria*, celandine, $2n = 16$, $4n = 32$, $5n = 40$, $6n = 48$).

Allopolyploidy (cross-polyploidy) involves hybridisation between two species. Normally interspecific hybrids, even if they grow, are sterile, since the chromosomes cannot pair in meiosis. If, however, a restitution nucleus forms, as in autopolyploidy, the F_1 hybrid may become fertile and will be a new species, separated by breeding barriers from the original species. For example, a new species of rice grass, known as *Spartina townsendii*, arose in Southampton Water in 1870, due to hybridisation between an introduced American species, *Spartina alterniflora*, and the native British species, *Spartina stricta*:

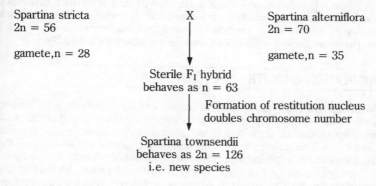

Spartina stricta
$2n = 56$
X
Spartina alterniflora
$2n = 70$

gamete, $n = 28$
gamete, $n = 35$

Sterile F_1 hybrid
behaves as $n = 63$

Formation of restitution nucleus
doubles chromosome number

Spartina townsendii
behaves as $2n = 126$
i.e. new species

Spartina townsendii possesses hybrid vigour and has rapidly replaced *Spartina stricta* as the main coloniser of coastal mudflats in Britain.

Allopolyploidy has been a very frequent and important mechanism in angiosperm evolution, and it is also exploited by plant breeders.
◄ Hybrids, Hybridisation, Out-breeding, Variation ►

POLYSACCHARIDES

A polysaccharide is a polymer of monosaccharides joined by condensation links.
◄ Cellulose, Glycogen, Starch ►

POPULATION

A group of individuals belonging to the same species in a given area at a given time is described as a population. Gene flow occurs freely between all members of the population, so they share the same gene pool.
◄ Communities, Population genetics, Population growth ►

POPULATION GENETICS

In genetics the **population** can be considered as a large group of individuals sharing a common gene pool. The sample of this gene pool that is passed on from one generation to the next can be considered as the unit of inheritance. It is important to be able to estimate **gene** and **phenotype** frequencies in order to study the genetic composition of populations, and to find out how the sample of genes is inherited. In fact, inheritance at the population level seems to occur through the simple Mendelian processes of segregation and random combination of pairs of **alleles**. This can therefore easily be predicted, using a basic law of population genetics, the Hardy-Weinberg law. When genotypes are undisturbed by mutations or **selection**, and can make equal contributions to their progeny, the law predicts constant gene frequencies.

◄ Hardy-Weinberg equilibrium, Mendelian inheritance, Mutation ►

POPULATION GROWTH

Population growth is an increase in numbers in a **population**. If no **limiting factors** are present, a population increases in numbers exponentially with time, but unless the environment has been disrupted in some way, external factors will limit this growth. The **carrying capacity** (symbol K) of the environment for a particular species, is the maximum density of population that the environment can support over a sustained period, without lasting damage to the environment itself. Many species can regulate their birth rate in order to maintain the optimum population density. Since this equals the carrying capacity, they are termed K-species. The usual population growth curve is the S-shaped (Fig. P.8) or logistic curve, which reflects the changing ratios between birth and death. During the acceleration stage, the birth rate

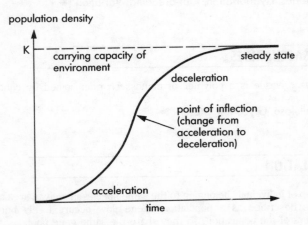

Fig. P.8 S-shaped population growth curve

greatly exceeds the death rate since conditions in the environment are optimum for population growth. During the deceleration stage the birth rate is lower than the death rate, either because the birth rate is falling or the death rate is rising, or both. Certain environmental factors must now be operating on the population to limit it. These factors are referred to as 'density-dependent factors', such as available space, available food and the build-up of waste products. As the population nears the carrying capacity, the birth and death rates should become steady and equal, resulting in a steady state population or **dynamic equilibrium**. Such a population may suddenly crash to a much lower level if a 'density-independent' factor operates, such as an adverse change in the weather, the introduction of a virulent pathogen or human interference (ploughing, pollution, land drainage, etc.).

PORIFERA

◄ Sponges ►

POST-NATAL GROWTH

Post-natal growth of a mammal occurs after it has been born. Such growth is characteristically allometric – that is, different organs grow at different rates to the rest of the body. This means that as the organism increases in size, the proportions of the body parts may change in relation to each other. For example, in human babies the head is large in proportion to the rest of the body while the genitalia are small. After puberty the genitalia are much larger in proportion while the head is smaller in proportion (but not in actual size). Growth in mammals is limited to a particular size determined genetically, and is regulated by growth hormones.
◄ Growth hormone, Pituitary gland, Thyroid gland ►

POTASSIUM

Potassium is an element of atomic weight 39 whose ions (K^+) help to maintain the fluid volume and pH of cells particularly in plant cells, which contain much less **sodium** than animal cells do. Potassium ions also have a key role in establishing and maintaining membrane potentials and are thus important in the functioning of nervous and muscular tissues. The levels of K^+ in the mammalian body are regulated by the hormone **aldosterone** secreted by the adrenal cortex. In both plants and animals, potassium ions are required as cofactors for the **glycolysis enzyme** pyruvate phosphokinase.
◄ Cofactor, Ion ►

PREDATION

Predation is a loose interspecific association in which a secondary consumer obtains its nutrients by the killing of another consumer, such as a **herbivore** which it eats. In natural habitats, a predator will normally feed on several different prey species, and the prey may be eaten by more than one type of **carnivore**. If this is not the case, and a particular predator feeds on just one prey species not predated by any others, then a closer relationship exists. Here the **population** numbers of both species fluctuate about the **carrying capacity**, with the predator population slightly lagging behind. See Fig. P.9.

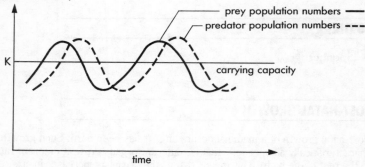

Fig. P.9 Predator–prey population numbers

◀ Population growth ▶

PREGNANCY

Pregnancy is the development of the **fetus** in the **uterus** from conception/**fertilisation** until **birth**, and is a characteristic of eutherian **mammals**. The period of pregnancy is called the gestation period, which in humans is forty weeks and in rabbits is about thirty days. During the gestation period the **placenta** acts as a life support system for the fetus, by allowing exchange between fetal and maternal blood, and by secreting hormones to maintain the pregnancy.

PRESSURE POTENTIAL

Pressure potential (ψp) is the hydrostatic pressure to which water in a liquid phase is subjected. It used to be termed wall pressure or **turgor** pressure but these terms are no longer acceptable. Pressure potential will be a positive

pressure in a circulating erythrocyte or a turgid plant cell. In the xylem, however, because of the tension, it is usually negative.
◀ Erythrocytes, Water potential ▶

PRIMARY GROWTH

Primary growth refers to the formation of stem and root systems by the activities of the apical meristems, and of the zone of elongation behind the meristems, and the zone of differentiation where the various adult plant tissues form – that is, parenchyma, sclerenchyma, collenchyma, xylem, phloem and epidermis.
◀ Apical meristem, Cell differentiation, Root systems, Secondary thickening, Stem elongation, Stem structure ▶

PRODUCERS

Producers are organisms on the first trophic level in food chains. They are autotrophic green plants that fix CO_2 into carbohydrates, fats and proteins, using energy from sunlight. In aquatic habitats it is the phytoplankton that act as producers. The producers transfer energy to the second trophic level when they are eaten by herbivores.
◀ Trophic levels ▶

PROGESTERONE

Progesterone is a steroid female sex hormone, produced by the corpus luteum during the menstrual cycle, and during the first ten weeks of pregnancy, and then by the placenta until the end of pregnancy. High levels of progesterone inhibit follicle stimulating hormone secretion from the pituitary gland by a process of negative feedback, and hence prevent further ovulation. In the menstrual cycle the role of progesterone is to stimulate development of the uterine wall and glands in preparation for implantation and pregnancy. If pregnancy does not occur, then the corpus luteum degenerates and the consequent fall in progesterone (and oestrogen) concentration triggers menstruation. Progesterone in pregnancy inhibits contraction of uterine smooth muscle, thus preventing abortion, and stimulates mammary gland development in the mother.

PROKARYOTAE

Prokaryotae are a kingdom of organisms including the bacteria and Cyanobacteria, or blue-green bacteria. (These used to be known as blue-green algae, but this is not recommended since all algae are eukaryotic). Prokaryotic organisms lack a distinct nucleus bounded by a membrane, they lack membrane-bound organelles such as mitochondria, and lack 9+2 microtubule organelles such as cilia. They contain many ribosomes for polypeptide synthesis, and their DNA is in the form of a single long chromosome and small circular **plasmids**. In some autotrophic forms, such as the blue-green bacteria, the bacterial plasma membrane is invaginated to form mesosomes. These contain **pigments** (chromatophores) which are capable of **photosynthesis**. The cell wall contains lipid and protein and a polysaccharide known as murein, which is absent in eukaryotic cell walls.

◄ Kingdoms, Ribosome ►

PROLACTIN

Prolactin is a hormone produced by the adenohypophysis (anterior pituitary) that promotes lactation. Levels start to build up during later **pregnancy** but there is no milk secretion at this stage since the high levels of oestrogen and **progesterone** stimulate the **hypothalamus** to release prolactin inhibiting factor (PIF). Just after birth, the levels of oestrogen and progesterone fall and the hypothalamus releases prolactin releasing factor (PRL), which causes prolactin release and milk synthesis. Suckling promotes PRL release by the pituitary but inhibits PIF release, thus a continual milk supply is formed, by the mammary glands, though a further hormone, **oxytocin**, is required for milk to be released into the nipple.

◄ Lactation, Oestrogens, Pituitary gland ►

PROPHASE

Prophase is the initial stage in **mitosis** and **meiosis**.

PROPRIOCEPTORS

Proprioceptors are **receptors** located in **joints**, ligaments, tendons and muscles which relay information to the **brain** about tensions, pressures and stretching. This information is used to interpret the location, position or movement of the limbs and trunk of the body, enabling **balance** and coordination.

PROTEINS

Proteins are complex **organic compounds** always containing the elements C, H, O and N, and sometimes S as well or P. They are assembled in the spaces of the rough **endoplasmic reticulum** and Golgi body from the polypeptides manufactured in the ribosomes. The arrangement of polypeptides in a protein is called its quarternary structure. Proteins may be fibrous, insoluble, and structural (e.g. collagen of white connective tissue fibres and keratin of skin). Other proteins are globular, soluble, and either enzymes or with some other metabolic role (e.g. gamma globulins are antibodies). Proteins are essential constituents of all living organisms. Plants manufacture proteins using carbohydrate from photosynthesis and nitrate from the soil, while animals must ingest protein as part of their diet. In humans, a lack of protein in the diet results in Kwashiorkor.

◀ Fibrous proteins, Globular proteins, Polypeptide, Protein synthesis ▶

PROTEIN SYNTHESIS

Polypeptide synthesis occurs in the ribosomes either on rough endoplasmic reticulum or free in the cytoplasm. A strand of mRNA attaches to a ribosome, where the enzyme peptide synthetase is used to couple adjacent amino acids together by peptide bonds. The sequence of amino acids is determined by the codon sequence of the gene for that polypeptide. About twenty-one types of amino acid can be incorporated into protein strucure, and they attach to specific molecules of transfer RNA (tRNA) in the cytoplasm. Each amino acid is first activated using adenosine triphosphate (ATP) and the enzyme amino-acyl-kinase, which phosphorylates the amino acid, which can then join to the tRNA. Another part of the tRNA molecule contains an anticodon which relates to the specific amino acid that it carries. The ribosome allows the amino-acyl-tRNA complexes to enter the ribosome and to attach to the specific codons on the mRNA relating to the complementary anticodons on the tRNA. The joining of complementary bases of codon and anticodon is by hydrogen bonds. The correct amino acids lie adjacent and can be coupled together by peptide bonds. At the end of the gene will be a stop–go codon on the mRNA. This allows the polypeptide to be released from the mRNA and to enter the spaces of the rough endoplasmic reticulum and Golgi body. Here polypeptide chains may be coupled together, forming protein, the cross-bonding involving hydrogen bonds and sulphur bridges. The molecules of tRNA are released back to the cytoplasm for reuse.

◀ Peptide linkage, Ribosomal RNA, Transcription, Translation ▶

PROTHALLUS

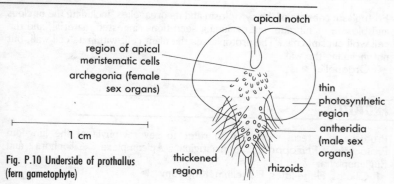

Fig. P.10 Underside of prothallus (fern gametophyte)

apical notch

region of apical meristematic cells

archegonia (female sex organs)

thin photosynthetic region

antheridia (male sex organs)

thickened region

rhizoids

1 cm

A prothallus (Fig. P.11) is an independent stage in the life cycle of ferns (phylum Filicinophyta), reminiscent of the thallus of liverworts. It is the haploid gametophyte stage of the fern and is a flat heart-shaped parenchymatous structure which photosynthesises and is attached to the substratum by rhizoids. It bears the female sex organs, the archegonia, and the male sex organs, the antheridia.

◄ Fern, Haploidy, Liverwort, Photosynthesis ►

PROTOCTISTA

Protoctista is one of the five kingdoms in the natural classification of organisms, defined as eukaryotic organisms that are neither animals, plants nor fungi. It contains the green, red and brown algae, the slime moulds, and the protozoa.

PROTON PUMP

The proton pump is a component of the chemiosmotic theory of Mitchell (1961). Basically an electrochemical gradient of hydrogen ions (protons) across a membrane is used as a source of energy for adenosine triphosphate (ATP) synthesis. Systems producing proton gradients occur in the membranes of chloroplasts, mitochondria and bacteria. Electrons originating from the photolysis of water or from reduced co-enzymes are passed along the series of electron carriers associated with the membrane. The free energy derived from the process is used to pump protons against the proton gradient to the opposite side of the membrane. The backflow of protons, when it occurs, can be used to synthesise ATP, or in bacteria, for instance, to transfer lactose into the cell, coupled to protons.

◄ Chloroplast, Co-enzyme, Electron carrier, Mitochondrion ►

PROTOPLASM

Protoplasm consists of the cytoplasm and its organelles, including the nucleus and plasma membrane, but excluding secretions, ingested material, and the cell wall of plant cells. The protoplast is the plant cell, within its cell wall, but not including the wall.

◄ Organelle ►

PROTOZOA

Protozoa is a term used now to refer to several phyla of the kingdom Protoctista: Rhizopoda, Zoomastigina, Apicomplexa, Ciliophora and Euglenophyta.

◄ Ciliates, Flagellates, Flagellum, Kingdoms ►

PTERIDOPHYTES

Pteridophytes is no longer a taxonomic group. The horsetails and ferns all now have separate phylum status in the kingdom **Plantae**.
◀ Alternation of generations, Fern, Kingdoms, Selaginella ▶

PULMONARY BLOOD CIRCULATION

The pulmonary **blood circulation** through the **lungs** allows blood to be reoxygenated. Blood is pumped from the right ventricle through the pulmonary arteries to the lungs, where there is a profuse capillary network round the alveoli. After **gaseous exchange**, the oxygenated blood is returned to the left atrium of the **heart** through the pulmonary veins.
◀ Double circulation, Ventilation ▶

PUPIL REFLEX

The pupil is the hole, surrounded by the iris, that allows light to pass through the lens into the posterior chamber of the **eye**. The size of the pupil is regulated by the iris muscles which are in turn governed by the brightness of the light. The iris contains circular smooth muscles, which when stimulated will decrease the aperture of the pupil under parasympathetic control and reduce the amount of light reaching the retina. The iris also contains radial smooth muscles which contract under sympathetic control to dilate the pupil and allow more light to enter the eye. This is a **reflex action**, the **stimulus** being excessive light received by the retina and sensory impulses being passed to the **brain** via the optic nerve.
◀ Parasympathetic nervous system, Smooth muscle, Sympathetic nervous system ▶

PYRAMIDS OF NUMBERS, BIOMASS AND ENERGY

A pyramid of numbers (Fig. P.11a)) shows that the number of organisms at each trophic level usually decreases (i.e. most producers, less primary consumers, even less secondary consumers). This is because the loss of energy through the chain means that the higher levels can support fewer numbers and also the animals at the top of the chain tend to be larger anyway. There are exceptions, however, as when a single producer, such as a tree, supports large numbers of **consumers**, or a single host organism supports many parasites. Pyramids of numbers are therefore not very accurate representations of feeding relationships.

A pyramid of biomass (Fig. P.11b)) reflects the decrease in **biomass** at each trophic level in a food chain. The biomass is the total weight of living matter, so it reflects both the numbers of organisms at each trophic level and also their size. It is therefore a clearer representation than a pyramid of numbers, but gives no indication of the relative energy contents of plant and animal tissues.

A pyramid of energy (Fig. P.11c)) represents the total energy content of each successive trophic level in a food chain. As material passes up through the food chain, energy is lost in respiration as heat so the sizes of bars decrease sharply. The efficiency of transfer of energy from plants to herbivores, for example, is only about 20 per cent.

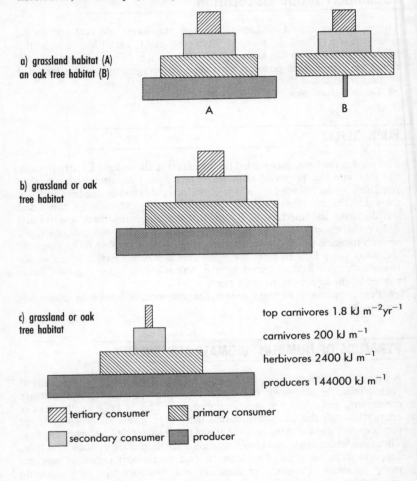

a) grassland habitat (A)
an oak tree habitat (B)

A B

b) grassland or oak tree habitat

c) grassland or oak tree habitat

top carnivores 1.8 kJ $m^{-2}yr^{-1}$

carnivores 200 kJ m^{-1}

herbivores 2400 kJ m^{-1}

producers 144000 kJ m^{-1}

tertiary consumer primary consumer

secondary consumer producer

Fig. P.11 Ecological pyramids

◀ Food chains, Food webs, Producers, Trophic levels ▶

PYRUVATE, PYRUVIC ACID

Pyruvate is a 3C compound which is the end product of **glycolysis**. It is transferred into the mitochondria, to be further respired by **Krebs cycle**. During anaerobic respiration in **skeletal muscle** it forms **lactic acid**, while in yeast fermentation it eventually forms alcohol.

◄ Mitochondrion, Oxygen debt ►

QUADRAT FRAMES

A quadrat frame is used to mark out a random square of vegetation for study. Quadrats are usually a square metre in area but smaller frames can be used if the species diversity is low. The quadrat frame may be made of metal or wood, and the area can be divided into a grid by cross wires. This makes it easier to count and record the plant species in the quadrat. The frame is thrown over the shoulder at random, in order to sample the area of vegetation.

◀ Sampling techniques ▶

QUALITATIVE ANALYSIS

Qualitative analysis involves the observation or identification of components without recording measurements (e.g. testing for the presence of carbohydrates, proteins and lipids in certain food substances or sugars and proteins in the urine of sick people). Qualitative observations describe appearance, colour, taste and so on.

◀ Quantitative analysis ▶

QUANTASOMES

Quantasomes are the regularly arranged large and small sub-units found in the thylakoid lamellae of chloroplasts. Small particles are thought to contain the pigments for photosystem 1 of photosynthesis, while larger particles contain the pigments of photosystem II. There are probably about 300 chlorophyll molecules per subunit.

◀ Chloroplast ▶

QUANTITATIVE ANALYSIS

Quantitative analysis involves measurement of the amounts of components within a material (e.g. measurement of the glucose levels within the blood stream when checking on a patient with sugar diabetes or of oxygen tensions in fresh water during pollution studies). Quantitative observations can be analysed using statistics and can be represented graphically.

◀ Graphs, Qualitative analysis, Statistical analysis ▶

QUOTAS

In order to preserve fish stocks and allow them to breed and recover from the activities of fishermen, quotas are imposed annually upon the fishing industry. Only certain tonnages of fish may be caught and landed, and once these have been reached, no further fishing for those species must take place that season. Overfishing has caused depletion of fish stocks in recent years, particularly of cod and herring.

◀ Fishing regulations ▶

RADIAL SYMMETRY

Radial symmetry is characteristic of sessile animals such as those of the phylum Cnidaria (e.g. *Hydra*, *Obelia* and sea anemones). The body parts are arranged regularly around a central line, and the body could be cut through any longitudinal axis to give mirror-image halves. The organism can receive stimuli with equal ease from all directions, which is of particular value to fixed organisms. Actinomorphic flowers, such as the buttercup, are also radially symmetrical.

◀ Stimulus ▶

RADIATION AS POLLUTANT

The peaceful uses of atomic energy are here to stay and thus there is a potential danger that some nuclear pollution will occur. The biological effects of radiation depend upon the dose absorbed, though different types of radiation have different effects. For safety purposes, a unit called a rem (radiation equivalent man) is used (SI unit is the Sievert (Sv) and equals 100 Rem). The safe exposure of the general public is based on a 'maximum genetic dose' of 5 rems over thirty child-bearing years, with no more than 170 millirems per year. It is particularly important that exposure should be low during growth and development, before and after birth.

Alpha-, beta- and gamma-rays cause damage by raising atoms to a higher energy level, often causing ionisation due to electron loss, and so making molecules more reactive. Various radioactive substances may contaminate the environment, the most dangerous being those with a long half-life, since they will persist in the environment and can be accumulated up the food chain. Examples include those shown in the table:

Radioactive substance	Half life	Comment
Sr^{90} (strontium^{90})	28 years	accumulates in bone since similar to calcium, irradiates bone marrow, causing leukaemia
I^{129} (iodine^{129})	16×10^6yrs	soil to grass to cow to milk to human, irradiates thyroid, causing cancer of the thyroid
Cs^{137} (caesium^{137})	30 years	similar to potassium so taken into cells, irradiates bone marrow, causing leukaemia

Accidents at nuclear power stations causing radiation pollution have occurred (e.g. Windscale, England 1957; Three Mile Island, USA 1979; Chernobyl, Russia 1987).

◀ Food chains, Food webs, Ionising radiation, Pollution ▶

RADIOACTIVE TRACERS

Radioactive isotopes which can be used to mark out a particular biochemical pathway, or to visualise a body organ or tumour, are called radioactive tracers. The biochemical substance or body organ containing the tracer will emit radiation, which can be detected by autoradiography.

◀ Tracers ▶

RARE BREEDS

Modern farming methods use relatively few breeds of domestic animal, and these have been selectively bred over the years to enhance the required characteristics (e.g. high milk yield, lean tender meat, high quality wool). Many of the older breeds of farm animals are not used any longer, because their yield is less, and such breeds have become rare. It is now realised however, that rare breeds may contain various traits and genes that could have value in a world of changing requirements, and thus it is important to preserve them. This applies to crop plants as well as to animals. On a wider horizon, it is similarly important to preserve all wild species of plants and animals, for instance, in the tropical rainforests, since the potential values of these organisms, inherent in their genes, has yet to be realised. This is one of the aims of the **World Conservation Strategy**. Examples of rare breeds are Chillingham cattle, Tamworth pigs, Gloucestershire Old Spot pigs.

◀ Selective breeding ▶

RATCHET MECHANISM

Within the sarcomeres of **striated muscle** are two types of myofilaments. The thin myofilaments are made mainly of **actin** molecules, though they also contain two other proteins, tropomyosin and troponin. The thick myofilaments contain **myosin** molecules, the heads of which project out of the filaments to form cross-bridges that spiral around the main axis. During contraction the **sarcomere** shortens but the myofilaments do not. The myosin cross-bridges react with portions of actin on the thin filament, moving rather like the oars on a boat on the actin surface. Thus the filaments slide past each other shortening the sarcomere. This is the ratchet mechanism.

◀ Muscle contraction ▶

RECEPTORS

Receptors are cells which perceive stimuli or changes within the external or internal environment. If the **stimulus** exceeds a minimum threshold value, it will depolarise the receptor and set up nerve impulses in the sensory nerve fibre. Receptors may be isolated cells or small groups of cells, e.g. baroreceptors (blood pressure); chemoreceptors (blood bicarbonate); **proprioceptors** (muscle/tendon tension); or be grouped into large structures with a **sense organ** (e.g. rods and cones in the **retina**).

◀ Depolarisation, Nerve impulse, Reflex action, Reflex arc ▶

RECESSIVE ALLELES

Recessive alleles have no apparent effect on the **phenotype** unless present in the homozygous, double recessive state. In the heterozygous state they are masked by the dominant allele, which is always expressed.

◀ Dominant alleles ▶

RECIPROCAL ALTRUISM

Altruism is putting others first, or having consideration for the needs of others before seeing to one's own needs. In biology the organism showing altruism is reducing its own chances of reproductive success and survival while increasing the chances of others. This takes place particularly in highly social animals that are related to one another and can also be termed **kin selection** (e.g. a parent defending its young against predators, childless monkeys and apes caring for the offspring of others, and wild dogs bringing meat back to the den to feed other dogs). In reciprocal altruism, the altruistic act is performed in the recognition that the act will be repaid in some way in the future. This implies that the individual organisms within the society can recognise each other as individuals.

◀ Behaviour ▶

RECOMBINANT DNA

Bacteria contain part of their DNA in the form of **plasmids** and if bacteria are placed into a medium containing free plasmids some of the bacterial cells will pick up plasmids and thus be transformed. Recombinant DNA technology involves the **recombination** of eukaryotic 'foreign' DNA with plasmid DNA, which then transforms the bacterial cell into one that will translate 'foreign' genes.

Examples of products made by bacteria through recombinant DNA technology are human insulin, human growth hormone, bovine growth hormone, interferon (only small yields so far) and silk.

◀ Genetic engineering ▶

RECOMBINATION

Recombination is the formation within the offspring of combinations of **alleles** that are not present in the parents. It occurs because:
- **crossing over** occurs between **homologous chromosomes**;
- there is **independent assortment** of chromosomes to the poles of the dividing nuclei in anaphase of meiosis,
- there is random fusion of male and female gametes during **fertilisation**.

RECYCLING

It is important in nature that when organisms die, the constituents of their bodies are broken down and returned to the environment, so that they may be re-used by other organisms in later generations. This also applies to the substances in excreted waste. The resources of the earth and its ecosystems are finite, and must be used time and time again to prevent them running out. This is the purpose of decay and of the carbon, nitrogen and sulphur cycles in nature.

◀ Carbon cycle, Nitrogen cycle ▶

RED BLOOD CELLS

◀ Erythrocytes ▶

REDUCING SUGARS

Most sugars have reducing properties, the exception being **sucrose**. Glucose will reduce Benedict's solution to cuprous oxide, turning the solution from blue to red (the glucose is in turn oxidised to gluconic acid). Fructose, galactose, **maltose** and lactose are also reducing sugars.

◀ Food tests, Non-reducing sugars ▶

REDUCTION

In biological systems reduction is usually by the addition of hydrogen or electrons to a substance, and only occasionally by the removal of oxygen. It is usually an energy-storing process, and is best seen during the redox reactions of respiration.

◀ Electron transfer, ET systems, Oxidative phosphorylation ▶

REFLEX ACTION

Reflex actions are automatic responses mediated through the **nervous system**. They are important in:

- adjusting the tone of muscles to maintain posture;
- causing reciprocal inhibition within **antagonistic muscles**;
- adjusting the activity of internal organs to the physiological requirements of the body;
- producing protective reactions such as blinking, coughing, sneezing.

◀ Reflex arc ▶

REFLEX ARC

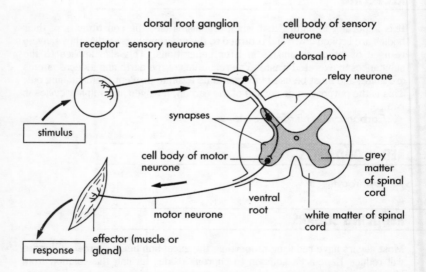

Fig. R.1 Reflex arc (spinal)

A reflex arc (Fig. R.1) is the simplest functional unit of the nervous system, involving the complete pathway from receptor to effector. The basic arc will consist of, in order, a sensory receptor, a sensory neurone, a synapse located in or near the central nervous system, a motor neurone, and an effector (muscle or gland). The basic plan may be complicated since the motor neurone may receive impulses from several sensory neurones, some excitatory, some inhibitory, and there may also be involvement of relay or association neurones to carry impulses to higher or lower levels of the central nervous system.

◀ Effectors, Receptors ▶

REFRACTORY PERIOD

The refractory period is the time interval during which an excitable tissue, such as nerve or muscle, is incapable of responding to a second stimulus after responding to a first stimulus. It is the time for ionic redistribution and adequate repolarisation to occur.

◀ Depolarisation, Nerve impulse ▶

REGENERATION

Regeneration is the regrowth by an organism of tissues or organs which have been removed. In mammals it is restricted to healing of wounds and regrowth of peripheral nerve fibres, but in some animals, such as platyhelminthes, a small part of the body can regenerate a complete organism. Regeneration of plants can occur from activation of dormant buds, or activation of secondary meristems. In plant tissue culture, whole plants may now be grown from a few plant cells. Sea stars and hydroids can be cut into small pieces and each will regenerate the whole, earthworms can regenerate new heads or tails, salamanders and lizards can regenerate new tails or limbs.

◀ Earthworm, Hydra, Hydroids, Meristem ▶

RENAL DIALYSIS

Dialysis is the removal of substances through a membrane by diffusion. It is used to replace the normal function of the kidneys in patients with renal failure. There are two types of renal dialysis: peritoneal dialysis and haemodialysis. In peritoneal dialysis, the dialysing fluid is run into, and then out of, the patient's abdominal cavity. The blood is dialysed across the huge capillary networks that lie in the mesenteries, particularly around the gut. This does not require complicated, expensive equipment and is used in short-term acute renal failure. In haemodialysis, blood is constantly removed from the patient, passed through a kidney machine and returned to the patient. Each chronic renal failure patient will require two or three dialysis sessions per week, each up to eight hours' duration. Such patients have to have permanent silicone rubber arteriovenous shunts established at the extremity of an arm or leg, so that attachment to the dialysis machine is easily made each time, and the blood has to be treated to prevent clotting. Waste products such as urea and uric acid are removed during dialysis, and the blood pH regulated, as well as the blood electrolyte balance.

RENIN

Renin is an enzyme secreted into the blood by the juxtaglomerular cells of the nephrons, in response to a fall in blood pressure. This could be due to factors such as dehydration, Na^+ deficiency or haemorrhage, which all cause a decrease in blood volume and hence a drop in blood pressure. Renin converts angiotensinogen, a plasma protein produced by the liver into the substance angiotensin I. This is then converted by a plasma enzyme into a **hormone** called angiotensin II, which stimulates the adrenal cortex cells to secrete **aldosterone**. Aldosterone increases Na^+ and water reabsorption from the nephrons so blood volume and pressure is raised. Angiotensin II is also a powerful vasoconstrictor, and will thus raise blood pressure directly as well.

RENNIN

Rennin is an enzyme in the stomach of young animals, but absent in the **gastric juice** of most adults. Rennin and Ca^{2+} act upon the milk protein, casein, to curdle it. This curd cannot leave the stomach as rapidly as liquid foods can, so is held in the stomach long enough for **pepsin** to act on it.

REPRODUCTION

Reproduction is the process of generating new individuals, so that the species is perpetuated. It may be by asexual means, in which case the offspring are genetically identical to the parent and to each other, since the cell division involved is only **mitosis**. Alternatively it may be by sexual means, involving the production of haploid gametes by two parents, and the fusion of the gametes in **fertilisation** to restore the **diploid** state. Since **meiosis** as well as mitosis is involved, sexual reproduction produces **genetic variation** – that is the offspring differ from the parents and from each other. This variation may be of survival value in **natural selection** and **evolution**.

◀ Asexual reproduction, Gametogenesis, Haploidy, Ovule, Pollination, Reproductive behaviour, Sexual reproduction, Stamen, Urinogenital system ▶

REPRODUCTIVE BEHAVIOUR

Reproductive behaviour is shown in animals during their reproductive seasons, and is designed to allow successful courtship, **fertilisation** and production of offspring. The behaviour is often ritualistic, consisting of innate, instinctive patterns of movement. For example, the three-spined stickleback has complex reproductive behaviour patterns, consisting of several separate actions occurring in a definite sequence, each activity triggering the next. In the spring, the female is attracted by the bright-red undersurface and zigzag swimming motion of the male, while the male is stimulated by the swollen egg-filled abdomen and head-up posture of the female. If the sequence of movements is correct, the male turns and swims towards the nest that he has prepared, stimulating the female to follow him. The male makes a number of rapid thrusts into the nest entrance with his snout, and then turns on his side and raises his dorsal spines. The showing of the nest entrance to the female induces her to enter it, which in turn makes the male push his snout against her rump in a series of rhythmic, trembling movements. These cause the female to spawn, which in turn causes the male to release sperm over the eggs to fertilise them. This elaborate courtship ritual ensures that only the same species of stickleback will mate, and also synchronises egg and sperm release.

Other examples of reproductive display behaviour are male spiders using their pedipalps to semaphore signals to female spiders, light flashing patterns of male fireflies, birdsong and highly coloured plumage coupled with various ritualistic movements.

Some behavioural activity is stimulated via **pheremones** – chemicals that are released into the air (or water) and which, when sensed by the opposite partner, act as a releaser, stimulating an immediate and reversible behavioural change. For example, a silkworm moth releases a sex attractant which is so powerful that it will attract males from two miles away, even though the female releases only about 0.01 microgramme of the chemical pheromone.

◀ Courtship behaviour, Reproduction ▶

REPRODUCTIVE ORGANS

In animals the reproductive organs are the **gonads** and ancillary ducts and glands. The male gonad is the **testis** and produces spermatozoa; the female gonad is the **ovary** and produces female gametes (eggs, oocytes, depending on organism). In plants the male organs may be antheridia or stamens, and the female organs, archegonia or ovules, depending on the organism.

◀ Ovule, Stamen, Urinogenital system ▶

REPTILIA

Reptilia is a class of the phylum *Chordata*. Reptiles have a scaly skin, possess lungs and lay eggs with shells that are usually soft (e.g. lizards, snakes, tortoises, turtles, terrapins, crocodiles, alligators and the now extinct dinosaurs).

rER

Rough endoplasmic reticulum or rER is found in the cytoplasm of eukaryotic cells. It is a system of pairs of parallel membranes enclosing narrow cavities of varying shapes, which form a communicating network of channels or cisternae through the cytoplasm. The channels are continuous with the nuclear membrane, and the membranes are covered with ribosomes, which are the sites of polypeptide synthesis. Assembled polypeptides are secreted into the channels, where they may be built up into proteins or passed on to the Golgi complex for combination with carbohydrate.
◄ Ribosome, Smooth endoplasmic reticulum ►

RESISTANCE

Resistant organisms are able to tolerate certain substances which would normally kill or inhibit them. For example, bacteria develop strains resistant to antibiotics, mosquitoes develop strains resistant to insecticides and rats develop resistance to warfarin (rat poison). Development of such resistance is essential for the survival and further evolution of the species involved. The development of immunity in man against various disease organisms is another aspect of resistance. Antibiotic resistance can develop by a gene mutation on the plasmid DNA within the bacterial cell and plasmid transfer may disperse the resistance-giving gene through the population.

In higher animals organisms that develop genes which give resistance will be selected while the non-resistant organisms will die out.
◄ Gene transfer in bacteria, Plasmids, Selection pressure ►

RESPIRATION

Respiration is the oxidation of food substances inside the cells of the body, liberating energy in a form which the organism can use to do biological work. The main type of oxidation is dehydrogenation. Much of the process occurs in the mitochondria and the usable energy is in the form of an energy-rich phosphate bond. The main biochemical processes of respiration are as follows:

- Glycolysis, which occurs in the cytoplasm and oxidises hexose sugars to pyruvate and then to acetyl Co-A.
- Beta-oxidation, which oxidises fatty acids to acetyl Co-A.

- Pentose shunt, which oxidises 4C, 5C and 7C sugars to acetyl Co-A.
- Krebs cycle, which oxidises acetyl Co-A to CO_2.
- The **electron transfer** chain, which receives hydrogen atoms from the above pathways and attaches them to oxygen to produce water. During the transfers that occur, energy from the oxidised foods is conserved for use by **oxidative phosphorylation**.

With the exception of glycolysis, all processes occur in the mitochondria.
◀ **Adenosine triphosphate, Anaerobic respiration, Mitochondrion, Ventilation mechanisms** ▶

RESPIRATORY GASES

The respiratory gases are oxygen and carbon dioxide. Oxygen is required to accept the hydrogen in the **electron transfer** chain and carbon dioxide is produced as a byproduct of **respiration**. Oxygen has to be obtained from the surrounding environment and carbon dioxide has to be removed from the organism.
◀ **Haemoglobin, Ventilation, Ventilation mechanisms** ▶

RESPIRATORY MEDIA

The respiratory medium for terrestrial animals or plants is air, which contains 21 per cent by volume of **oxygen**. For aquatic organisms, it is water, which contains dissolved oxygen. The solubility of oxygen in water and in blood plasma is rather low, and decreases with rise in temperature, so animals require respiratory pigments, such as **haemoglobin**, to transport adequate amounts of oxygen to meet their respiratory needs.

RESPIRATORY QUOTIENT (RQ)

This is the ratio of the volume of carbon dioxide liberated to the volume of oxygen consumed during the same time interval. Theoretically the RQ for respiring carbohydrates is 1.0, for lipids is 0.7 and for proteins is 0.8. The interpretation of an organism's RQ value is not easy, since the organism may be respiring carbohydrates, fats and proteins at the same time, and other metabolic processes can also produce CO_2 as a byproduct.

RESPIRATORY SURFACES AND SYSTEMS

The respiratory surface is the surface through which exchange of **respiratory gases** occurs, between the respiratory medium and the inside of the organism. In small organisms the body surface is large enough to absorb enough oxygen to meet the organism's needs, but in larger organisms respiratory surfaces with huge moist, highly vascularised surface areas have to be developed to meet the body's requirements for oxygen uptake and carbon dioxide removal (e.g. alveolar surfaces of lungs, gills and gill filaments, tracheole surfaces in insect tracheal systems. Ventilation mechanisms are required to bring air or water across the respiratory surfaces, so that gaseous exchange can occur. Ancillary structures such as air tubes (e.g. trachea, bronchi) and muscles in order to make ventilation movements all make up a respiratory system.

◀ Respiratory media, Tracheal system ▶

RESPIROMETRY

Respirometry is the measurement of respiration. Techniques usually involve measurement of the oxygen uptake by living materials. If this is carried out in conjunction with the use of selective metabolic inhibitors, data can be obtained about the initial substrates used, and about the pathways followed, particularly when using radioactive tracers to tag compounds, and chromatography to separate the intermediate compounds formed.

Simple respirometers use manometers to measure the gas volume changes caused by oxygen uptake or carbon dioxide release. In medicine, volumes of either inspired air or expired air can be measured by having small turbines with rotating blades in the air tubes to or from the patient. The number of turns of the turbine is proportional to the gas volume passing and this can be counted and recorded directly as litres of air.

RESPONSE

The response is the change that occurs when an organism is challenged by a stimulus. Plants respond slowly by growth movements towards such stimuli as unilateral light (positive phototropism of stems) or to gravity (positive geotropism of roots). Animals respond rapidly using nerves and effector organs, such as skeletal muscle or glands. Responses in animals due to hormone control tend to be slower, with the exception of those due to adrenalin. The stimuli may be external (e.g. response to a food source or a predator) or internal (e.g. increases in cardiac output and ventilation rate when blood hydrogencarbonate concentration rises).

◀ Reflex action ▶

RESTING POTENTIAL

The inside of cells tends to be electrically negative with respect to the outside, so the cell membranes tend to be positively charged on their outer surfaces. This charge is the resting potential, and is particularly important in nerve cells, since it allows the action potential to develop, and in muscle cells and fibres, where it allows contraction mechanisms to be initiated. The cell membrane at rest is impermeable to Na^+, but a powerful sodium pump removes sodium ions from the cytoplasm to the outside tissue fluid. The membrane is permeable to K^+, and since there is a deficiency of positive ions in the cytoplasm, potassium ions move in to restore the ionic balance. Potassium uptake never quite catches up with the outflow of sodium, however, so there are always surplus negative ions in a resting cell. This gives rise to the resting potential, the value of which is usually in the range 65–95 millivolts.

◄ Nerve impulse ►

RESTRICTION ENZYMES

Restriction endonuclease enzymes cleave DNA chains at specific points and at no others, the cleavage points being related to certain nucleotide sequences (e.g. enzyme Eco RI recognises and cleaves DNA at the sequence GAATTC, while enzyme Hind III recognises AAGCTT). The enzymes are of microbial origin and were first discovered in 1974. They have been invaluable in DNA sequencing studies and in **genetic engineering** using **recombinant DNA**.

◄ Nucleotides ►

RETINA

The retina (Fig. R.2) is the layer at the back of the posterior chamber of the eye which contains the light receptors, the rods and cones. It also contains bipolar relay neurones, and various cells which integrate the mosaic of signals that are transmitted via the optic nerves to the **visual cortex** of the brain. Behind the retina is a cuboidal **epithelium**, containing melanin, a **pigment** which absorbs light that has passed through the photoreceptors and so prevents internal reflection. The cones are for colour vision and require bright light for stimulation, while the rods are for black and white vision and are sensitive to dim light. This is because several rods synapse with one relay **neurone**, so summation occurs, but in cones it is a 1:1 ratio between cone and relay cell. The cones are in the fovea at the centre of the retina, where light rays are focused. Around the periphery only rod cells are present.

◄ Eye, Retinene, Retinol, Transducers, Trichromatic vision ►

RETINOL, RETINENE

Retinol is Vitamin A. It is transported by the **blood** to the **retina** and absorbed into the rods and cones. Here it is dehydrogenated to form visual yellow or retinene. In the rods this combines with a protein called scotopsin to form visual purple. When light of any wavelength or intensity strikes rhodopsin, it goes through a series of chemical stages before breaking down to retinine and scotopsin. These chemical changes alter the ionic balance of the rod and cause **depolarisation**. In dark or dim light the rhodopsin can be resynthesised, but in bright light it is completely bleached faster than it can reform. The 'dark adaptation' time required when entering a dark room from bright sunlight is due to the need to regenerate rhodopsin, a fairly slow process. The retinine in cones combines with proteins known as photopsins. These products break down only in bright light and respond only to certain wavelengths of light, which is the basis of colour vision. The visual pigments in cones regenerate quickly after bleaching.

◀ Eye, Retina, Trichromatic vision, Vitamins ▶

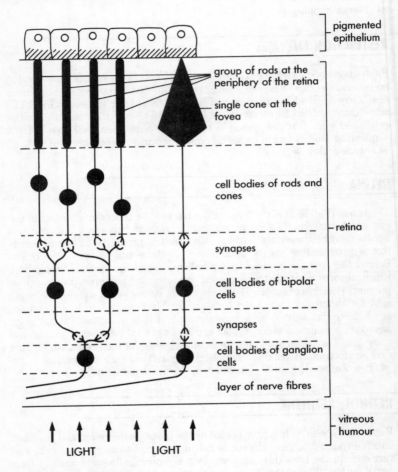

Fig. R.2 Structure of the retina

RHESUS BLOOD GROUPS

Rhesus blood groups were first discovered in Rhesus monkeys, but also occur in humans. In Rhesus positive (Rh-positive) people the erythrocyte surfaces contain the antigenic rhesus protein, while Rhesus negative (Rh-negative) people have no rhesus **antigens** on their red cells. Under normal circumstances, plasma does not contain Rhesus antibodies but if a Rh-negative person receives a transfusion of Rh-positive cells, then they will become sensitised as their immune response starts to produce Rhesus antibody (anti-D). This will not have an effect at the first blood transfusion since the red cells will have had their normal life span and been destroyed before problems occur. If a second transfusion of Rh-positive blood is given, then there will be a serious problem. Since the patient is sensitised, large amounts of anti-D will be produced quickly, and will clump the rhesus positive cells, blocking many small blood vessels. The patient usually dies from acute kidney failure as all the glomeruli become blocked. Towards the end of **pregnancy**, some fetal cells leak across the **placenta** into the maternal blood. If a Rh-negative mother is bearing a Rh-positive fetus, then this leakage induces the mother to produce anti-D. The baby is born before amounts are large enough to damage it, but in subsequent pregnancies, the now-sensitized mother will produce massive amounts of anti-D as soon as she is challenged by Rh-positive fetal cells. The anti-D will cross the placenta back to the baby and haemolyse its red cells. This is Rhesus disease of the newborn and would normally be fatal. The problem can be avoided by giving the mother an injection of anti-D as soon as the first baby is born. This will 'mop up' the few Rhesus positive baby cells in her blood and prevent her developing an immune response of her own.

◀ Erythrocytes, Immunity ▶

RHIZOBIUM

Rhizobium is a genus of symbiotic nitrogen-fixing **bacteria** which infect the root hairs and cause the development of root nodules on leguminous plants (peas, beans, clover). The bacteria multiply and grow in the nodules, and fix atmospheric nitrogen to ammonia (*not* to nitrate).

$$N_2 + 3H_2 \rightarrow 2NH_3$$

The legume can use the ammonia to manufacture **amino acids** and **nucleic acids**, while the bacterium obtains a sugar source from the legume. Thus both partners profit by the association and it is an example of **mutualism**. Leguminous crops, because of **nitrogen fixation**, are of great benefit in maintaining and improving soil fertility.

◀ Nitrogen cycle ▶

RHIZOIDS

Rhizoids are hair-like structures which serve as 'roots'. They may be single celled or multicellular. They are found in **fungi**, penetrating the **substratum** for extracellular **digestion** and food **absorption**, in mosses, at the stem base, and on the underside of the prothalli of liverworts and ferns.

◀ Fern, Liverwort, Moss, Prothallus ▶

RHIZOPODA

Rhizopoda is a phylum of the kingdom **Protoctista**. They possess pseudopodia for locomotion and the best known example is **Amoeba**.
◄ Kingdoms ►

RIBOFLAVIN

This is vitamin B_2. It is water-soluble.
◄ Vitamins ►

RIBONUCLEIC ACID (RNA)

RNA is a **polymer** of ribo-nucleotides. Each nucleotide contains **ribose** sugar and a nitrogenous **base**, the bases being either purines (adenine and guanine) or pyrimidines (cytosine and uracil). Adjacent **nucleotides** are attached by phosphate bridges, forming a long chain molecule which unlike DNA is single-stranded. All the components are joined by **condensation reactions**.

There are three types of RNA in cells, **messenger RNA, transfer RNA** and **ribosomal RNA**. Each has characteristic molecular weights and base compositions and each performs specific roles in the cell cycle. The **genetic code** from which polypeptides are synthesized is found on messenger RNA, while transfer RNA carries specific **amino acids** to the **ribosome**, which is made of ribosomal RNA. The ribosomes are involved in translating the code on the messenger RNA into a **polypeptide**.
◄ Protein synthesis, Translation ►

RIBOSE

Ribose is a **pentose** or five-carbon sugar of **aldose** type. It occurs in **nucleotides** such as **adenosine triphosphate** (ATP) and in the nucleic acid RNA.

RIBOSOMAL RNA (rRNA)

Ribosomal RNA is made in the **nucleolus** in **eukaryotic cells**, and it is the type of RNA contained in the ribosomes. Prokaryotic, mitochondrial and **chloroplast** ribosomes contain 30S and 50S types of rRNA. Eukaryotic cells contain ribosomes on the **rough endoplasmic reticulum** that contain 60S and 40S rRNA. S stands for Svedberg units, which are a measure of how fast the molecules sediment in a centrifuge tube.
◄ Mitochondrion, Prokaryotae, Prokaryotic cells, Ribosome, RNA ►

RIBOSOME

Ribosomes are tiny organelles responsible for assembling proteins in living cells. Some occur in other organelles, some are free in the cytoplasm and others are attached to endoplasmic reticulum, thus making it rough endoplasmic reticulum. They are only about 20 nm diameter and are the last items to be sedimented by ultra-centrifugation, requiring 100,000 g for up to 2 hours. Centrifugation of the contents of a cell yields two types of ribosomes. The smaller 70S ribosomes contain the 30S and 50S rRNA found in chloroplasts and mitochondrion, and 80S ribosomes contain 60S and 40S rRNA, which are the typical rRNA molecules of eukaryotic cells. Each ribosome consists of a small sub-unit and a large sub-unit, and both sub-units contain rRNA and protein. The proteins probably act as enzymes and binding sites for polypeptide synthesis, during which process messenger RNA attaches to a specific binding site on the small sub-unit of the ribosome.

◄ Ribosomal RNA, Protein synthesis, Transfer RNA, Translation ►

RIBULOSE BISPHOSPHATE (RuBP)

RuBP is a five-carbon compound that accepts carbon dioxide during the dark stage of photosynthesis.

$$RuBP + CO_2 + H_2O \xrightarrow{\text{RuBP carboxylase}} 2.GP$$
$$\text{(glycerate 3-phosphate)}$$

GP is the first product of photosynthesis. The carboxylase enzyme is abundant in the stroma of chloroplasts.

◄ Chloroplast ►

RNA

◄ Ribonucleic acid ►

RODENT

Rodents are placental mammals, and include rats, mice, squirrels, beavers, gophers and porcupines. They are gnawing mammals with a pair of large, continually growing, chisel-shaped incisors in each jaw.

ROOT HAIRS

Root hairs are outgrowths from the piliferous layer cells of the root. They are unicellular and have thin delicate cellulose cell walls, which are in intimate contact with the soil particles and solution. They are numerous behind the root tip zone and greatly increase the absorptive surface area of the root.

They wither after a few days, but are constantly replenished by the new root tissue formed by the **apical meristem**.

◀ Root systems, Water uptake in roots ▶

ROOT NODULES

Root nodules are small swellings found on the roots of leguminous plants (peas, beans, lupins) which contain millions of nitrogen-fixing **bacteria** of the genus **Rhizobium**. The bacteria are housed in enlarged parenchymatous cells, surrounded by vascular strands which connect with the **xylem** and **phloem** of the root. The bacteria fix nitrogen from the soil atmosphere, forming **ammonia**, which the host plant can use to make **amino acids**. The bacteria gain a sugar source from the host plant, so this is a mutualistic relationship.

◀ Mutualism, Nitrogen fixation ▶

ROOT PRESSURE

Root pressure is a force exerted by the roots, which pushes water into the **xylem** and then up the xylem. The maintenance of root pressure requires energy expenditure by the root, but the precise origin of the pressure is not fully understood. When **transpiration** cannot occur (if the air is fully saturated, for example), root pressure is still strong enough to force water out of the leaf vessel ends. This forms water droplets on the leaf edges and is called guttation.

ROUGH ENDOPLASMIC RETICULUM

◀ rER ▶

ROOT SYSTEMS

Root systems anchor the plant, absorb adequate quantities of water and salts, and may also contain storage tissue. The tap root systems of **dicotyledons** have a main primary root (Fig. R.3a)) with lateral branches off it called secondary roots, which in turn have smaller lateral branches called tertiary roots. Fibrous root systems of monocotyledons tend to have many main roots all arising from the bottom of the stem, and these branch randomly and extensively.

The root grows from the apex, where the **meristem** is situated, protected by a hood-shaped root cap. Just behind the mitotic zone of the meristem is the region of elongation where the cells elongate before **differentiation**. Behind this is the region of differentiation, where the cells differentiate into the tissues of the mature root. The dermal cells remain thin-walled and produce outgrowths, which are the **root hairs**, for absorption of water and salts (Fig. R.3b)). Other cells differentiate either into cortical parenchyma and the endodermis or into the tissues of the stele (i.e. **xylem** and **phloem**). The outer layer of the stele remains as a parenchymatous single cell thick layer called the pericycle.

a)

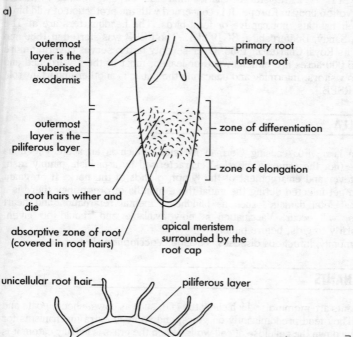

outermost layer is the suberised exodermis

outermost layer is the piliferous layer

root hairs wither and die

absorptive zone of root (covered in root hairs)

primary root

lateral root

zone of differentiation

zone of elongation

apical meristem surrounded by the root cap

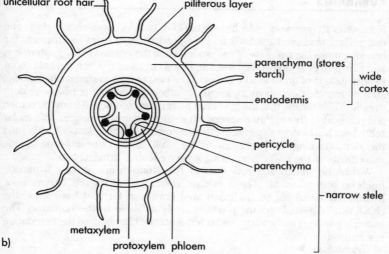

unicellular root hair

piliferous layer

parenchyma (stores starch)

endodermis

pericycle

parenchyma

metaxylem

protoxylem phloem

wide cortex

narrow stele

b)

Fig. R.3 Primary root structure

◀ Dicotyledon, Monocotyledon, Secondary thickening ▶

ROYAL SOCIETY FOR THE PROTECTION OF BIRDS (RSPB)

The RSPB is a registered charity and the largest voluntary wildlife conservation body in Europe. It is concerned with the protection of wild birds and their habitats, not captive or feral birds. The headquarters are at The Lodge, Sandy, Bedfordshire, SG19 2DL. The RSPB was started in 1889 and gained its Royal Charter in 1905. Over seventy bird reserves covering more than 85,000 acres are either owned or leased, most of them wardened and open to visitors. Informing and educating the public is another important role of the RSPB.

RUBELLA

Rubella is a virus causing German measles, which is an acute infectious disease (not the same as measles) characterised by a pinkish, pimply rash, slight fever and enlargement of the lymph glands of the neck. If pregnant women get infected during the initial three months of pregnancy there is a risk that fetal damage, such as blindness, mental retardation and heart defects, will occur. Vaccination is now available and should be given, particularly to girls, before puberty.

◄ Immunity, Infectious diseases, Vaccine, Vaccination ►

RUMINANTS

Ruminants are mammals which chew the cud, such as cows, sheep, goats and deer. They feed predominantly on grass, and so need extra mechanisms for breaking down the cellulose of cell walls. When the grass is initially eaten, it is stored in a large region of the stomach, called the rumen, which can hold about twenty gallons of grass in a large cow. The oesophagus in ruminants contains striated muscle throughout its length (in other mammals it is mainly smooth muscle). This means that the grass can be regurgitated at will from the rumen and masticated thoroughly a second time, at the animal's leisure. The molar teeth bear heavy ridges to enable efficient smashing of the plant cell walls, and the joint attaching the lower jaw to the skull allows sweeping side-to-side movements of the lower jaw, giving a very effective grinding action.

Within the rumen and reticulum of the stomach are various symbiotic bacteria and protozoa. These contain cellulases, which are enzymes for hydrolysing cellulose, so the masticated grass can ferment here while the cellulose is digested and the products made available to the ruminant. The bacteria gain food and a warm, moist fermentation chamber, so the association is a mutualistic one.

◄ Mutualism ►

SALMONELLA POISONING

Salmonella poisoning may be caused by various species of *Salmonella* bacteria, which can contaminate poultry, eggs, shellfish and many other foods. The bacteria reproduce in the gut lymph vessels and then spread to the liver, spleen, bone marrow and other tissues, setting up a wide infection.

Toxins are released which cause high fever and severe abdominal discomfort. Treatment is by antibiotics and control by good sanitation. Some humans act as carriers and have the bacteria in their bodies but without disease symptoms; such people could unintentionally contaminate foods, so good kitchen and personal hygiene is essential.

◀ Toxicity, Toxins, Typhoid ▶

SALT BALANCE

Cells are intolerant of changes in the salt (and osmotic) balance of the fluids surrounding them. Thus there are many methods in nature of regulating salt balance. For example, when *Carcinus* (shore crab) is in sea water, its body fluids are isotonic to the sea water, but in brackish water its body fluids are hypertonic to the sea water and thus salt tends to leave the animal. To overcome this problem there are special salt-control cells on the gills, which take up salt from the sea water and actively secrete it into the blood to compensate for the salt loss. A similar mechanism operates in the gills of fresh water fish. In marine fish the blood is hypotonic to the sea water and thus salt tends to leak into the fish. This is removed back to the sea by special salt-excretory cells on the gills. In mammals the salt level of the blood and salt loss in urine are regulated by the nephrons and ADH — aldosterone mechanism, under negative feedback control. Since plant cells are surrounded by cellulose cell walls, they are not as susceptible to osmotic damage as animal cells.

◀ Osmoregulation ▶

SAMPLING TECHNIQUES

These are techniques of recording and/or collecting organisms in a standard way in order that valid comparisons of sites within ecosystems can be made where abiotic and biotic factors are being investigated. For instance, a line transect may be used to sample when it is suspected or known that there is a transition in habitats and populations through an area. A tape is strung between two poles in a straight line across the area and species which touch the tape are recorded.

A belt transect is a strip of chosen width, usually 1 metre, taken across the area in which all species are recorded and counted in every square metre. If height variations are recorded along the line or belt transect, these become profile transects. Quadrat frames are metal or wooden frames of known area which can be placed along a line transect or belt transect to facilitate sampling. In an apparently uniform habitat they may be thrown at random and the species recorded where the quadrat falls. They can be left in place permanently to allow changes to be recorded over periods of time.

◀ Statistical analysis, Zone ▶

SAND DUNE SYSTEM

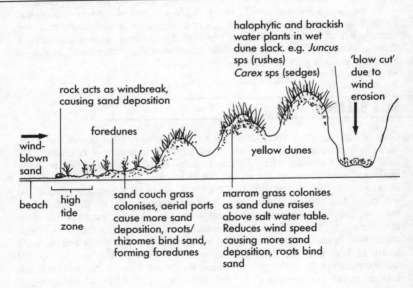

Fig. S.1 Sand dune succession

Accumulations of blown sand on the sea shore, on shores of great lakes or in deserts may form sand dune systems. If an onshore wind is carrying grains of sand, it will deposit that sand around any structure such as a small rock, that reduces the wind speed. Certain plants such as sand couch grass may colonise the pile of sand formed, their roots binding the sand and their aerial parts impeding the windflow, causing the deposition of more sand. In this way a foredune may be built up (Fig. S.1). Sand couch grass (*Agropyron junceiforme*) is a good pioneer as it can withstand immersion in salt water and it has long, creeping rhizomes which bind the sand, and aerial shoots which act as windbreaks. Associated plants are Sea Sandwort (*Honkenya peploid*), Sea Rocket (*Cakile maritima*) and Saltwort (*Salsola kali*). The succession continues when the foredune builds up above tide level and the most important establishing species colonises. This is Marram Grass (*Ammophila arenaria*), which has vigorous vertical and lateral extension, thus trapping and binding more sand. Associated species are Sea Lyme Grass (*Elymus arenarius*), Ragwort (*Senecio jacobaea*), Hawkweed (*Hieracium umbellatum*), Sea Holly (*Eryngium maritimum*) and Sand Fescue (*Festuca rubra*). This latter plant, together with various mosses, helps to bind the surface, so forming a permanent dune. Between the dunes may be wet slacks where the water table is near the surface; here aquatic and marsh vegetation may occur.

◄ Colonisation, Sere ►

SAP

Sap may consist of water and dissolved salts moving in the xylem, or dissolved organic compounds moving in the phloem, or the cell sap within the cell vacuoles of plant cells.

◄ Vacuole ►

SAP-FEEDING ARTHROPOD PESTS

Species of the insect genus *Aphis*, commonly known as greenfly, blackfly, dolphin fly, blue fly, etc. are sap-feeding pests. They have mouthparts adapted for piercing and sucking the stems and leaves of plants, tapping into the phloem and xylem. Attacked plants are weakened, shoots and leaves often curl up and crop yield is reduced. The insects frequently act as vectors of plant virus diseases, but fortunately most species are wingless, so their influences are local. They can reproduce at a tremendous rate and achieve huge population densities, but they are preyed upon by ladybirds and can be controlled using systemic insecticides.

◄ Vector ►

SAPROBIONTS

Saprobionts are organisms which absorb organic materials in solution from their environments, the organic materials originating from the dead plants and animals at that site. Some animals feed saprozoically, (e.g. soil nematodes feeding on dead soil organisms). Some fungi and bacteria feed saprophytically.

◄ Saprophyte, Saprophytism ►

SAPROPHYTE/SAPROPHYTISM

Saprophytes are organisms, such as many fungi and bacteria species, which obtain their nutrition in solution from the decaying tissues of animals and plants. This mode of life is called saprophytism and is responsible for decay and the recycling of carbon, nitrogen and salts in the biosphere. The saprophytes usually secrete digestive enzymes into the surrounding organic matter for extra-cellular digestion. The products of digestion are then absorbed by **diffusion** or **active transport/facilitated uptake** into the fungal mycelium or bacterial cells. Enzymes that are secreted include amylases, proteases, lipases and cellulases. Thus many saprophytes can break down **cellulose** during the decay process. Yeasts cause alcoholic **fermentation** and are important in the brewing and baking industries. Many saprophytes will grow on bread, fruit, cheese, damp leather, etc. and thus cause spoilage.

◄ Enzyme, Heterotrophs, Heterotrophic nutrition, Yeast ►

SARCOMERE

The repeating units of a single **striated muscle** fibre are called sarcomeres (Fig. S.2). They are made of the contractile proteins **actin** and **myosin**. At the ends of each sarcomere are the Z-discs, to which the parallel actin filaments are attached, and between the actin filaments are thicker filaments of myosin. The arrangements of these filaments give the sarcomere the appearance of alternating light I-bands and dark A-bands.

◄ Muscle structure ►

SATURATED FATS

Saturated fats contain **fatty acids** which have the maximum possible number of hydrogen atoms attached to their carbon atoms. A high intake of such fat in the diet is thought to be a factor causing atherosclerosis, a disease in which fatty deposits in the artery walls impede the blood flow.

◄ Lipids ►

SCANNING ELECTRON MICROSCOPE (SEM)

The scanning electron microscope can be used to study surface structures and does not require the cutting of thin sections. Electrons are reflected back to a detector by the solid surface, producing a dark-ground image. The microscope has great depth of focus so can give three-dimensional images.

◄ Electron microscope, Transmission ►

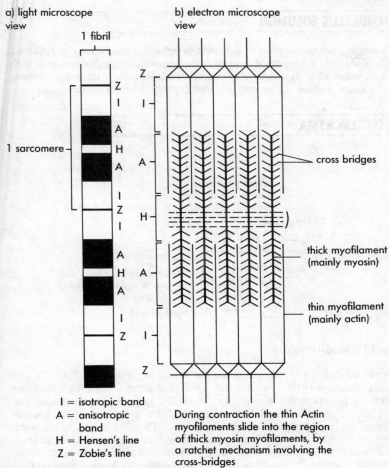

a) light microscope view

1 fibril

1 sarcomere

b) electron microscope view

cross bridges

thick myofilament (mainly myosin)

thin myofilament (mainly actin)

I = isotropic band
A = anisotropic band
H = Hensen's line
Z = Zobie's line

During contraction the thin Actin myofilaments slide into the region of thick myosin myofilaments, by a ratchet mechanism involving the cross-bridges

Sarcomeres are arranged end to end to give fibrils (myofibrils)

The H line has fine cross threads that connect the thick myofilaments together.

Fig. S.2 Sarcomere structure (striated muscle)

SCAPULA

The scapula, or shoulder blade, is the main **bone** of the pectoral girdle. It is a flat bone which forms the shoulder joint with the **humerus**.
◀ Skeleton ▶

SCHULTZE'S SOLUTION

Schultze's solution is used to indicate the presence and location of **cellulose**. Plant sections are mounted directly in the solution. Unlignified cellulose walls stain violet while lignified, suberised or cutinised walls stain yellow–brown. The iodine content means that any **starch** present is stained blue-black.

SCLERENCHYMA

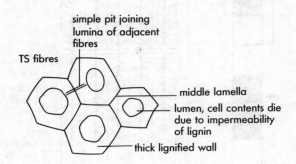

Fig. S.3 Sclerenchyma fibres

Sclerenchyma is a mechanical or support tissue in plants (Fig. S.3). The cell walls become very thick, usually with **lignin** (e.g. hemp fibres), but sometimes with much extra cellulose (e.g. flax fibres), and as a result of this thickening, the cell contents die. Before thickening, the cells may have become elongated, with tapering interlocking ends. When thickened, these form inelastic fibres which have high tensile strength to withstand pulling strains.

Fibres may be found associated with **xylem** and **phloem** elements within vascular bundles or be outside the vascular bundles as bundle caps and they may also form complete rings, such as the pericycle. They are most abundant in stems and in the midribs of leaves where they have an essential strengthening role.

◄ Vascular bundle ►

SEA ANEMONE

Sea anemones are marine animals belonging to the phylum **Cnidaria**, class Anthozoa. They consist of sessile polyps only, with no medusal stage. The enteron is divided by mesenteries and they show **radial symmetry**. They are commonly found attached to rocks on the sea shore and are closely related to the corals.

SECONDARY CELL WALL

The primary cell wall in young cells consists of the middle lamella and a thin layer of cellulose. Later the protoplasm may lay down further chemicals over the primary wall to thicken and strengthen it, so forming the secondary cell wall. Examples of such chemicals are cellulose, in collenchyma, lignin, in xylem and sclerenchyma, and suberin, in phellem, or cork.

SECONDARY THICKENING

Secondary thickening occurs in the stems (Fig. S.4) and roots of many dicotyledonous plants and in conifers (formerly gymnosperms). Additional vascular tissue in the form of secondary xylem and phloem is formed by the intra-fascicular cambium and interfascicular cambium. This causes an increase in girth, in mechanical strength and in the amount of conducting tissue. Since large xylem elements are formed in the spring and small ones in the late summer/autumn, one year's growth of xylem is distinct from the next year's growth – hence annual rings appear.

◄ Conifer, Dicotyledon ►

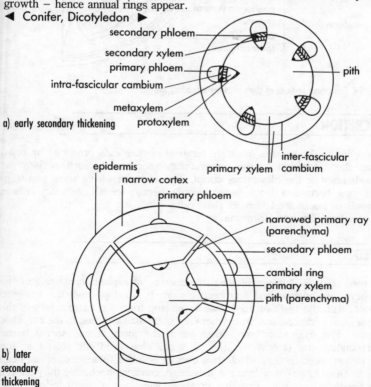

secondary phloem
secondary xylem
primary phloem
intra-fascicular cambium
metaxylem
protoxylem
pith
inter-fascicular cambium
primary xylem

a) early secondary thickening

epidermis
narrow cortex
primary phloem
narrowed primary ray (parenchyma)
secondary phloem
cambial ring
primary xylem
pith (parenchyma)

b) later secondary thickening

secondary xylem

c) transverse secion one-year-old woody stem

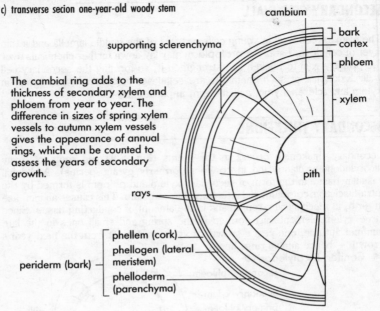

The cambial ring adds to the thickness of secondary xylem and phloem from year to year. The difference in sizes of spring xylem vessels to autumn xylem vessels gives the appearance of annual rings, which can be counted to assess the years of secondary growth.

Labels: cambium, bark, cortex, phloem, xylem, supporting sclerenchyma, pith, rays, periderm (bark) — phellem (cork), phellogen (lateral meristem), phelloderm (parenchyma)

Fig. S.4 Transverse sections of stem showing secondary growth:

SECRETION

Secretion is the passive or active removal of chemicals produced by cells, from the **cytoplasm** to the extracellular environment, such as into the bloodstream or the **alimentary canal**. The secretions have some use (e.g. enzymes, hormones, tears, sweat, mucus, nectar, scent). Secretory cells in animals or plants are known as gland cells.
◄ Enzyme, Glands, Hormone ►

SEED

A seed (Fig. S.5) is a reproductive structure of a plant, consisting of the embryo, stored food and a protective coat. It develops from the fertilised **ovule**, with the testa or seed coat developing from the integuments of the ovule, and it has one scar from where the ovule was attached to the carpel or ovary. The food store can either be in the form of endosperm tissue surrounding the embryo (castor oil seed, pine seed) or stored in the cotyledons/seed leaves, which thus become swollen (pea seed, broad bean seed). One or two cotyledons are present, depending on whether the plant is a **monocotyledon** (e.g. orchids, grasses, lilies) or a **dicotyledon** (e.g.

buttercups, roses, plums). Conifers generally have several cotyledons per embryo.

◄ Conifer, Fruit, Seed dormancy, Seed germination ►

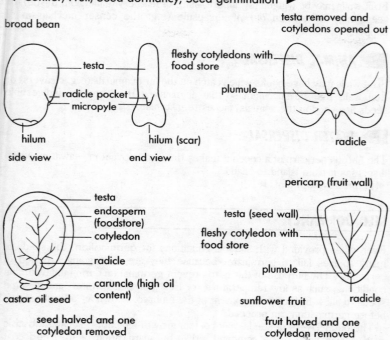

Fig. S.5 Structure of seeds: a) broad bean b) castor oil seed c) sunflower fruit

SEED DISPERSAL

To prevent overcrowding it is obviously advantageous for the seed to be transported or dispersed some distance away from its parent plant. This also allows **colonisation** of other areas,. Usually the seed is housed within a **fruit** formed from the **ovary** and it is the fruit which is adapted for dispersal. Dehiscent fruits will open in an organised manner to release the seeds for germination, but indehiscent fruits do not split (except by accidental breakage or decay), the seeds actually germinate from inside the fruit wall (pericarp).

► MECHANICAL DISPERSAL

This is found in 'explosive' fruits, where tensions are set up in the fruit wall as it dries. The wall eventually splits open suddenly and forecefully, flinging the seeds a considerable distance (e.g. legumes such as gorse, peas, beans).

 WIND DISPERSAL

Fruit walls may be winged (sycamore, ash), or feathery (dandelion, thistle), or seeds may be shaken out of a capsule (e.g. the censer mechanism of poppy).

ANIMAL DISPERSAL

Fruit walls may have hooks which catch on the fur of aminals (e.g. cleavers) or fruit walls may be succulent so that animals eat them and the indigestible seeds are shed in the animals' faeces (e.g. tomato).

WATER DISPERSAL

The fibrous pericarp of a coconut makes the fruit buoyant in seawater, which disperses it from island to island.

◀ Fruit development ▶

SEED DORMANCY

Even when provided with suitable conditions for **germination**, the seeds of many species fail to germinate, because they are undergoing a period of dormancy. The purpose of this is to prevent germination during unfavourable conditions, such as low temperatures or lack of available water, and in some seeds to allow further development of the embryo, known as 'after ripening', before germination can proceed.

The outer layers of seeds may contain growth inhibitors, such as **abscisic acid**, which have to be removed either by scarification of the **seed** coat (damage/scratching of the seed coat) or by washing away in water. If growth inhibitors are not removed, their effect may be overriden by an increase in concentration of **gibberellin**, which is a growth promotor. This increase may be caused by light. Gibberellins may also induce the embryos in seeds to produce hydrolytic enzymes for the mobilisation of **starch** or lipid food reserves. Sometimes a period of cold temperatures will induce gibberellin production and reduce inhibitor activity. This is called stratification and is common in cereals.

◀ Enzyme, Lipids ▶

SEED GERMINATION

Germination is the start of the growth of the embryo plant, usually following a period of **seed dormancy**. It requires the presence of water, a suitable temperature and the presence of a suitable oxygen tension. The water is taken up by the seed by inbibition, in which **starch, protein**, pectins and hemicelluloses adsorb water molecules and consequently swell up, causing the rupturing of the testa. The water is used to dissolve enzymes so that they may digest and mobilise the stored foods within the seed; all the respiratory and growth reactions also occur in aqueous solution. A suitable temperature is required so that the enzymes can work at reasonable rates, preferable near or at their optimum temperatures. Depending on the normal environment of the seed, the optimum temperature for growth may be between 10 and 40°C. The oxygen is required for a reasonable level of aerobic respiration.

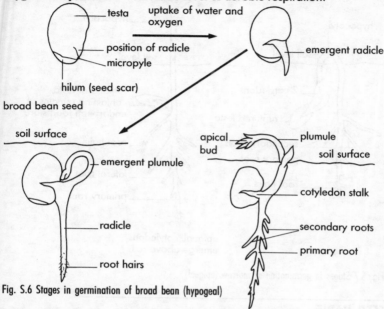

Fig. S.6 Stages in germination of broad bean (hypogeal)

The embryo grows by **mitosis** in the **apical meristem**, by cell elongation and by cell differentiation. The radicle emerges from the testa first and grows down, being positively **geotropic**. The plumule grows upwards, being negatively geotropic and positively phototropic. In hypogeal germination the cotyledons containing the food store remain underground (e.g. broad bean, Fig. S.6). In epigeal germination (Fig. S.7) the cotyledons, which may or may not contain food, depending on the species, come above the ground and act as the first green photosynthetic leaves.

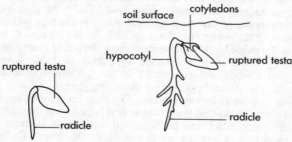

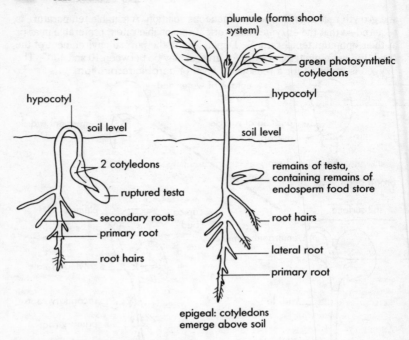

Fig. S.7 Stages in germination of marrow (epigeal)

SEED HABIT

The seed habit is the result of an evolutionary sequence which started among ancient **pteridophytes**. The first advance was the development of **heterospory** – that is, the production of microspores and megaspores. The microspore contents become the male **gametophyte** and the megaspore contents the female gametophyte. The trend that developed was for the free-living female gametophyte that was dependent on water for **fertilisation** to become reduced and eventually retained within the **sporophyte** tissues, where it was protected and supplied with food. The male gamotophyte developed into the pollen grain, which germinates by a pollen tube without the need for water. Fertilisation of the egg cell in the retained female gametophyte in the **ovule** by the male nucleus from the pollen grain results in seed formation. The seed habit started to evolve in fossil Lycopods (clubmosses) and Cycads and culminated in the modern Gymnosperms (conifers, cycads, yews) and Angiosperms (flowering plants).

The seed habit is valuable for two reasons. The plant becomes independent of water for reproduction and can thus colonise land habitats and the embryo is protected in the seed, which can be dispersed and remain dormant over unfavourable conditions. There are some drawbacks, however. The seeds require a large food reserve for germination, dispersal mechanisms may be risky, resulting in great wastage, and **pollination** relies on external agents, such as wind or insects.

◀ Colonisation, Dispersal ▶

SEGMENTATION

Segmentation (metameric segmentation) is the subdivision of an animal into basically similar units along the anterior–posterior axis. In the evolutionary sequence it is first shown clearly in the annelids, but has remained as a basic body plan in all later evolved groups, up to and including man. The segmentation initially appears in the mesoderm and each segment has a pattern of blood vessels, nervous system, excretory organs and epidermal structures. This repeating pattern may be modified by specialisations in different segments.

SEGREGATION

This is the separation of the genes of all allelomorphic pair into different gametes. Mendel's first law states only one of a pair of allelomorphic genes may be represented in a single **gamete**. Since the contrasting genes are on separate **homologous chromosomes** (on corresponding loci), when the homologous pairs separate to the poles during anaphase of **meiosis**, the allelic genes are also carried apart. This is a random process since it is purely chance which pole of the cell each one of the homologous chromosomes migrates to as they separate.

◀ Mendelian inheritance ▶

SELAGINELLA

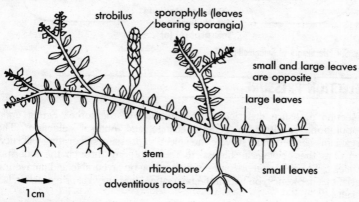

Fig. S.8 Selaginella sporophyte

Selaginella is a clubmoss, an example of the phylum Lycopodophyta. Most modern species are tropical and the only British species is *Selaginella selaginoides*. It has a creeping stem that is prostrate and short erect branches. The leaves are small, in four rows and arranged in opposite pairs, each with a lower larger leaf and an upper smaller leaf (see Fig. S.8). Rhizophores, which are root-like structures, grow down from the stem and form adventitious roots in the soil. The plant requires moist conditions and is found in north-western Britain, generally near streams. Reproduction is heterosporous and involves the production of vertical branches bearing strobili or cones. The mature gametophytes are dependent on food present in the spores, and do not lead an independent existence. **Fertilisation** requires water for the sperm to swim from the male gametophytes in the microspores to the archegonia on the female gametophytes in the megaspores. The zygote develops from the base of the archegonium. (See Fig. S.9.)

◀ Heterospory ▶

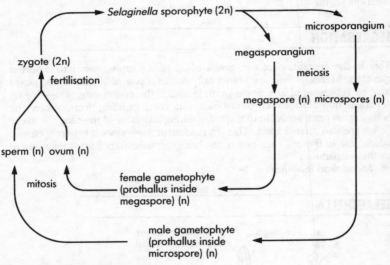

Fig. S.9 Life history of Selaginella

SELECTION PRESSURE

Selection pressure describes the sum total of the forces acting upon a **population**, resulting in genetic change and **natural selection**. Those organisms best fitted to survive the selection pressures operating will survive and pass their biological 'fitness' to their progeny through the inheritance process. The selection pressure is thus acting on favourable and unfavourable variations in **phenotype** within the population, and survival or extinction is the result.

◀ Darwin, Variation ▶

SELECTIVE BREEDING

This is a breeding programme used with animals or plants to select and stabilise characteristics which have some usefulness to man. The process used is **artificial selection** – that is, restricting breeding to those organisms that exhibit the required trait. Thus Hereford and Aberdeen Angus cattle have been selectively bred to enhance the quality and quantity of their meat, whereas Jersey and Friesian cattle have been selected for the quantity of their milk. In order to obtain good milkers, for example, the farmer will only breed from Friesian cows which show a high milk yield, not from the cows which have poor yields. The bulls used will have been 'progeny tested' – that is, they must have sired calves of proven ability for the required trait. All modern breeds of domestic animals, vegetables, fruits, crops and garden flowers have been produced by selective breeding.

It is important to conserve the world's **species**, for instance, in the tropical rain forests, since in those species must be many genes that could be of great benefit to mankind and they could be 'extracted' for use by artificial selection.

◀ Hybrids, Hybridisation ▶

SELECTIVE UPTAKE

Selective uptake means the uptake of specific chemical substances by cells. It occurs in root hair cells during uptake from the **soil**, in the **alimentary canal** during **absorption** of products of **digestion**, in liver cells when absorbing metabolites from the hepatic portal vein blood, in the **nephron** tubules when reabsorbing substances from glomerular filtrate, and in many other examples. The absorption may be active, requiring energy and a specific carrier, probably an intrinsic cell membrane protein or a permease **enzyme**. Alternatively the uptake may be facilitated – that is, still requiring a permease enzyme but not involving energy expenditure. The selective absorption may concentrate metabolites in cells against the diffusion gradient or against the electrical gradient caused by ionic charges (e.g. active uptake of K^+ ions into animal cells, active reabsorption of glucose from glomerular filtrate to the cells of the first convoluted tubules.

◀ Absorption, Active transport, Facilitated uptake, Vein, Root hairs ▶

SELFISH GENE CONCEPT

The selfish gene concept was developed by Richard Dawkins during the 1970s. He argued that the fundamental unit of selection is not the **species** or individual but the **gene**, since this is the unit of **heredity**. Thus selfishness is important to the survival of an individual and to its genes – the individual must survive at the expense of others.

◀ Kin selection ▶

SEMICIRCULAR CANALS

The semicircular canals arise from the utriculus in the inner **ear** and lie in three different planes at right angles to one another. They contain the fluid endolymph. At their ends are swellings called ampullae, which each contain an organ called a crista. This consists of a gelatinous mass, the cupula, attached to sensory hair cells. Any movement of the head will move endolymph in at least two canals. This will thus displace the cupula to one side, setting up nerve impulses via the hair cells. The information received by the brain is used in the **balancing** reflexes.

◀ Balance, Ear ▶

SEMICONSERVATIVE REPLICATION OF DNA

After replication of **DNA**, the two 'daughter' strands each consist of a single strand of newly synthesised DNA and a strand of the original parent, or primer, DNA. This is referred to as semiconservative replication.

SENESCENCE

Senescence means ageing, and is due to the deterioration and death of tissues which cannot be replaced, or cannot be regenerated at a rate sufficient to maintain life. It may be that the ageing process and death is triggered genetically, since it is of disadvantage to the species to have many old, non-reproductive individuals competing for space and food. All cells are thought to contain oncogenes, for example, and if these are switched on, they initiate the development of cancer, which results in death if it runs its natural course.

SENSE ORGAN

A sense organ is an organ composed of receptor cells and the tissues associated with them. The **eye**, for example contains light receptor cells concentrated in the **retina**, and associated parts concerned with gathering and focussing light, supporting and moving the eyeballs and relaying the information to the **brain**. Examples of other sense organs are ears for hearing and balance, tastebuds, olfactory organs for smell, simple and compound eyes in insects, and lateral line systems in fishes for echo-perception.

◀ Ear, Receptors ▶

SENSORY NEURONE

Neurones which carry impulses from receptor cells to the **central nervous system** are called sensory neurones. Aggregates of sensory neurones make up sensory nerves (e.g. optic nerve), but many nerves are mixed, containing both sensory and motor neurones (e.g. sciatic nerve). In vertebrates the cell bodies of the sensory neurones are situated in the dorsal root ganglia of the spinal cord. Sensory neurones usually have myelinated fibres for rapid saltatory conduction, thus allowing rapid response. Some sensory fibres concerned with the autonomic nervous system are non-myelinated, however, and so conduct impulses relatively slowly.

◀ Autonomic nervous control, Neurone ▶

SERE

A sere is a developmental step occuring during **succession** in an **ecosystem** or community. For example, of the successive stages in the **sand dune system** succession is called a sere.

SESSILE

Sessile means 'without a stalk' (e.g. the leaves of mosses which have no petioles). In animals it means 'fixed to the **substratum'** or sedentary (e.g. sea anemones).

SEX DETERMINATION

Maleness and femaleness are determined by genes carried on the sex **chromosomes.** There is one pair of sex chromosomes per **nucleus,** all the other chromosomes are called autosomes. In a female there are two X-chromosome present – that is, XX, the homogametic sex. In a male there is one **X-chromosome** and one Y-chromosome present – that is, XY, the heterogametic sex. The X-chromosomes and Y-chromosomes are usually different shapes. Females can produce only eggs which contain an X-chromosome, but sperm will contain either an X-chromosome or a Y-chromosome. Y-chromosomes contain few genes, but the presence or absence of a Y-chromosome in the genotype determines the sex of the individual.

Parent	Male	x	Female
	XY		XX
Gametes	50% Ⓧ 50% Ⓨ		100% Ⓧ
	sperms		eggs
F$_1$	50% XY male		50% XX female

In some groups of animals the methods of sex determination differ (e.g. in birds the homogametic sex is male and the heterogametic sex is female; in many insects it is the proportion of X-chromosomes to the autosomes which determines the sex).

SEX LINKAGE

All the genes on a particular chromosome form a **linkage** group. Those genes present on the sex chromosomes are sex-linked. Sex linkage concerns characteristics which have a special distribution with respect to sex. (e.g. **Haemophilia**, red–green colour blindness, which occur mainly in the human male).

In humans the Y-chromosomes is much shorter than the X-chromosome, so any recessive character carried on the X-chromosome section which has no corresponding Y-chromosome section must manifest itself in the male. In the female, such a recessive allele could be masked by the dominant allele on the second X-chromosome. For example,

Let N = allele for normal colour vision (dominant)
 n = allele for colour blindness (recessive)

Parents	Carrier female XN.Xn.		Normal male XN.Y.	
Gametes	50% XN	50% Xn eggs	50% XN	50% Y sperm
F_1	XN.XN.	XN.Xn.	XN.Y	Xn.Y
	normal female	carrier female	normal male	colour blind male

About one in thirty-three human males have red–green colour blindness, but colour-blind females are relatively rare, since they can result only from a cross between a colour-blind male and a carrier female.

Other examples of sex-linked inheritance include the recessive white-eyed mutation of *Drosophila*, yellow body in *Drosophila*, the presence of feathers on the shanks of Black Langshan poultry.

SEXUAL REPRODUCTION

Sexual reproduction involves the fusion of haploid nuclei, or gametes resulting in the formation of a **diploid zygote**. It results in **variation**, which is of survival value in evolutionary terms, since it gives the possibility of withstanding **selection pressure** in at least some of the population members. The variation arises because, firstly, **meiosis** is involved somewhere in the life cycle, usually during the production of gametes, so the gametes vary genetically. Second, two parents are involved who vary genetically, unless in-breeding is occuring, and thus **fertilisation** involves fusion of genetically different gametes. Sexual reproduction occurs in the majority of animal and plant species, and in general does not produce the large numbers of offspring that **asexual reproduction** does.

◀ Gametogenesis, Genetic variation, Haploidy, Pollination ▶

SEXUALLY TRANSMITTED DISEASE

Sexually transmitted diseases can be transmitted from an infected person to another person during sexual intercourse. The infected person may not be exhibiting symptoms of the disease and may not even know they are infected. The main diseases transmitted this way are AIDS, genital herpes, gonorrhea and syphilis. They are spread through the population by people having more than one sexual partner. AIDS is also spread by infected needles among drug addicts.

SHOULDER JOINT

The shoulder joint is a synovial ball and socket joint between the socket on the scapula and the head of the humerus. It attaches the forelimb to the body, the scapula being attached to the thoracic cage by muscle. This gives resilience to the forelimb, unlike the bony attachments of the hindlimb to the body, which give rigidity for weight bearing. The socket on the scapula is shallow, allowing almost universal movement by the shoulder joint.
◄ Forelimb of mammal, Joints ►

SICKLE CELL ANAEMIA

Sickle cell anaemia is an inherited disease caused by a mutation that changes one amino acid in haemoglobin. The sufferer makes abnormal haemoglobin, which as it unloads its oxygen, tends to form stiff rod-like structures that bend the red cells into a sickle shape. These cells rupture (haemolyse) very easily, and quicker than they can be replaced, so the patient becomes anaemic. The sickled cells can also get stuck in small blood vessels, cutting off the blood supply to tissues. A sufferer from sickle cell anaemia is homozygous for the sickling gene. The heterozygous individuals are said to have the sickle cell trait, but they do not develop anaemia. Such people have a high resistance to the malarial parasite, since the gene seems to stop red cells from rupturing during a malarial attack; it also causes potassium to leak from red cells to plasma and low potassium levels in the red cells kills the malarial parasites. Sickle cell genes are thus found mainly in malarial areas of the world.
◄ Gene mutation, Heterozygous genotype, Homozygous genotype ►

SIEVE PLATE, SIEVE TUBE

The sieve tubes (sieve elements) are the cells of phloem (Fig. S.10) that transport organic solutes through the plant. When mature the elements have no nucleus, ribosomes, or Golgi complex, having lost these during development, and have only a few small mitochondria. The cytoplasm is restricted to a thin layer bounded by a plasma membrane, just inside the cell wall. Each sieve tube has one or more companion cells closely associated with it, which have all the usual cell organelles, dense cytoplasm and small vacuoles. The fact that they contain many mitochondria and ribosomes suggests that they are metabolically very active, – indeed, sieve tubes cannot function if companion cells die. The cell walls at the end of the sieve tubes become modified into sieve plates as the **plasmodesmata** enlarge to form sieve pores, and the pores become lined by a veneer of the **glucose** polymer, callose. A fibrous protein, called 'phloem protein', develops in the cytoplasm and runs through the sieve pores (although there is some doubt about this fact since in electron micrographs the sieve pores are often empty – however, this may be due to a processing artefact). The phloem protein used to be known as the 'slime strand'. In older phloem the sieve pores may become completely blocked with callose as the cells become redundant.

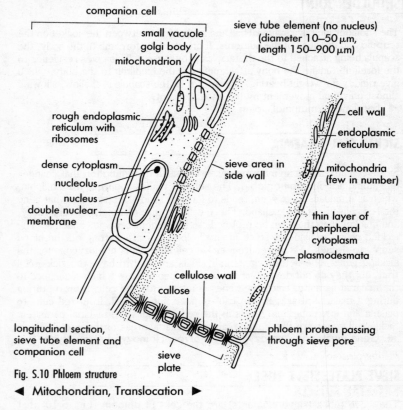

Fig. S.10 Phloem structure

◄ Mitochondrian, Translocation ►

SILVICULTURE

Silviculture is the culture and growing of trees, and ultimately woodland. The Forestry Commission is the largest body in the British Isles carrying out silviculture. In the past the policy was to plant monoculture forests in formal blocks, which cut across and spoiled the natural landscape. Nowadays the policy is to plant mixed conifer and broad-leaved deciduous forest, and to contour the forest to the natural landscape, giving a more aesthetic appearance. Since the number of tree species has been increased, so the number of associated plant and animal species has increased. Sitka Spruce (*Picea sitchensis*), Lodgepole Pine (*Pine contorta* var. *latifolia*), Corsican Pine (*Pinus nigra* var. *maritima*), Scots Pine (*Pinus sylvestris*) and Common Larch (*Larix decidua*) are all commonly found in British planted forests, interspersed with areas of oakwood, ashwood or beechwood.

◄ Forestry ►

SINGLE CELL PROTEIN (SCP)

Single cell protein is made from the mass commercial culture of particular micro-organisms. **Bacteria, fungi** and yeasts can all be grown to form a crop. When washed and dried the cells provide a powder that is very rich in protein, **carbohydrate** and fat. The production costs of such protein are much less than with conventional protein (e.g. meat), but the problem of getting people to accept it as a new sort of food has not yet been overcome.

◄ Biotechnology ►

SITES OF SPECIAL SCIENTIFIC INTEREST (SSSIs)

These are sites which contain habitats and populations which are of biological or geological importance, and which require **conservation** and preservation. Man's activities in such areas are limited by law and restricted to activities that will not disrupt the special features of the site. The SSSIs usually come under the control of the Nature Conservancy Council.

SIZE INCREASE

Size increase could be an increase in volume, girth or height, and if it is permanent, it is a parameter of **growth**. Temporary size increase may be due to storage of fat, or overstorage of fat in **obesity**, to **pregnancy** in female mammals, or to **water uptake** in roots causing a plant to change from wilting/**plasmolysis** to **turgor**.

SKELETAL MUSCLE

Skeletal muscle is striated voluntary muscle that attaches to the **skeleton**. It is responsible for movement of joints and bones. In an **endoskeleton** the muscle is attached to the outside of the bones; in an **exoskeleton** it is attached to the inner surfaces of the skeletal components (e.g. apodemes in insects).

◄ Striated muscle ►

SKELETON

Skeletons have the following basic functions:

- They provide a **support** and framework for the body, giving it a recognisable shape.
- They provide cover for vital organs, thus giving it a recognisable shape.
- They provide attachment bases for muscles, so that together with **joints**, movements can be made.

Endoskeletons are inside the body, particularly in **vertebrates**, and are made mainly of **bone**, but with some **cartilage**. Exoskeletons are on the outer surface of organisms, occurring particularly in **arthropods** and echinoderms. In arthropods they are made largely from **chitin**.

The **endoskeleton** of the human (Fig. S. 11), for example, can be classified in the following way: the axial skeleton, consisting of the skull, the vertebral column and rib cage with sternum; and the appendicular skeleton, consisting of the pectoral girdle and forelimb bones, and the pelvic girdle and hindlimb bones.

the sclerites are the thick plates of chitin and are joined by thinner, flexible, chitinous joint membranes muscles are internal

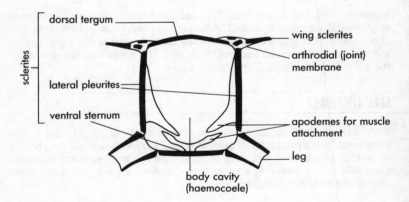

Fig. S.12 Insect exoskeleton

The chitinous **exoskeleton** of insects (Fig. S.12) is divided into tough plates or sclerites, joined by thinner areas of chitin called arthrodial membranes. Muscles are attached to the apodemes, which are inwardly projecting rigid processes.

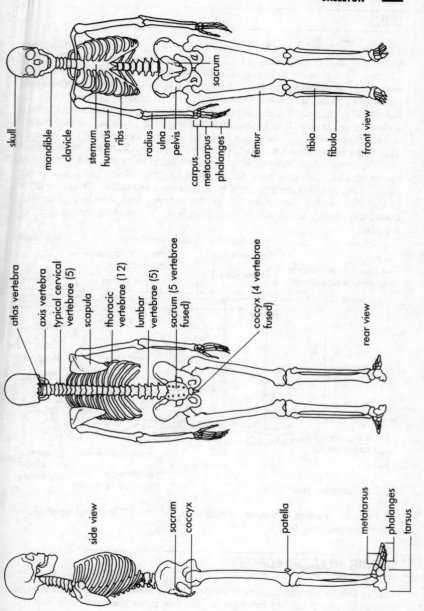

front view

- skull
- mandible
- clavicle
- sternum
- humerus
- ribs
- radius
- ulna
- pelvis
- carpus
- metacarpus
- phalanges
- femur
- tibia
- fibula
- sacrum

rear view

- atlas vertebra
- axis vertebra
- typical cervical vertebrae (5)
- scapula
- thoracic vertebrae (12)
- lumbar vertebrae (5)
- sacrum (5 vertebrae fused)
- coccyx (4 vertebrae fused)

side view

- sacrum
- coccyx
- patella
- metatarsus
- phalanges
- tarsus

Fig. S.11 Human skeleton

SKIN

The skin (Fig. S. 13) is the largest **organ** of the body. Its main importance lies in the fact that it interfaces the organism with its environment, thus it is adapted for receiving sensory stimuli, for preventing water loss in land animals, for preventing erosion by friction, for preventing entry of **pathogens** into the organism, and allowing stretching to accommodate movements by the animal. The outermost layer of the skin is a stratified squamous epithelium known as **epidermis**. It is constantly shedding cells and skin flakes from its surface (exfoliation) and these are replaced by mitotic divisions from its base. This helps to withstand friction. The dead upper epidermis is impregnated with the fibrous protein alpha-keratin, which helps to harden and waterproof the skin. The epidermis may be modified to give rise to hairs and sweat glands, both of which are important in temperature regulation. The inner layer of the skin, under the epidermis, is the dermis. This consists of areolar **connective tissue**, which allows stretching while maintaining the integrity of the skin.

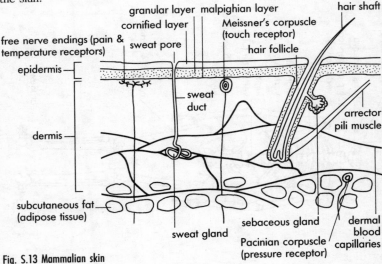

Fig. S.13 Mammalian skin

◀ Fibrous proteins, Squamous epithelia, Stimulus, Stratified epithelium, Thermoregulation ▶

SLIDING FILAMENT CONCEPT

This refers to the mechanism of contraction in **skeletal muscle**. During the contraction, by a **ratchet mechanism**, the thin **actin** filaments slide into the thick **myosin** filaments, thus shortening the sarcomeres.
◀ Muscle contraction, Sarcomere ▶

SMALL INTESTINE

The small intestine is a long tube starting at the pyloric sphincter of the stomach and ending at a valve into the large intestine. The duodenum, which is about 25 cm long in humans, is the first part. It has crypts of Lieberkuhn and Brunner glands in its walls which secrete intestinal juice, and it also receives bile from the liver and pancreatic juice from the pancreas. The middle section is the jejunum, which is about 2.5 m long in humans, and the final portion, where most absorption occurs, is the ileum, which is about 3.6 m long in humans.

The inner lining of the small intestine bears millions of *villi*, which in turn bear microvilli, thus providing a huge surface area for absorption into blood and lymph.

◄ Digestion, Gut histology, Villus ►

SMOKING, EFFECTS OF

The pseudostratified epithelium of the trachea and bronchi contains three types of cells: columnar ciliated cells, columnar goblet cells, which secrete mucus, and basal cells, which divide mitotically to regenerate the epithelium. Inhaled smoke has a very irritating effect on this epithelium, since it causes, firstly, an enlargement of the goblet cells, which then secrete excess mucus, and, secondly, an increase in the mitotic rate, so that excess basal cells are produced, filling spaces which should be occupied by ciliated cells. The cilia become less and less effective, and since mucus is not removed to the throat, it causes a 'smoker's cough'. The cells eventually become malignant and lung cancer develops.

Bronchitis is inflammation of the bronchi, the most common cause of which is smoking. The symptoms are a constant cough, which brings up a greenish-yellow sputum. The constant irritation also damages the alveoli, which become replaced with thick elastic tissue. Millions of alveolar sacs rupture, reducing the surface area for exchange. This is emphysema and is irreversible.

◄ Goblet cell ►

SMOOTH ENDOPLASMIC RETICULUM (SER)

This is the area of endoplasmic reticulum in the cell ultrastructure which has no associated ribosomes. Apart from having a role in supporting the cytoplasm, it is concerned with intracellular transport, detoxification of drugs and synthesis of non-protein material for export (e.g. steroids).

◄ Ribosome ►

SMOOTH MUSCLE

Smooth muscle (Fig. S.14) is involuntary since it is not under conscious

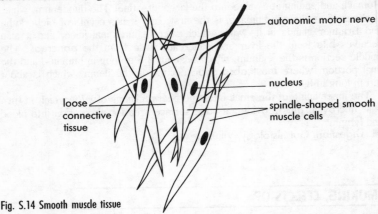

Fig. S.14 Smooth muscle tissue

control. It is controlled by the autonomic nervous system and has the power of slow sustained contraction. In the gut it shows characteristic waves of contraction and relaxation called **peristalsis**. It consists of spindle-shaped cells with tapering ends. These interlock with those of adjacent cells to form sheets of smooth muscle tissue.

◄ Autonomic nervous control ►

SOCIAL BEHAVIOUR

Apart from when mating, most animal species show no intraspecific cooperation and are often antagonistic to each other. In some species, however, there are degrees of cooperative interaction, for the benefit of the individual animal as well as the species. Some interactions are relatively loose, such as the flocking together of swallows before **migration**, or of fish when confusing predators. Other interactions are much closer and more evolved, such as those of honey bees or human society. For the society to remain integrated, it is important that the animals can recognise one another (e.g. colony odour and pheromones in honey bees), and that the individuals can communicate with each other (e.g. dances and pheromones in honey bees). Often within the society there is a 'pecking order', worked out as a result of **aggression** between the members, as, for example, within a flock of birds. The largest most aggressive birds will dominate the flock while weaker birds will be subservient. Within the society aggression may be triggered when an animal comes too close to another: each animal requires its own 'individual distance', a volume of space that it treats as its own. This can be seen in the spacing-out of flocks of birds lined up on telephone wires.

◄ Predation ►

SODIUM

Sodium is the most abundant extracellular ion in animals, being pumped out of cells into surrounding tissue fluid by the sodium pump during active transport. It occurs in **blood plasma**, **lymph** and tissue fluid, making up about 90 per cent of extracellular ions. Its level in the blood of mammals is regulated by **aldosterone** from the adrenal cortex, which acts on the ascending limbs of the loops of Henle in the nephrons stimulating the reabsorption of sodium to the blood. Sodium is necessary for the transmission of action potentials in nerve and muscle, and for contributing to the **solute potential** of blood, maintaining blood volume and pressure.

Sodium does not occur in plant tissues in such high quantities and is termed a trace element for plants. The main ion in plant tissue is potassium.

◀ Action potential, Trace elements ▶

SOIL

The scientific study of soil is pedology and soil factors which affect the communities in the ecosystem are said to be **edaphic factors**. The soil is the layer lying over the rocks of the Earth's crust, and its main importance is to supply **nutrients** to allow healthy plant growth. Soil is a dynamic structure, since it changes and develops with time as a result of factors such as climate, underlying rocks, local topography and organisms. Basically it has four structural components; mineral skeleton, organic matter, water and air. Living in and on the soil will be dependent organisms.

▶ THE MINERAL COMPONENTS

These are formed from the parent rock by weathering into smaller and smaller particles. The size of the particles in a soil determine the properties of that soil. The smallest clay particles are less than 2 micrometres in diameter and often behave in a colloidal way. Silt particles are between 2 and 20 micrometres in diameter, and fine sand is between 20 and 200 micrometres in diameter (0.2mm).

In a sandy soil the particles are predominantly large and do not aggregate together to give the soil a structure. Since the pore spaces between the particles will be large, aeration is good, but so is drainage, so the soil can hold little water and tends to be dry. Though the soil is warm due to its lack of water (as water evaporates, it cools due to latent heat of vaporisation), it is rapidly leached of its salts by the water as it drains through. Bases are particularly leached out and the soil becomes acidic as humus acids accumulate.

In a clay soil the particles are mainly fine and can aggregate to form crumbs if calcium ions are present (liming helps this). The soil can form large sticky clods when wet and becomes hard and cracked when dry. It has small pores so is badly aerated and often waterlogged, since the water is held by capillarity and adsorption to the large surface area of particles. It tends to be cold due to its waterlogged nature, but does not leach to a great extent.

Equal proportions of clay and silt give an excellent soil with a good tilth and fertile porous crumb structure. This is called a loam.

▶ THE ORGANIC MATTER OF THE SOIL

This is derived from the decay of dead animals and plants, and from excreta. Undecomposed material, such as freshly fallen leaves, is called litter. The final decomposed brown-black amorphous organic matter is called humus and this is in a colloidal state. It releases minerals into the soil which are then available to recycle through the food chains. Organic matter is largely present in the topsoil with very little in the subsoil.

▶ THE SOIL WATER

This exists in several fractions. Gravitational water drains freely down through the soil until it reaches the water table, the depth of which depends largely on rainfall. When draining down, the water may wash out, or leach, soluble salts. Hygroscopic water is tightly adsorbed to the surfaces of soil particles, and not very accessible to plant roots. Capillary water is held in the pores by capillary attraction, and is readily available to plant roots. The total amount of water that can be held by a soil is the field capacity.

▶ THE SOIL ATMOSPHERE

This also exists in the pores, though in a waterlogged soil the soil air is displaced. Lack of soil air inhibits the growth of aerobic micro-organisms which aid decay, and promotes the growth of anaerobic bacteria. These tend to produce carbon dioxide, which contributes to soil acidity.

◀ Colloid, Colloidal properties, Leaching ▶

SOIL EROSION

Soil erosion is the removal of soil from one area to another. The area which has lost the soil is said to be eroded. The erosion may be natural, as for example, when soil is washed off a hillside by rain water into valleys, or when soil is blown from an exposed area and deposited in a more sheltered area. Erosion may also be caused by the activities of humans. For example, the removal of hedges which act as windbreaks, the removal of rain forests which act as windbreaks and bind the soil, and the compaction of soil by livestock or heavy machinery can all lead to wind and water erosion.

SOLUTE POTENTIAL

This denotes the change in the water potential of a phase due to the presence of solute molecules. The solute molecules lower the water potential, thus solute potential is always negative.

◀ Solutes ▶

SOLUTES

A solute is a compound which dissolves in a solvent to form a solution. Examples of solutes in biology are sugars, amino acids, salts, vitamins and so on.
◀ Solvents ▶

SOLUTION

A solution consists of a solute dissolved in a solvent. Most solutions in biology are aqueous – that is, water is the solvent.
◀ Solutes, Solvent ▶

SOLVENT

A solvent is the medium in which the solute is dissolved in a solution.
◀ Solutes ▶

SORUS

A sorus comprises a group of sporangia situated on the underside of fertile leaves, or sporophylls, of ferns. There may be a protective cover, which is called an indusium.
◀ Ferns ▶

SPECIALISATION OF CELLS

During growth and development, cells become specialised to perform different functions. This is called differentiation and it allows division of labour among cells and tissues. In a plant, for example, all tissues, such as parenchyma, collenchyma, sclerenchyma, xylem and phloem, develop from the original meristematic cell derivatives. Since the type of cell division during growth is mitosis, it follows that all cells in a line back to the original zygote will have identical genetic codes, and a full complement of all the genes received from the gametes. As the cells develop into different types, certain genes are turned on to cause the development of certain characteristics, and other genes must be switched off so that they do not express themselves. A fat cell would have the genes activated which are concerned with the mechanism of fat storage, but the genes concerned with haemoglobin synthesis, which must also be present, would be inhibited.

The inhibitory mechanisms may involve the proteins (histones) of the chromosomes; or hormones (such as gibberellins, human growth hormone, sex hormones); or genetic mechanisms such as regulator, inducer and repressor genes, which can produce substances that act as gene switches.

The details of gene regulation, however, are still far from being completely understood.

◄ Gamete, Gene, Genetic code, Gibberellin, Histone, Hormone, Jacob-Monod model of gene control ►

SPECIATION, SPECIES

Speciation is the formation of new species of organism. There are various ways of defining a species: from a genetical view they can be considered as a group of organisms capable of interbreeding to form **fertile offspring**, or a group of organisms showing very similar genetic make-up; from an ecological point of view they can be thought of as a group of organisms sharing the same ecological **niche**; or from an evolutionary view they can be considered as a group of organisms possessing a unique collection of anatomical and functional features.

A particular species does not usually exist as a single big population but tends to be split by an isolating mechanism into small interbreeding groups called demes. Different sorts of **selection pressure** may operate on different demes, and this, coupled with **variation** arising within the demes, may result in differences in **phenotype** and **genotype** between one deme and another. This may result in different races appearing within the species. For example, the British Pied Wagtail (*Motacilla alba yarrellii*) is a sub-species or race of the White Wagtail (*Motacilla alba alba*), which is found on the other side of the English Channel in Continental Europe.

A gradual change in the characteristics of a species across its geographical range is called a cline. Species showing marked phenotypic differences according to their geographical distances apart are called polytypic species. For example, the British and Scandanavian varieties of the Lesser Black-backed Gull (*Larus fuscus*).

Intraspecific speciation is when a single species gives rise to a new species. Interspecific speciation is when two different species interact to give rise to a new species. Allopatric speciation is when intraspecific speciation occurs whilst the populations are geographically separated. Sympatric speciation is when intraspecific speciation occurs in a population in the same geographical area.

In intraspecific speciation it is crucial that gene flow between populations must be stopped so that each population can become genetically isolated. Within an isolated population, natural selection acts on the phenotypic variations produced by **mutation**, **meiosis** and **fertilisation**, and new races or sub-species may develop. Eventually these may have diverged so much from other populations of the original species that they will not interbreed with them to form fertile offspring. They can then be given the status of new species. Barriers which cause reproductive isolation between populations or demes are called **isolating mechanisms**. This barrier may be geographical in which case allopatric speciation results. For sympatric speciation, a seasonal, ecological, behavioural, mechanical or physiological barrier is required, in order to prevent fertilisation.

An example of allopatric speciation is that of Darwin's finches on the

Galapagos Islands. An original stock of finches must have arrived on the islands from the South American mainland. In the absence of **competition** from species already present on the islands, selection occurred to produce a variety of species adapted to fill various ecological niches (adaptive radiation). When these species dispersed from island to island they were reproductively isolated from other finches and therefore coexisted as distinct species.

An example of interspecific hybridisation is that of *Spartina townsendii*. This is thought to have arisen in about 1870 in Southampton Water, by hybridisation between the endemic British species of Cord Grass (*Spartina maritima*) and an introduced American species, *Spartina alterniflora*. These interbred to form a sterile hybrid, but due to a doubling in chromosome number, the hybrid became fertile. This was the allopolyploid plant *Spartina townsendii*. It has widely colonised coastal mudflats throughout Britain, and is said to possess 'hybrid vigour'.

◀ Darwin, Evolution, Hybrids, Hybridisation, Isolating mechanisms, Polyploidy ▶

SPECIFICITY

This refers to enzymes which are substrate-specific – that is, they will react only with one particular substrate or group of substrates. Some enzymes, such as those involved in digestion, show group specificity (e.g. lipase will hydrolyse all types of lipid). Other enzymes show absolute specificity (e.g. succinic dehydrogenase). This is usually explained by a 'lock and key' hypothesis to demonstrate the chemical affinity between the active sites of the **enzyme** and the specific substrate to which they attach, and the lack of chemical affinity between the active sites and other substrates.

Enzymes are also reaction specific and will not catalyse other types of reaction, (e.g. polymerases catalyse condensation reactions while dehydrogenases catalyse oxidation/reduction reactions).

Enzymes are named according to their substrate and reaction specificity (e.g. Glucose-6-phosphate dehydrogenase, Succinic dehydrogenase, Glucose-6-phosphate isomerase).

◀ Active site ▶

SPERM

Sperm (Fig. S.15) are haploid male gametes, carrying the male genetical material in the male nucleus to the female **gamete** so that **fertilisation** can occur. They have a head, containing the haploid nucleus, and an acrosome for egg penetration, a middle piece with many mitochondria, and a tail or flagellum for swimming and motility.

◀ Gametogenesis, Haploidy, Mitochondrion ▶

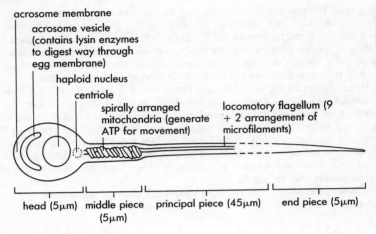

acrosome membrane

acrosome vesicle
(contains lysin enzymes
to digest way through
egg membrane)

haploid nucleus

centriole

spirally arranged
mitochondria (generate
ATP for movement)

locomotory flagellum (9
+ 2 arrangement of
microfilaments)

head (5μm)　middle piece (5μm)　principal piece (45μm)　end piece (5μm)

Fig. S.15 Mammalian sperm cell

SPIDERS

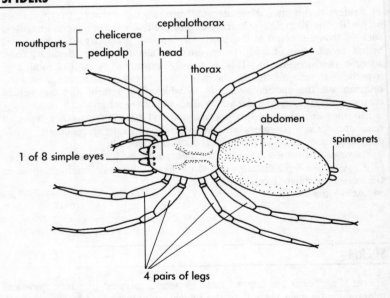

mouthparts —
chelicerae
pedipalp

cephalothorax

head

thorax

abdomen

spinnerets

1 of 8 simple eyes

4 pairs of legs

Fig. S.16 Dorsal view of a spider

Spiders (Fig. S.16) are terrestrial members of the phylum *Arthropoda*, class *Arachnida*. They are characterised by having four pairs of legs attached to a

cephalothorax, mandibles and poison fangs, spinnerets for producing silk, and simple eyes (2, 6 or 8) but no compound eyes. Some species weave webs (orb or sheet variety), others are hunting spiders, some are jumping spiders.
◀ Arachnids, Arthropods ▶

SPINAL CORD

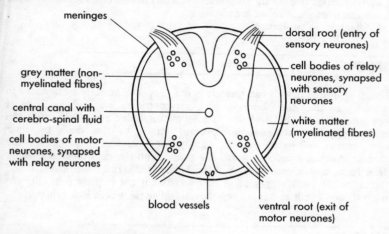

Fig. S.17 Transverse section of the spinal cord

The spinal cord (Fig. S.17) is the part of the **central nervous system** that is housed in the neural canals of the **vertebrae** and runs down the mid-dorsal length of the body. Its functions are to:

- relay impulses coming in and going out at the same level;
- relay impulses going up and down the cord to other levels;
- relay impulses to and from the brain.

In the human there are thirty-one pairs of spinal nerves, each consisting of a dorsal, sensory root on which is the dorsal root ganglion that holds the cell bodies of the sensory neurones, and a ventral, motor root with no ganglion. The two roots join to make a mixed nerve where they leave the neural canal. In the spinal cord, **grey matter** is located in the centre and white matter round the outside.

◀ Neurone, Spinal reflec arc ▶

SPINAL REFLEX ARC

A spinal reflex is an automatic **response** to a **stimulus** mediated through the **spinal cord** without directly involving the **brain reflex arc**. Spinal reflexes are important in adjusting the tone of muscles to maintain posture and in producing reciprocal inhibition of antagonistic muscles. They also cause protective withdrawal responses, and make homeostatic adjustments in breathing rate and blood pressure.

The arc consists of, in sequence, a sensory receptor to perceive the stimulus, a sensory **neurone**, a **synapse** in the **central nervous system**, an association or relay neurone, another synapse in the central nervous system, and a motor neurone which carries the impulses to an effector muscle or gland, which carries out the response. The relay neurone and second synapse is absent from some reflex arcs.

◄ Effectors, Receptors ►

SPINDLE

Spindles form in **mitosis** and **meiosis** in late prophase or early metaphase. In animal cells they form between the two **centrioles** which come to lie at opposite ends of the **nucleus**. Spindle **microtubules** stretch towards the nuclear equator, where **chromosomes** attach to the ends by their centromeres. When the spindle microtubules contract in anaphase, the chromosomes are pulled towards the poles, with the centromeres leading. Near to the centrioles is an array of short blind-ending radiating tubules, called the aster. These are present in animal cells but not in plant cells. Spindle microtubules occur in plants even though higher plant cells lack centrioles.

SPIRACLE

Spiracles are pores in the insect **exoskeleton** that lead into the **tracheal system**. In the cockroach there are ten pairs of spiracles, one pair on the prothorax, one pair on the mesothorax, and one pair on each of the first eight abdominal segments. Entry of air into the spiracles may be by **diffusion** at rest, but aided by **ventilation mechanisms** (dorso-ventral flattening and expanding) when activity is increased. Much of the CO_2 produced diffuses out through the cuticle rather than exiting through the spiracles. This helps to reduce water loss via the spiracles.

SPONGES

Sponges are sessile, mostly marine animals belonging to the **Porifera**. Though multicellular they show a very low level of organisation, having no organs and only ill-defined tissues. They generally have a sac-shaped body with pore-like perforations. Water flows through the pores into the central body cavity and out through a large opening at the top of the body. The wall has three layers; an outer layer of flattened epidermal cells, a middle gelatinous layer with wandering amoeboid cells and an inner layer of flagellated cells. The amoeboid cells secrete an internal skeleton of spicules, which can be composed of calcium carbonate, silicates or protein.

SPORANGIA

A sporangium is a plant structure that produces spores. Sporangia occur in many plant groups but are well illustrated in the phyla **Lycopodophyta** (club mosses), Sphenophyta (horsetails) and Filicinophyta (ferns). In **fern** sporophytes sporangia are borne in large numbers on the undersides of the fronds, in groups called sori. Within a **sorus** the development of sporangia is staggered so that they will mature at different times. The sporangium consists of a wall, one cell thick, within which is a tapetum of nutritive layer, and archesporial tissue inside. The spore mother cells in the archesporium divide meiotically to form tetrads of spores, with sixty-four spores formed per sporangium. The head of the sporangium is circled by a special row of cells called the annulus. The inner walls of these cells are very heavily thickened so that tension develops as their protoplasts dry out, which ruptures the sporangium at a weak point called the stomium. A jerky movement occurs, ejecting the spores into passing air currents for dispersal.

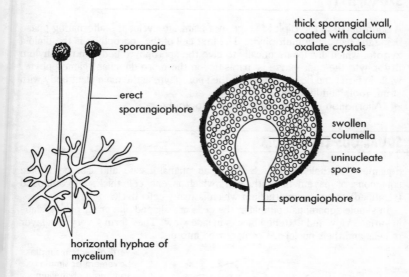

Fig. S.18 Sporangia of mucor (fungus)

In the club moss **Selaginella**, there are microsporangia and megasporangia and similarly, in the seed plants, where the spores can be considered to be within pollen grains and ovules.

Simpler types of sporangia occur in the algae and fungi (Fig. S.18) and the capsules of mosses and liverworts can be considered to be sporangia.

◀ Gametophyte, Spore, Sporophyte, Sporulation ▶

SPORE

Spores are units of asexual reproduction that may be single-celled or several-celled. They are produced in large numbers by **sporophyte** plants and a few animals such as **protozoa**, and dispersed by air, water or animals. In plants, they germinate to form a **gametophyte**. Spores are often thick-walled resting stages, capable of lying dormant during unfavourable conditions.

◀ Sporangia ▶

SPORULATION

Sporulation is the release of spores from a sporangium, usually by splitting of the sporangial wall (dehiscence).

◀ Sporangia, Spore ▶

SPOROPHYTE

A sporophyte is the **diploid** stage in a plant life cycle, the alternating phase being the haploid **gametophyte**. The first cell of the sporophyte is the diploid **zygote**, which divides mitotically to give the sporophyte body. In the phylum Bryophyta the sporophyte is 'parasitic' on the more dominant gametophyte, while in ferns and **flowering plants** the sporophyte is the main plant body with stem, roots and leaves.

◀ Alternation of generations, Fern, Haploidy ▶

SQUAMOUS EPITHELIUM

Squamous epithelium (Fig. S.19) is an animal tissue and can be simple squamous or pavement epithelium, which is one cell thick, or compound (stratified) squamous epithelium which is many cells thick.

In simple squamous epithelium the cells are shaped like crazy paving slabs in surface view and flattened blocks in side view. They form a very thin layer of cells and their nuclei are compressed into discs.

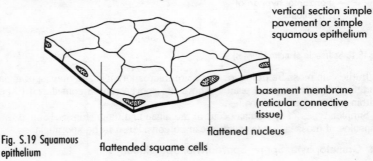

vertical section simple pavement or simple squamous epithelium

basement membrane (reticular connective tissue)

flattened nucleus

Fig. S.19 Squamous epithelium

flattended squame cells

The epithelium is found in many places in the body. It occurs where a smooth lining tissue is required in order to minimise friction (e.g. lining arteries, veins and the heart chambers. It also occurs where a protective covering is needed that is thin enough to permit diffusion of molecules in solution (e.g. lining blood capillaries and the lung alveoli, and lining the Bowman's capsules of the kidney nephron, where the squamous cells are modified into podocytes).

Compound squamous epithelium makes up the epidermis of the skin, and is found lining structures such as the buccal cavity, oesophagus and vagina. The basal cells divide constantly by mitosis, forming cuboidal or columnar cells. This pushes older cells upwards towards the surface, where they become flattened and squamous. In skin the outer cells become modified by the deposition of the protein keratin, which waterproofs the skin and makes it resistant to infection and to friction. The keratinised cells are dead, however, and ultimately they flake off, to be replaced by cells from lower down.

STABILISING SELECTION

In polygenic inheritance of a character a normal distribution ('top-hat' distribution) of the character will often be shown, with the commonest phenotypes around the mean and the less common variations tailing off either side. If selection acts against these 'tail' variations, it tends to allow individuals around the mean to survive. This is stabilising selection, as opposed to disruptive selection, which would select against the mean and divide the population into two.
◄ Natural selection ►

STAGE MICROMETER

A stage micrometer is a scale, either on a microscope slide or incorporated into an eye piece, which allows measurement of microscopic sizes. The divisions of the scale will usually be in micrometres (10^{-6} metre).

STAINS

Stains are dyes which are used to stain specific tissue components, allowing them to be visualised more readily. A stain must contain a chemical grouping called a chromophore which absorbs certain wavelengths of visible light and thus transmits colour, and another group which will form a salt link with the tissue components, thus binding the stain in place. Basic stains (e.g. basic fuchsin) tend to stain acid tissue components (e.g. DNA, RNA, nuclei). Acid stains (e.g. eosin) tend to stain basic tissue components (e.g. many cytoplasmic proteins). Basic stains are usually blue; acidic stains red. Other stains (e.g. haematoxylin) require an intermediate compound, usually a metal salt, to attach them to specific tissue components.

STAMEN

The stamens are the male organs of a flower and make up the androecium. Each stamen consists of a stalk or filament, at the apex of which is the anther. This consists of two lobes, each containing a pollen sac which produces the pollen grains (microspores) which are released when the anthers dehisce.

◀ Anthers, Fertilisation, Floral morphology, Pollination ▶

STANDARD DEVIATION

Standard deviation is a measure of the spread of a distribution curve. It can be used as a measure of precision in experimental work and measurements.

$$\text{Standard Deviation } (\sigma) = \sqrt{\frac{\Sigma \ (x-\bar{x})}{n-I}}$$

Sigma (σ) = standard deviation $\qquad \bar{x}$ = mean of the distribution
Σ = 'sum of'
x = every single observation in turn which makes up the mean
n = number of observations (should be more than 30 for an adequate measure)

An application of this can be seen, for example, in the quality control of daily blood glucose level measurements in hospital pathology laboratories. The mean value obtained from a large set of analyses and the allowable spread (usually two standard deviations either side of the mean) are shown on a wall chart. Each days results are plotted and must fall within the acceptable range. If they do not, the reason for the divergence must be corrected and the patient's measurements repeated.

◀ Statistical analysis ▶

STANDING CROP

The standing crop is the biomass or amount of living material in a given population of organisms at a certain time. The standing crop of various fish species has become drastically reduced by overfishing in recent years. It is therefore essential to limit fish quotas to enable the stocks to rebuild to satisfactory levels.

◀ Fishing regulations ▶

STARCH

Starch is a storage polysaccharide of green plants. It consists of a mixture of two main compounds, alpha-amylose and amylopectin. Alpha-amylose is a polymer of between 300 and 3000 alpha-D-glucose molecules joined by 1,4 glycosidic links. This polymer is coiled into a helix forming a minute starch grain or micelle. Amylopectin is similar to alpha-amylose but is highly branched, with each branch forming a 1,6 glycosidic link with the stem. Alpha-amylose can be completely hydrolysed to maltose by salivary and pancreatic amylases in humans, but amylopectin can be digested only down to its first branch links by these enzymes, thus maltose units and dextrin result. If the branch links are hydrolysed by cooking, the amylopectin can be completely broken down to maltase by amylases.

◀ Amylase, Carbohydrate, Polysaccharides, Storage polymer ▶

STARFISH

Starfish (Fig. S.20) are marine, radially symmetrical animals with five-part symmetry, belonging to the phylum **Echinodermata**, class Stelleroidea.

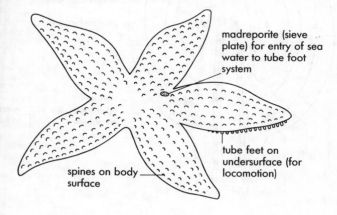

madreporite (sieve plate) for entry of sea water to tube foot system

tube feet on undersurface (for locomotion)

spines on body surface

Fig. S.20 Starfish, showing penta-radial symmetry and position of tube-feet

◀ Radial symmetry ▶

STATISTICAL ANALYSIS

Statistical analysis is an essential tool in biological investigation, since it is by applying statistical techniques to analyse sets of results that these can be correctly interpreted and reasonable conclusions drawn. The statistical test that is used must be suitable to fit the measurements or investigations being carried out. For example, **standard deviation** is useful to measure the spread or dispersion of a distribution, or to monitor the quality control or precision of measurements. A **t test** would be used to test the significance of differences between two means, whereas a chi^2 test would measure goodness of fit or the significance of an observed result, or ratio, against an expected hypothesis.

STEM ELONGATION

Fig. S.21 Longitudinal section of stem apex (apical bud)

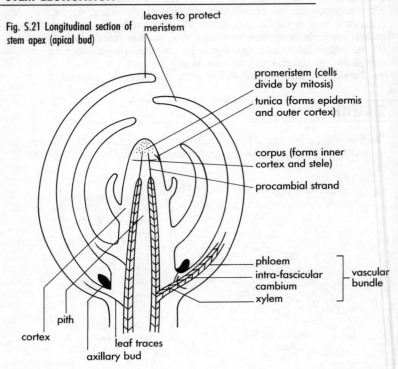

leaves to protect meristem

promeristem (cells divide by mitosis)

tunica (forms epidermis and outer cortex)

corpus (forms inner cortex and stele)

procambial strand

phloem
intra-fascicular cambium
xylem
} vascular bundle

pith

cortex

leaf traces

axillary bud

In dicotyledonous plants stem elongation takes place from the stem apex (Fig. S.21), or tip. Cells in the **apical meristem** divide by **mitosis** in order to add cells to the stem length, while also maintaining the meristem. The new cells just behind the meristem undergo enlargement and elongation, aided by water uptake and vacuole development in their cytoplasm. The enlarged cells then differentiate into the adult tissues of the primary plant stem; epidermis, parenchyma, sclerenchyma, collenchyma, phloem, xylem and procambium.

In monocotyledons the activity of intercalary meristems at the bases of the internodes adds to the stem length. The growth of the plant stem is regulated by plant growth substances, such as auxins, gibberellins and kinins, and also is affected by the stimuli of light (**phototropism**) and gravity (**geotropism**).

STEM, PRIMARY STRUCTURE

The stem structure produced by the apical meristems is the primary plant structure. In many dicotyledons a secondary stem structure arises, due to the activity of lateral meristems.

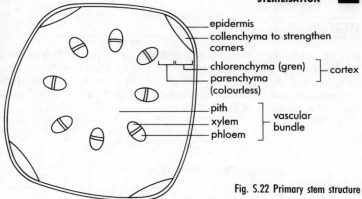

epidermis
collenchyma to strengthen corners
chlorenchyma (gren) ⎤ cortex
parenchyma (colourless) ⎦
pith ⎤ vascular bundle
xylem
phloem ⎦

Fig. S.22 Primary stem structure

The primary structure of the stem (Fig. S.22) consists of an epidermis, the fundamental tissues of the cortex and pith and the vascular bundles.

- The epidermis forms a lining on the outside of the stem. It is one cell thick and the cells possess a **cuticle** and cutinised walls to reduce water loss.
- The **cortex** and pith mainly contain **parenchyma** and in the cortex there are often chloroplasts. In young stems, and those of **herbaceous plants**, **collenchyma** develops at the outer edge of the cortex to add extra support, while in grasses **sclerenchyma** performs this function. The inner part of the pith parenchyma may be destroyed during growth leaving a large air space.
- The **xylem** and **phloem** are arranged in vascular bundles with the two tissues on the same axis.

In dicotyledons, the vascular bundles form a ring around the inside of the cortex and are open – that is, they have an intrafascicular **cambium** which allows **secondary growth** in some species. In monocotyledons, the vascular bundles are closed – that is, no cambium – and dispersed throughout the parenchyma of the stem.

◄ Chloroplast, Sieve plate, Sieve tube, Vascular bundle ►

STERILISATION

Sterilisation involves the killing of all micro-organisms, including their spores, thus making an article safe to handle or use. It is an absolute process, unlike disinfection, which only reduces microbial contamination to safe limits and does not kill all spores. Sterilisation may use dry heat in a hot-air oven, the minimum treatment being a holding time of one hour at 160°C. Alternatively wet heat may be used in an autoclave. The saturated steam under pressure gives a temperature of 121°C, and the holding time must be fifteen minutes. Irradiation with gamma rays is a third method of sterilisation. This is used for the bulk sterilisation of syringes, for instance.

◄ Disease transmission, Micro-organism, Spore ►

STEROIDS

Steroids can be classed as **lipids** although they do not contain **fatty acids**. They are abundant in plants and animals, with many important roles. The sex hormones and those of the adrenal cortex are steroids, (e.g. **testosterone, progesterone** and **oestrogens, aldosterone** and **cortisone**). The structure of a steroid is as shown in Fig. S.23.

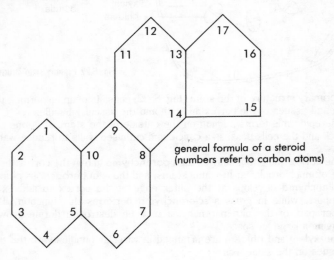

general formula of a steroid
(numbers refer to carbon atoms)

Fig. S.23

In a sterol there is an alcohol (-OH) group attached to carbon 3 and a side chain attached to carbon 17. Sterols are abundant in tissue (e.g. cholesterol in cell membranes, and ergosterol which is Vitamin D.

◄ Vitamins ►

STIMULUS

A stimulus is a change in the external or internal environment of an organism which is strong enough to produce a **response**. In animals an example of a stimulus might be a rise in blood hydrogencarbonate concentration. This will induce an increase in **cardiac output** and an increase in the depth and frequency of **breathing**. In plants, the stimulus of unilateral light on their stems, for example, induces them to grow towards the light source. The mechanisms causing such responses may be nervous, in animals only, or chemical, by hormones, in both plants and animals.

◄ Hormone, Reflex actions ►

STOMATA

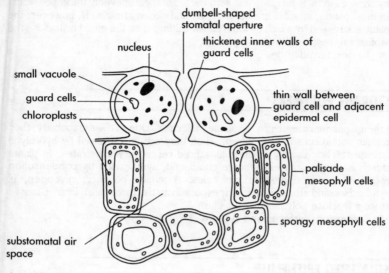

a) V.s. of stoma

Labels: dumbell-shaped stomatal aperture; thickened inner walls of guard cells; nucleus; small vacuole; guard cells; chloroplasts; thin wall between guard cell and adjacent epidermal cell; palisade mesophyll cells; spongy mesophyll cells; substomatal air space

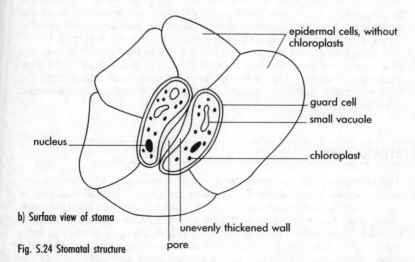

b) Surface view of stoma

Labels: epidermal cells, without chloroplasts; guard cell; small vacuole; nucleus; chloroplast; unevenly thickened wall; pore

Fig. S.24 Stomatal structure

Stomata (Fig. S.24) are pores in the plant epidermis, present in very large numbers, especially on leaves. They are concerned with **gaseous exchange** for **photosynthesis** and **respiration**, and also with loss of water vapour in transpiration, which maintains the flow of water through the plant. They are bordered by photosynthetic guard cells, which can open and close the stoma by changes in their turgidity and with the aid of their unevenly thickened walls. In most plants, stomata are open by day and closed at night. If, however, the plant is stressed by a lack of water, as in wilting, then the guard cells close the stomata to reduce transpiration.

◀ Turgor, turgidity ▶

STORAGE POLYMERS

Storage polymers are large, insoluble molecules. Due to their immobility, they remain within cells until required, when they can be mobilised by hydrolytic enzymes. They usually function as stored respiratory substrates. In plants starch is the commonest storage compound, synthesised by condensation reactions between glucose molecules. A similar polymer, glycogen, is synthesised and stored in animals, especially in the mammalian liver. Grasses store a fructose polymer called inulin.

◀ Respiratory surfaces and systems ▶

STRATIFIED EPITHELIUM

Stratified epithelium is several layers of cells thick. The two main types found in mammalian bodies are transitional epithelium and stratified squamous epithelium. Transitional epithelium is found only in the bladder and ureters, where it is designed to allow expansion and to contain the hypertonic urine. The epithelium may be between two and seven cells thick, since the cells can slide over one another sideways when the bladder is emptying and filling, thus changing the volume. The surface of the outer transitional cells is thick and fairly rigid; this apparently waterproofs it so that osmotic exchange cannot occur with the urine.

STRATOSPHERE

The stratosphere is the middle layer of the atmosphere. The lower layer, which contains nearly all the water vapour and clouds of the atmosphere, is the troposphere and extends to a height of 4 miles at the poles and 11 miles at the equator. Above this is the stratosphere, which reaches to a height of 50 to 60 miles. The middle of the stratosphere is rich in ozone, a gas which absorbs much of the ultra-violet light from the sun and prevents it from reaching the lower atmosphere. There is worry at present about pollutants such as the CFCs in aerosol propellants, which are destroying the ozone layer. Higher intensities of potentially harmful ultra-violet rays are therefore reaching the Earth's surface.

STREAMLINING IN AQUATIC ORGANISMS

Aquatic organisms such as fish need to move through the water meeting as little resistance as possible and causing as little turbulence as possible, since this would attract predators. A streamlined shape means that less energy needs to be expended in propulsion, even at low speeds, since the resistance of the relatively dense water has less effect. Most fish are streamlined, with a torpedo shape. In the dogfish, for instance, the anterior end is smoothly rounded, maximum girth is reached about a third of the way along the body length, and this then tapers gradually to the tail. The skin is covered with placoid scales, which are backward pointing, so when stroked from head to tail, the skin feels smooth.

◀ Predation ▶

STRESS, EFFECTS OF

Stress is any stimulus that causes an imbalance in the internal environment. Such stress may come from the external environment, in the form of cold, heat, intense noise or lack of oxygen, or it may originate inside the body, in the form of raised blood pressure, pain or unpleasant thoughts. Homeostatic devices oppose the forces of stress and bring the body's internal environment back into balance. In deserts, for example, external temperatures may range from 49°C by day to sub-zero at night, but man's temperature is maintained around 37°C. People used to living at sea level, who spend a length of time at high altitudes, adjust to the lower oxygen tension by developing a higher red cell count. An appreciable increase in red cell formation occurs within five days of experiencing low oxygen tensions, and adjustment is completed in about three weeks. If stress is extreme, normal homeostatic mechanisms may not be adequate to maintain stability, and the stress triggers a wide-ranging set of changes known as the General Adaptation Syndrome. This gears up the body to face an emergency (e.g. blood sugar level and blood pressure rise well above normal). The response involves the hypothalamus, sympathetic nervous system, adrenal medulla and anterior pituitary.

◀ Adrenaline, Homeostasis, Pituitary gland ▶

STRIATED MUSCLES

Striated muscle (Fig. S.25a) and b)) is voluntary muscle, and also known as skeletal muscle since it is attached by tendon to the skeleton. It can undergo rapid contraction at will. This contraction may be isotonic, when the muscle length shortens but the tension in the muscle stays the same, or it may be isometric, when the tone in the muscle is raised but the length stays the same.

The smallest working unit of striated muscle is the sarcomere, and sarcomeres are arranged end to end to make myofibrils. Each sarcomere has dark and light bands due to different arrangements of the proteins actin and myosin in its structure, and the fibrils are grouped to form muscle fibres in such a way that the light and dark bands correspond giving the fibre a striped appearance. A muscle fibre is not divided into cells but forms a syncytium – that is, a mass of cytoplasm, called sarcoplasm – and many nuclei. **Connective tissue** and collagen fibres are found between and around the fibres within the muscle, and form the tendons at the ends of the muscle. The protein filaments of actin and myosin interact by a **ratchet mechanism**, allowing contraction and relaxation.

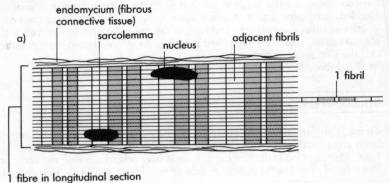

a)

endomycium (fibrous connective tissue)

sarcolemma

nucleus

adjacent fibrils

1 fibril

1 fibre in longitudinal section

a) fibre in longitudinal section

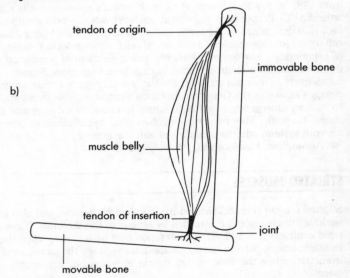

b)

tendon of origin

immovable bone

muscle belly

tendon of insertion

joint

movable bone

Fig. S.25 Striated muscle structure: b) skeletal muscle, general anatomy

◀ Muscle structure, Tendon ▶

STROMA

The stroma is the colourless matrix that surrounds the grana in a chloroplast. It is the site of the dark reaction of photosynthesis and contains ribulose bisphosphate and all the enzymes of the Calvin cycle.
◀ Enzyme ▶

SUBERIN

Suberin is a polymer of fatty acids. It is laid down on the cell walls of cork cells in the bark, or periderm, in order to provide a waterproof coating for the plant. It also occurs in the endodermis of plant roots, where it forms the impermeable casparian strips. These ensure that water and mineral ions must pass through the symplastic pathway before they can enter the xylem.

SUBSTRATUM

Substratum has several meanings and could refer to any of the following.
- The ground or soil to which organisms such as plants are attached, or upon which animals walk;
- the medium upon which micro-organisms grow, such as host organism, culture medium or dead body;
- the substrate upon which an enzyme works.

◀ Micro-organisms ▶

SUCCESSION

Succession is the progressive change which occurs in a community of organisms over a period of time, towards a climax community which is stable. It starts with the initial colonisation of a bare area and will probably progress through several distinct stages before the climax occurs.
◀ Communities, Sand dune system, Sere ▶

SUCCUS ENTERICUS

Succus entericus is intestinal juice, secreted by the crypts of Lieberkuhn and Brunner glands in the small intestine. It is alkaline due to a high hydrogencarbonate concentration and contains water as a solvent, mucus as a lubricant, peptidase (erepsin) for the hydrolysis of polypeptides to amino acids, sucrase for the hydrolysis of sucrose to glucose and fructose, maltase for the hydrolysis of maltose to glucose, lactase for the hydrolysis of lactose to glucose and galactose, and enterokinase for the activation of trypsinogen to trypsin.
◀ Enzyme, Gut histology, Hydrolase, Hydrolysis, Polypeptide, Solvent ▶

SUCRASE

Sucrase is an **enzyme** produced by the duodenum that hydrolyses **sucrose** to **glucose** and **fructose**. It is known as invertase, because if polarised light is passed through sucrose as it is digested, the plane of the polarised light is inverted.

◀ Hydrolase, Hydrolysis ▶

SUCROSE

Sucrose, cane sugar, is produced as a result of a condensation reaction between **glucose** and **fructose**. The linking glycosidic bond involves the reducing groups of both sugars, thus sucrose is non-reducing.

◀ Carbohydrates, Condensation reactions, Disaccharides, Non-reducing sugars ▶

SULPHATE

Sulphate is a salt required by animals and plants as a source of sulphur. In plants sulphur is used to make the **amino acids** cysteine and methionine, which are constituents of several **proteins** in animals also. Only small amounts of sulphate occur in mammalian blood and it does not undergo reabsorption from the urine to the blood.

SULPHUR DIOXIDE POLLUTION

Sulphur dioxide, together with sulphur trioxide and nitrogen dioxide, are present in automobile exhaust fumes. They can combine with water to form a mist of acid droplets. If there is also a lot of dust in the air, these acid droplets may condense to produce an unpleasant smog, which attacks the conjunctiva of the **eye** and the alveolar epithelium of the **lungs**. Dust is present in smoke, from coal-burning and other sources. The major source of sulphur dioxide pollution is from the combustion of fossil fuels by cars, industry and power stations. Much of the SO_2-containing smoke is carried by prevailing winds from Britain to Scandinavian countries, where it falls as **acid rain**. The acid rain causes defoliation and death of coniferous trees, and runs off from the soil into lakes and rivers, where it reduces the **pH** to a level which kills all **fish** and many other aquatic organisms.

Clean Air Acts now prohibit the burning of coal in open fires over much of Britain and many other countries, so urban smogs have largely disappeared.

◀ Pollution ▶

SUMMATION

Summation occurs in synapses and in receptors due to the additive effect of separate stimuli. If neurone X receives impulses from neurones Y and Z via interneuronal synapses, an action potential is initiated and an impulse passes along X. If it receives impulses from only Y or Z, then an impulse is not established in X. The phenomenon relates to the amount of sodium drift of the post-synaptic membrane that is required in order to initiate an impulse. Summation may be temporal, when impulses arrive at the same synapse in rapid succession. It can also be spatial, when impulses arrive at different synapses on the same neurone at the same time.
◄ Nerve impulse, Transmission, Stimulus ►

SUPPORT

Most biological structures require some sort of support to maintain the spatial arrangements of their parts with one another (e.g. mesenteries support the gut organs of animals within the body cavity). Organisms also require support to raise them off the ground, allowing locomotion in animals and upward growth in plants.
◄ Support systems ►

SUPPORT SYSTEMS

Examples of these are the cytoskeleton of microtubules, supporting the ultrastructure of the cell; mechanical tissues such as sclerenchyma, xylem, collenchyma, supporting the stems and leaves of plants; the cellulose cell wall – turgidity mechanisms operating in plant cells to support stem and leaf tissues; the exoskeleton in arthropods; hydrostatic skeleton in annelids; shells in molluscs; the bony endoskeleton in vertebrates.
◄ Arthropoda, Annelida, Mollusca, Turgor, Turgidity ►

SURFACE AREA/VOLUME RATIO

The smaller a structure is, the greater the ratio of its surface area to its volume. This has many implications in biology. For example, Protozoa can gain adequate amounts of oxygen to meet their bodily requirements by diffusion across their body surface, but larger animals cannot, since their body surface is relatively smaller in relation to their volume. They have consequently evolved special respiratory surfaces for gaseous exchange, which are highly folded to increase the surface area (gill filaments, lung alveoli). Similarly, since large animals cannot absorb enough nutrients across their body surface for maintenance, they have evolved a long, folded alimentary canal for food absorption into the blood. Smaller animals also tend to have high metabolic rates, producing much heat as a byproduct. Their larger relative surface area mean that they face a problem of heat loss, so more heat is produced to compensate. This is best seen in endotherms, where a shrew, for instance, has a far higher metabolic rate than an elephant.

When individual cells grow to a certain size, **cell division** is initiated, so the cells do not 'outgrow' their surface area limitations.

◀ Endothermy, Metabolism ▶

SURVEY METHODS

Some survey methods are qualitative, to gain an impression of an area (e.g. observation by naked eye and binoculars to identify the birds present in an area). Other methods are quantitative and precise (e.g. the use of line transects, belt transects or **quadrat frames** to plot the flora of an area of zonation. **Edaphic factors** may also be measured across the **succession**. Estimation of animal populations (e.g. moths) can be made by applying capture–recapture techniques, and by trapping the animals in a standard way at each capture, thus allowing valid comparisons.

◀ Population, Sampling techniques, Zone ▶

SUSPENSION

A suspension consists of solid particles dispersed throughout a liquid medium. Examples of suspensions include the following:

- very fine particles of clay making a colloidal suspension with soil water;
- a suspension of bacterial cells growing in nutrient broth;
- red and white blood cells suspended in blood plasma.

The term can also refer to the suspension of body organs in the body cavities by mesenteries, or to the suspension of the body weight on the vertebral column and appendicular skeleton.

◀ Colloid, colloidal properties ▶

SWIMMING IN BONY FISH

Propulsion is brought about by antagonistic blocks of segmental muscle called myotomes, which lie either side of the vertebral column. The myotomes on either side of the vertebral column contract and relax alternately. In most bony fish this affects the posterior half of the body only, so that the tail lashes from side to side in a wave-like motion. The tail and caudal fin provide resistance to the water in such a way that the greatest resultant force pushes the fish forward in the water. The large anterior part of the body and the dorsal median fin counteract any lateral drag caused by the beating of the tail. The swim bladder, which lies between the gut and vertebral column, provides buoyancy, giving the bony fish a density equal to that of the water. This means that the paired fins do not have to give lift, as they do in cartilaginous fishes, but can be used as brakes, stabilisers or turners (pivots). The swim bladder is full of gas.

◀ Antagonistic muscles, Vertebrae, vertebral column ▶

SYMBIOSIS

Symbiosis describes an association between dissimilar organisms in which the body of one organism generally provides a habitat for the other. If both organisms benefit from the association then it is termed **mutualism**. If only one organism benefits, then it is either commensalism, if the host organism neither loses nor gains, or **parasitism**, if the host is harmed.

◀ Interactions between organisms ▶

SYMMETRY

There are two forms of symmetry, radial and bilateral. **Radial symmetry** is shown by the phylum **Cnidaria** (jelly fish, sea anemones) and is where the body parts are arranged regularly around a central line; the body could be cut along any longitudinal axis to give mirror-image halves. Such an organism can receive stimuli, food, light, etc. with equal ease from all directions. This is of particular use to fixed animals. Radially symmetrical flowers, such as buttercups, are termed actinomorphic, and can shed pollen or be visited by bees with equal facility from all sides. In **bilateral symmetry** animals can be cut along only one longitudinal plane, in the mid-line, to form mirror-image halves. They thus have distinct upper and lower surfaces, and anteriors and posteriors. Bilaterally symmetrical flowers, such as the sweet pea, are termed zygomorphic, and have more complicated **pollination** mechanisms.

◀ Floral morphology ▶

SYMPATHETIC NERVOUS SYSTEM

The sympathetic nervous system is the part of the autonomic nervous system generally concerned with accelerating or enhancing physiological events. Some of the many effects of sympathetic stimulation are to increase **ventilation** rate, dilate the pupils, increase **cardiac output** and increase sweat release. Noradrenaline is released instead of **acetylcholine** as the transmitter substance at the **synapse** with the effector. This is chemically very similar to the **hormone adrenaline** which has similar effects to those of the sympathetic nervous system.

◀ Autonomic nervous control, Effectors, Parasympathetic nervous system ▶

SYMPATRIC SPECIATION

Sympatric **speciation** may occur where varieties of the same species, or sub-species, share the same geographical range. Since they are not geographically isolated, some other isolation mechanism is required.
◄ Isolation mechanisms ►

SYMPETALOUS

Sympetalous flowers are those in which the petals are fused together (e.g. primrose, which has a corolla tube). Sympetalous flowers may also be referred to as gamopetalous.
◄ Floral morphology ►

SYMPLASTIC PATHWAY

The symplasm is the mass of protoplasts in the plant which are interconnected with **plasmodesmata**. Water can therefore pass from cell to cell through the symplasm, without having to pass through any membranes (e.g. across the cortex of the root from root hairs to xylem).
◄ Apoplastic pathway, Water uptake in roots ►

SYNAPSE, SYNAPTIC TRANSMISSION

A synapse (Figs S.26a) and b)) is the junction between two nerve cells. They are found in three places: between a receptor cell and a sensory **neurone**; between two neurones; and between a neurone and an effector (e.g. the neuromuscular junction).

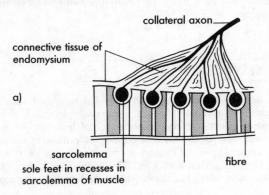

a) motor end plate (light microscope)

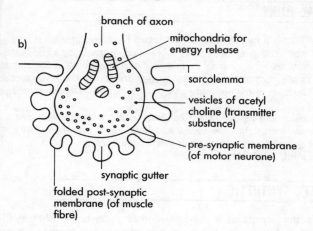

Fig. S.26 Synapse structure: b) diagram of sole foot (electron microscope detail)

The electrical resistance of the synaptic gap between the pre-synaptic membrane and the post-synaptic membrane is too high for the impulse arriving at the pre-synaptic membrane to cross. Chemical transmission is therefore required in order to generate an impulse in the post-synaptic membrane. When the impulse reaches the 'sole feet' it causes the rupture of **acetylcholine** vesicles, releasing the transmitter substance into the synaptic gap. Attachment of acetylcholine (Ach) to specific receptors on the post-synaptic membrane alters the permeability of the membrane to sodium ions. These flood into the post-synaptic neurone causing **depolarisation** and the establishment of an impulse. Acetylcholine esterase **enzyme** is then released. This detaches Ach from the receptors, thus allowing repolarisation, and hydrolyses Ach into acetate and choline. These are then recycled to synthesise more Ach.

◀ Nerve impulse ▶

SYNAPSIS

Synapsis is the pairing of **homologous chromosomes** with each other during prophase I of **meiosis**.

SYNECOLOGY

Synecology is the ecological study of a group of organisms associated together as a unit, or community. Examples of **communities** that may be studied include those of a rock pool or those of a hedgerow.

◀ Ecology, Hedgerows ▶

SYNOVIAL JOINT

A synovial joint is a mobile joint between two bones encapsulated by a tough capsule of white collagen fibres. This is bounded internally by a highly vascular cellular membrane, the synovial membrane, which secretes synovial fluid into the joint cavity. Synovial fluid acts as a lubricant and aids in metabolite transfer. The ends of the opposing bones are covered with protective hyaline cartilage.

The shoulder and hip joints are ball and socket joints, which give a wide range of movements, but the elbow and knee joints are hinge joints where movement is restricted to extension and flexion only.

◄ Hinge joint, Joints ►

SYNTHESIS, SYNTHETIC

In biochemistry, synthesis is the formation of a substance. Photosynthesis, for example, forms various sugars such as glucose and sucrose; starch can be synthesised by polymerisation of glucose; and proteins can be synthesised from amino acids. Synthetic reactions are anabolic and require an energy input, often in the form of adenosine triphosphate (ATP). They usually involve condensation — that is, the elimination of water, to establish the connecting or polymerising bonds. Compounds are sometimes referred to as synthetic if they have been manufactured in an industrial chemical process rather than by an organism in a biological process.

◄ Anabolism, Condensation reactions ►

SYNTHETIC SULPHONAMIDES

Sulphonamides are a group of drugs which have antibacterial action. They prevent the uptake of folic acid by bacteria, which cannot then complete their cell cycle. The drugs may have unpleasant side effects, such as nausea, diarrhoea and bone marrow damage, if treatment is prolonged.

T4 PHAGE

The T4 phage is a **bacteriophage** of particular interest, since it was used by Crick and his associates at Cambridge to investigate the nature of the **genetic code**. The results of these experiments supported the view that a **codon** consists of three adjacent **nucleotides**, and that the chain of codons is read from one end, taking each non-overlapping codon in turn.

T-LYMPHOCYTES

T-lymphocytes are the cells responsible for cellular **immunity**. They are referred to as T-cells since they are processed in the thymus gland before migrating to their positions in the lymphoid tissue (e.g. lymph nodes, spleen).

tRNA

Transfer RNA carries **amino acids** from the **cytoplasm** to the ribosomes. Here the **anticodon** on the tRNA matches with a **codon** on the **mRNA** so that the correct amino acid can be added to the **polypeptide** chain. A small soluble molecule, tRNA is about 80 nucleotides long and is held in a hair pin shape by hydrogen bonding between complementary bases. The anticodon of three nucleotides relates to the amino acid that the specific tRNA attaches to.
◀ Hydrogen bond, Protein synthesis, Ribosome ▶

t-TEST

A t-test is a statistical test designed to test the significance of differences between two means.

$$t = \frac{\text{deviations between observations or means to be compared}}{\text{pooled standard error of the distributions involved}}$$

$$t = \frac{d}{\frac{s}{\sqrt{n}}}$$

d = difference $\bar{x}_1 - \bar{x}_2$ between the two means

$\dfrac{s}{\sqrt{n}}$ = standard error where s = $\dfrac{\sqrt{\Sigma(x-x_1)^2 + \Sigma(x-x_2)^2}}{n_1 + n_2 - 2}$

n_1 and n_2 = no. of observations in each distribution

When a value for t is obtained, it must be used to gain a value for P (probability) from an appropriate t-table.

◀ Statistical analysis ▶

TACTIC RESPONSES, TAXES

A taxis is a directional movement of a cell or a complete organism in relation to a directional **stimulus**. Movement towards the stimulus is a positive taxis; movement away from the stimulus is a negative taxis. It applies to motile **algae**, such as *Chlamydomonas*, to whole animals and to single cells, such as motile gametes. Phototaxis is response to a directional light stimulus; chemotaxis to a directional chemical stimulus (e.g. the antherozooids of mosses are chemically attracted to a high concentration of maleic acid in the archegonial venters, where the egg cells are situated).

◀ Gamete, Moss ▶

TAXONOMY

Taxonomy is a system of **classification** of organisms based on how closely they are related. It results in a natural classification of **Kingdoms**, phyla and classes.

TCA CYCLE

TCA stands for the tricarboxylic acid or **Krebs cycle** (Fig. T.1). The enzymes controlling the Krebs cycle are housed mainly in the mitochondrial matrix. The Krebs cycle accepts **acetyl co-A** from **glycolysis** and attaches it to the carrier molecule, oxaloacetic acid, forming citric acid. The citric acid then undergoes four successive dehydrogenations, producing various organic acids and reduced $NADH_2$, which passes into the **electron transfer** system to synthesise **adenosine triphosphate** (ATP). At the end of the Krebs cycle the oxaloacetic acid is regenerated. One molecule of acetyl co-A yields 12ATP when completely oxidised in the Krebs cycle.

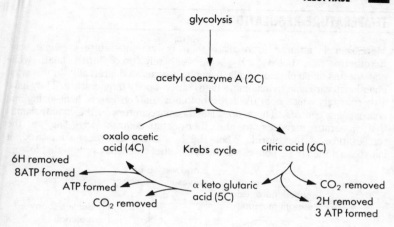

Fig. T.1 Krebs cycle

◀ Aerobic respiration ▶

TEETH

Mammals have four main types of teeth: incisors, canines, pre-molars and molars. Incisors are chisel-shaped for cutting, canines are spear-shaped for piercing and tearing, and molars (Fig. T.2) and premolars have broad surfaces, which tend to be ridged in **herbivores** for grinding plant cells, or cusped in the **carnivore** for shearing meat off bones. The tooth has a skeleton made of a bony substance called dentine, which is covered in the crown region by hard protective enamel. The dentine encloses a pulp cavity, which contains the **blood** and nerve supply. Depending on the type of tooth there may be one, two or three roots which anchor the tooth into the jawbone.

◀ Dentition ▶

TELEOST

Teleosts are bony **fish**, now classed in the phylum Chordata class **Osteichthyes**.

TELOPHASE

Telophase is the final stage in **mitosis** or **meiosis**. Nuclear division is completed by the formation of new nuclear membranes around the daughter nuclei, and cytoplasmic division takes place.

TEMPERATURE REGULATION

Most animals attempt to regulate their body temperature in some way. Ectotherms use behavioural means and rely on external heat, while endotherms do so physiologically using heat generated internally. In this way, endotherms are able to maintain a high constant body temperature. They have a thermostat, which is in the hypothalamus and consists of heat-losing and heat-gaining centres. There are also thermoreceptors in the hypothalamus that generate impulses to the thermostat centres according to the temperature of the blood. When the heat-losing centre is stimulated, it initiates a series of responses via the sympathetic nervous system that lowers

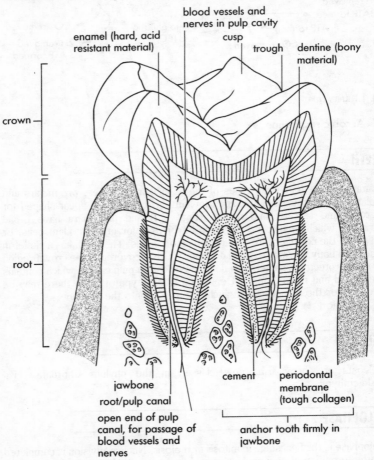

Fig. T.2 Vertical section through molar tooth

body temperature. When the heat-promoting centre is stimulated, it initiates responses via the **parasympathetic nervous system** that raise body temperature. Thermoreceptors in the skin also send information to the hypothalamus relating to the surface temperature of the body.

Most heat is produced by the oxidation of foods and the rate at which it is produced is called the metabolic rate. This can be affected by the body temperature itself, a rise of 1°C causing a 10° per cent increase in metabolic rate, or by exercise, by hormones such as **adrenaline** and **thyroxine**, or by sympathetic stimulation. Heat can be lost by radiation, conduction, convection and evaporation (latent heat of vaporisation of sweat).

When the environmental temperature is low or blood temperature is reduced, the heat-promoting centre generates impulses which cause the following responses to raise body temperature back to the norm:

- The **blood vessels** (arterioles) of the skin constrict, thus less heat is lost from the blood through the skin,
- The adrenal medulla is stimulated to release **adrenaline** and noradrenaline into the blood. These promote cellular metabolism, and so increase heat production,
- The **pituitary gland** is induced to release thyroid stimulating hormone into the blood, which stimulates the **thyroid** to release thyroxine. This increases metabolic rate and thus heat production.
- The muscles undergo involuntary spasms, called shivering, which also release metabolic heat.

When the environmental temperature is high or blood temperature is raised, the heat-losing centre generates impulses which cause the following responses to try and cool the body down:

- The blood vessels (arterioles) in the skin dilate, thus more blood is carried to the surface so that more heat can be lost,
- The sweat glands are activated to produce more sweat and as this evaporates, it cools the body surface down,
- Adrenaline and thyroxine release is curtailed so that metabolic rate falls and less metabolic heat is released.

As the body temperature reaches the norm, or mean, the controlling mechanisms are damped or curtailed. This is **negative feedback** control.

◄ Ectothermy, Endothermy, Hormone, Metabolism ►

TENDON

Tendons consist of bundles of parallel **connective tissue** fibres that arise from connective tissue within the muscle. Their function is to attach **skeletal muscle** to **bone** and they have a high collagen content, so are inelastic and resistant to pulling strains. The collagen fibres of the tendons are continuous with those of the bone periosteum and with the Sharpey fibres of the bone matrix.

◄ Striated muscle ►

TERRESTRIAL LIFE, ADAPTATIONS FOR

The main problem to be met by organisms living on land is to obtain an adequate water supply, and to conserve it once obtained. Terrestrial plants require deep roots and **root hairs** to absorb water from all levels in the soil and a **transpiration** stream to raise the water to all levels in the plant. This involves the development of vascular tissue (**xylem** tracheids and vessels) and **stomata**. Their surfaces need to be impermeable to reduce water loss by evaporation, hence the secretion of a **cuticle** on the **epidermis** and the development of corky bark. Methods of transferring male gametes have developed which do not need water: **pollination** is by insects or wind.

Terrestrial animals also require impermeable body surfaces (e.g. keratin in the outer layers of **epidermis** and wax over the **exoskeleton** and **cuticles** of **insects**. They need waste products that are less toxic, and so require less water loss to remove, than ammonia does (e.g. in mammals the ammonia is incorporated into **urea**, while birds excrete **uric acid**, which, since it is almost insoluble, has to be removed in solid form, thus curtailing water loss very efficiently). Terrestrial animals have walking limbs for locomotion on land, and they have internal **fertilisation** for sperm transfer, since an aquatic medium is no longer available.

◄ Water conservation ►

TERRITORIAL BEHAVIOUR

Territorial behaviour is common in **vertebrates** with the exception of the **Amphibia**, but is rare among invertebrates. A territory is a region held and defended by one or more animals against animals of the same or different species. In general terms the possession of territory means that the individuals, mating pairs or family units are spaced so that each receives an adequate share of the resources of the area, such as food and breeding space. **Aggression**, particularly by males, helps to maintain territorial rights, and the territorial boundary is often marked with scents or urine. Weaker animals may fail to establish a territory and thus fail to breed. This is 'survival of the **fittest**' due to **intraspecific competition**, and helps to regulate population size.

TESTA OF SEED

The testa is the protective outer covering of the **seed**. It is formed after **fertilisation**, mainly from the inner and outer integuments of the **ovule**. The cell walls may be thickened with cutin and **suberin**, making the testa impermeable to disease and decay organisms and to chemicals. It cannot remain impermeable to water for too long, since water must be absorbed for **germination**. Scarification will aid in causing water permeability.

◄ Seed dormancy, Seed germination ►

TESTIS

The testis is the male **gonad** responsible for producing male gametes. The two testes in mammals are usually descended out of the abdominal cavity into the scrotal sacs as an adaptation for cooling. The testes contain tightly packed, highly convoluted seminiferous tubules, which produce millions of **sperm** by spermatogenesis. Other cells in the testes produce **testosterone**, which is the male sex hormone.

◀ Gametogenesis, Reproduction ▶

TESTOSTERONE

Testosterone is the male sex hormone. It controls the growth, development and maintenance of the male sex organs, and also **bone** growth, protein **anabolism**, sexual behaviour and, in humans, the development of the male secondary sexual characteristics at puberty (wide shoulders, narrow hips, deep voice, facial hair, etc.) The secretion of testosterone by the testes is controlled by gonadotrophin from the **pituitary gland**, which is in turn regulated by a releasing factor from the **hypothalamus**. A low blood testosterone level stimulates secretion of the releasing factor, and visa versa, by **negative feedback**.

◀ Reproduction, Testis ▶

THERMONASTY

Thermonasty is a non-directional response to temperature change (e.g. the opening of flowers due to a temperature rise). In crocuses and tulips this is caused by more rapid cell elongation on the upper sides of the petals, but many other nastic responses are due to turgor changes in different parts of the responding organs.

◀ Nastic responses, Nasty ▶

THERMOREGULATION

Thermoregulation is the control of body temperature as shown by homoiothermic/endothermic animals, such as **birds** and **mammals**.

◀ Endothermy, Temperature regulation ▶

THIAMINE

Thiamine is Vitamin B_1, a water-soluble vitamin that is rapidly destroyed by heat. It is found in whole-grain products, and in eggs, pork, liver, nuts and yeast. It acts as a **co-enzyme** for the **decarboxylation** of pyruvic acid, and it is essential for **acetylcholine** synthesis. Deficiency leads to the following diseases:

- Beri-beri, in which there is partial paralysis of the gut smooth muscle, leading to digestive upsets, skeletal muscle paralysis, strophy of limbs and pyruvic and lactic acid build-up in tissues.
- Polyneuritis, in which there is degeneration of myelin sheaths of the neurones.

NB Do not confuse thiamine with **thymine**.

◄ Pyruvate, pyruvic acid, Vitamins ►

THORACIC VERTEBRAE

There are typically twelve thoracic **vertebrae** and their main feature is their very long dorsal neural spines. These are for muscle attachment and the attachment of a strong ligament which runs to here from the base of the skull. This ligament reduces the work load of the neck muscles in supporting the head. Thoracic vertebrae also have extra facets for rib articulation.

THORAX

The thorax in **vertebrates** is the part of the body which houses the heart and lungs – that is, the chest. It is bounded to the posterior by the diaphragm. In **insects** it consists of three segments – prothorax, mesothorax and metathorax – each of which bears one pair of walking legs. In many insects the meso- and metathorax each bears a pair of wings as well.

THYLAKOID

Thylakoids are flattened membraneous sacs containing an orderly arrangement of photosynthetic **pigments**. They are situated in the chloroplasts, where numerous disc-shaped thylacoids stack together to form the grana. The light reactions of **photosynthesis** occur in the thylakoids.

◄ Chloroplast ►

THYMINE

Thymine is a pyrimidine base found in **DNA**, but not **RNA**, which is complementary to **adenine** – that is, they will join together by hydrogen bonding.

NB Do not confuse thymine with **thiamine**.

◄ Hydrogen bond ►

THYROID GLAND

The thyroid gland is an endocrine gland in the neck. It is composed of hollow spheres of cuboidal epithelium, separated by connective tissue. The epithelium secretes the hormones thyroxine and tri-iodothyronine into the central cavity, while the connective tissue contains cells which secrete the hormone calcitonin. Calcitonin regulates blood calcium levels by reducing the release of calcium from bones, thus opposing the action of parathormone from the parathyroid glands.

The thyroid accumulates iodine in order to synthesise thyroxine and tri-iodothyronine, and deficiency of iodine in the diet may cause the thyroid to grow abnormally large. This is known as goitre. The growth, synthesis and release of thyroxine and tri-iodothyronine are regulated by thyroid stimulating hormone (TSH) from the anterior pituitary, which is in turn regulated by a releasing factor from the hypothalamus, which responds to a low blood concentration of thyroid hormones. This is a negative feedback controlling mechanism.

◀ Bone, Endocrine glands, Pituitary gland ▶

THYROXINE

Thyroxine is the main hormone secreted by the thyroid gland, unusual since it contains iodine. It generally speeds up the metabolic rate of cells, but unlike adrenaline it has an extended effect, often lasting for up to eight weeks after release from the thyroid. It also increases cardiac output, and increases wakefulness. In hyperthyroidism too much thyroxine is released into the blood, causing weight loss, heart strain and considerable excitability. In hypothyroidism, too little thyroxine is released, causing in young animals, retarded physical and mental development, or cretinism, and in older animals, lethargy, extreme obesity and mental dullness.

TISSUE

A tissue is an aggregate of cells, usually of similar type and function, often bound together by intercellular material. A complex tissue may have several types of cells, each with different functions, which are 'integrated' to perform the functions of the tissue as a whole (e.g. xylem tissue contains tracheids, vessels, fibres and parenchyma, and blood contains red and white cells plus platelets). Many tissues also contain elements which have been formed by the cells (e.g. loose connective tissue contains collagen fibres, elastic fibres and reticular fibres).

◀ Cell, Organ ▶

TISSUE COMPATABILITY, TISSUE REJECTION

Tissue compatability is important in organ transplants since the body tends to recognise transplanted tissue as foreign and produces antibodies against it. These antibodies destroy the foreign cells and the tissue is rejected. Compatability depends on there being a good match in tissue type groups between the recipient and the donor, and particularly requires matching of the HLA antigens. The best matches come from people with identical or similar genetic backgrounds – that is, identical twins or close blood relatives.

◀ Antibody, HLA system, Immunity ▶

TISSUE CULTURE

Tissue culture is the growth of cells and tissue in artificial culture medium. Glassware for this purpose has to be scrupulously clean, culture media must be sterile and microbial contamination prevented by incorporation of antibiotics into the medium. The medium contains sugars, amino acids, salts and vitamins and any other growth requirement of the cells to be cultured.

One purpose of tissue culture is for karyotyping, or analysis of the **chromosomes** present (e.g. fetal cells collected by amniocentesis may be kayotyped to diagnose **Down's Syndrome** and various other conditions). Plant cells may be cultured to form a parenchymatous mass called callus. By use of cytokinins, this can be made to differentiate into other tissues, or even into whole plants.

TISSUE FLUID

Tissue fluid is the interstitial fluid or lymph in the regions around the cells. Due to exchange of substances between the lymph and cells its composition is continually changing. The cells are absorbing metabolites from the tissue fluid and releasing their waste products.

TOADS

Toads are amphibians, belonging to the same order as frogs. They have an aquatic tadpole larva, and so return to the water to breed. Fertilisation is external and the eggs are laid in water. The adults have short, tailless bodies with long hind legs for leaping.

◀ Amphibia, Frogs ▶

TOBACCO SMOKE

Tobacco smoke contains various harmful compounds such as nicotine, carbon monoxide and tar.

Nicotine increases the tendency of the **blood** to clot and therefore increases the risk of death from coronary thrombosis, where the clot blocks a coronary vessel, leading to death of heart tissue.

Carbon monoxide combines with **haemoglobin** and reduces the oxygen-carrying capacity of the blood. The heart workload increases and ventilation is inefficient, resulting in breathlessness.

Tar products are carcinogenic, or cancer-causing, and there is therefore a high incidence of lung cancer among smokers.

◀ Smoking, effects of ▶

TONOPLAST

The membrane surrounding the **vacuole** in plant cells is called the tonoplast. It separates the cell sap from the **cytoplasm** and is able to maintain differences between them.

TOXICITY, TOXINS

Toxicity is possessed by toxins, chemicals which are poisonous. Amino acids are fairly toxic, which is why they cannot be stored in large amounts. Unwanted amino acids are therefore deaminated to urea and excreted. Cyanide is extremely toxic, because it inhibits cytochrome oxidase and thus renders the respiratory chain inoperative, so causing death. Many pesticides, insecticides and herbicides are toxic and must be used with caution, and the very toxic and persistent Aldrin and Dieldrin are now banned. One of the most dangerous toxins is that produced by *Clostridium botulinum*. This causes respiratory paralysis, very quickly resulting in death due to botulism food poisoning.

TRACE ELEMENTS

Trace elements are salts which are essential in small amounts to maintain health but become toxic if present in large amounts. Lack of the element will cause disease (e.g. in humans, lack of iodine will result in goitre, the development of an enlarged thyroid gland).

Flowering plants require traces of zinc, boron, manganese, molybdenum and copper. Mammals require traces of iodine, cobalt, copper, zinc and fluorine.

◀ Mineral nutrition ▶

TRACERS

Tracers are radioactive isotopes which may be used to label certain biochemical compounds or tissue components to make them visible or detectable. The isotopes emit gamma radiation, which can be detected on a photographic plate or by using a Geiger counter. The half-life of the isotope must be long enough to allow the measurement to be completed, but if the tissue is living, it must not persist to cause radiation damage.

The dark reaction of photosynthesis was worked out by using carbon dioxide labelled with radioactive C^{14}. At various times after exposure to the tracer CO_2 the products and intermediate compounds of photosynthesis were extracted into ethanol, separated by chromatography and then photographed to locate the labelled compounds. These were then identified and the reactions worked out in sequence.

Tracers are also used in medicine (e.g. iodine^{131} can be used in studies of the thyroid and its functioning).

◀ Radioactive tracers ▶

TRACHEA

The trachea, or windpipe, runs from the larynx to where it divides into the two bronchi just before entry into the lungs. It is supported by C-shaped rings of hyaline cartilage, which prevent it collapsing during the pressure changes of ventilation, and also allow it to increase in length and diameter. The inner surface is lined by a ciliated pseudostratified columnar epithelium, which secretes mucus to help trap dust particles, which the cilia waft up to the glottis. From here the mucus, dust and any bacteria are swallowed for disinfection by the stomach acidity.

TRACHEAL SYSTEM, TRACHEOLES

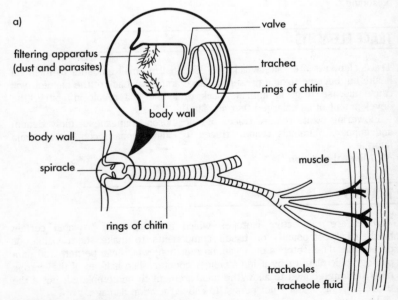

Fig. T.3a) Insect tracheal system

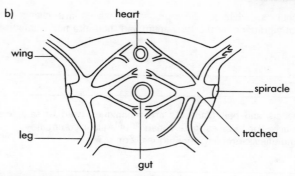

Fig. T.3b) Relationship of spiracle, trachea and tracheoles

Insects have a tracheal system (Fig. T.3a)) for gaseous exchange. Spiracles in the exoskeleton lead to tracheal tubes, which run to all areas of the body (Fig. T.3b)). At tissue level, the branching tracheae branch further into microscopic tubules called tracheoles, which carry the respiratory gases direct to the cells. They have a diameter of 0.2 to 0.3 micrometres. The ends of the tracheoles contain tissue fluid into which oxygen dissolves before being absorbed into the cells.

◀ Spiracles, Ventilation ▶

TRACHEID

A tracheid is a **xylem**-conducting cell. It is heavily lignified so that the cell contents die, and it transports water and salts up the plant.

TRANSCRIPTION

Transcription is the copying of the **DNA genetic code** on to **messenger RNA** and is the first stage of **protein synthesis**. A cistron of DNA unwinds and one strand acts as a template, attracting the complementary ribonucleotides to it. A sequence of 'adenine, cytosine, guanine, thymine' on the DNA strand, for example, is transcribed as 'uracil, guanine, cytosine, adenine' on mRNA. The ribonucleotides polymerise together in the correct sequence, catalysed by RNA polymerase **enzyme**, and mRNA leaves the nucleus to travel to the ribosomes in the **cytoplasm** for **translation**.

◀ Ribosome ▶

TRANSDUCERS

Transducers change one type of energy or signal into another type. They occur in instruments such as microphones and oscilloscopes, but also in living organisms. Rods and cones in the **retina** in the **eye** change light signals into nerve impulses, while in the ear, sound waves are changed first into mechanical vibrations by the tympanum and then into nerve impulses by the cochlea.

TRANSECT

Line transects and belt transects are techniques used to sample the flora across an area, or to investigate zonation of a plant communtiy.
◀ Communities, Sampling techniques, Zone ▶

TRANSFERASES

Transferases are enzymes which transfer certain chemical groups from one substance to another. Transaminases, for example, transfer amino groups during transamination.
◀ Enzyme ▶

TRANSFER RNA

◀ tRNA ▶

TRANSFORMATION

Transformation describes the way in which certain bacteria can change genetically. Under natural conditions, DNA released by the death of certain bacteria may be incorporated into other living bacteria, producing genetic changes. This was first observed by Griffith in 1928, who noted that a non-pathogenic strain of *Pneumococcus* became virulent when grown with a pathogenic strain. Avery, in 1943, showed that the transformation could be achieved in the laboratory, by incubating the non-pathogenic strain with an extract of DNA from the pathogenic strain. These discoveries led to the development of genetic engineering.
◀ Gene-transfer in bacteria ▶

TRANSLATION

Translation is the second stage of protein synthesis, in which the mRNA is translated into a sequence of amino acids. The process occurs in the ribosomes and results in the synthesis of a specific polypeptide as determined by the cistron of DNA in the nucleus that was transcribed.
◀ Ribosome, Transcription ▶

TRANSLOCATION

Translocation refers to the movement of mainly organic substances from one part of the plant to another part through the **phloem** – that is, the dissolved products of **photosynthesis**, such as **sucrose** and **amino acids**, may be carried from leaves to roots. There are several ideas concerning the mechanisms involved in translocation. It has been shown that the organic nutrients and some inorganic salts enter and leave the phloem sieve tubes by **active transport**. Within the tubes, they may move by mass flow, which occurs from a 'source' to a 'sink'. The source could be photosynthesising cells in the leaves or storage tissue, such as a potato tuber. The sink could also be storage tissue, or it could be meristematic growing regions.

This mass flow may receive an electro-osmotic boost at each **sieve plate**, where potassium ions can pass through but negative ions are repelled by the negative charge on phloem protein. This creates a potential difference across the plate, which triggers the release of hydrogen ions. The temporary positive charge above the sieve plate causes electro-osmosis of potassium ions through the pores, which in turn causes a mass flow of solution.

Other hypotheses for phloem transport include cytoplasmic streaming along **microtubules** that connect the cells, and a relay system in which the solutes bypass sieve plates by being pumped into adjacent overlapping sieve tubes.

TRANSMISSION ELECTRON MICROSCOPE (TEM)

The TEM is an **electron microscope** which looks at electrons transmitted through or past the object being visualised. Since electrons are passed through the tissue, extremely thin sections must be cut, so many sections may be needed in order to build up a complete picture.
◀ Scanning electron microscope ▶

TRANSPIRATION

Transpiration is the loss of water vapour from a plant, especially through the **stomata** on the leaves, but also to a lesser extent through the **lenticels** on woody stems. This evaporation creates the transpiration stream, which draws up more water and salts through the **xylem**. Water vapour diffuses from the air spaces in the **mesophyll** through the open stomata, which in dicotyledons are mainly on the lower side of the leaf. The vapour must first diffuse through a layer of still air below the stoma before it reaches moving air and is blown away, thus maintaining the **water potential** gradient. In effect, each stoma has a diffusion shell around it, although since stomata are so close together, these often overlap. The rate of transpiration can be increased by raising temperature, increasing light intensity and by increasing wind speed. It is also higher when relative humidity is low. Measurement of transpiration rates can be made indirectly, using a potometer (Fig. T.4), which measures water uptake by a stem.

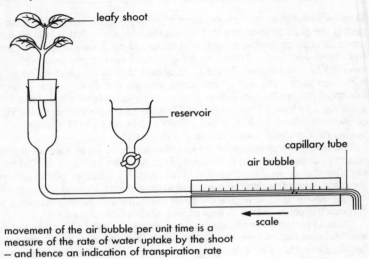

movement of the air bubble per unit time is a measure of the rate of water uptake by the shoot — and hence an indication of transpiration rate

Fig. T.4 A potometer

TRANSPORT

Transport means carrying of substances from one part of the organism to another. **Blood** is the main transporting medium in vertebrates, carrying cells, plasma proteins, salts, sugars, amino acids, lipids, respiratory gases, hormones and heat, etc. around the body. **Xylem** vessels and tracheids carry water and salts through plants, while **phloem** sieve tubes carry organic compounds through plants.
◀ Sieve plate, Sieve tube ▶

TREES

A tree is a large dicotyledonous or coniferous plant with extensive **secondary thickening.** Trees form the canopy layer in forests.
◀ Conifer, Dicotyledon, Forestry ▶

TRIAL AND ERROR LEARNING

In animal **behaviour**, trial and error learning is the development of an association by constant repetition, and usually occurs during feeding behaviour. For example, a racoon tied to a stake with the leash looped around another stake cannot reach its food; a human would walk round the second stake to unleash the lead, but the racoon must find out by trial and error how to reach the food.

◀ Learned behaviour ▶

TRICARBOXYLIC ACID CYCLE

◀ TCA Cycle ▶

TRICHROMATIC VISION

Trichromatic vision is the way in which light of different wavelengths and thus of different colours is perceived by the retina of the eye. The visual pigment of cones is similar to rods since both contain retinine, but the protein portions are different: cones contain photopsins whereas rods contain the protein scotopsin. There are three types of cone which contain different combinations of retinine and photopsin, and these absorb light of different wavelengths – that is, they have different absorption spectra. One type of cone responds best to red light, another to blue and another to green. It is thought that cones can perceive any colour by differential stimulation – a specific wavelength may stimulate more than one type of cone since their absorption spectra overlap. The bleaching of the visual pigment in a rod or cone causes chemical changes which result in depolarisation of the rod or cone and the establishment of nerve impulses.

◀ Absorption spectrum, Nerve impulse, Pigments, Proteins ▶

TRIGLYCERIDES

Triglycerides are condensation products of the alcohol glycerol and three molecules of fatty acid, and are also known as lipids. They are stored in seeds and in adipose tissue and used as respiratory substrates.

$$
\begin{array}{c}
\text{H} \\
\text{H}-\overset{|}{\text{C}}-\text{OH} \\
\text{H}-\overset{|}{\text{C}}-\text{OH} \\
\text{H}-\overset{|}{\text{C}}-\text{OH} \\
\text{H}
\end{array}
+ 3\,\text{R.COOH}
\underset{\substack{\text{hydrolysis} \\ \text{(digestion)}}}{\overset{\substack{\text{condensation} \\ \text{(synthesis)}}}{\rightleftharpoons}}
\begin{array}{c}
\text{H} \\
\text{H}-\overset{|}{\text{C}}-\text{O}-\overset{||}{\text{C}}-\text{R} \\
\text{H}-\overset{|}{\text{C}}-\text{O}-\overset{||}{\text{C}}-\text{R} \\
\text{H}-\overset{|}{\text{C}}-\text{O}-\overset{||}{\text{C}}-\text{R} \\
\text{H}
\end{array}
+ 3\text{H}_2\text{O}
$$

glycerol   fatty acids

triglyceride
where R = hydrocarbon chain

TRIOSE, TRIOSE PHOSPHATE

Trioses are three-carbon sugars. There are only two examples – glyceraldehyde and dihydroxyacetone. These are isomers.

$$\alpha-\text{D}-\text{glyceraldehyde} \quad \begin{array}{c} \text{H}-\text{C}=\text{O} \\ | \\ \text{H}-\text{C}-\text{OH} \\ | \\ \text{CH}_2\text{OH} \end{array} \quad \xrightleftharpoons{\text{triose isomerase}} \quad \begin{array}{c} \text{CH}_2\text{OH} \\ | \\ \text{C}=\text{O} \\ | \\ \text{CH}_2\text{OH} \end{array} \quad \text{dihydroxyacetone}$$

These are both products of **photosynthesis**, used to build up hexose sugars, and are both intermediates in **glycolysis**. They can be phosphorylated using **adenosine triphosphate** (ATP) to activate them for use, forming triose phosphate (glyceraldehyde-3-phosphate or dihydroxyacetone-3-phosphate).

$$\begin{array}{c} \text{H} \quad \text{O} \\ \diagdown \diagup \\ \text{C} \\ | \\ \text{H}-\text{C}-\text{OH} \\ | \\ \text{H}-\text{C}-\text{OH} \\ | \\ \text{H} \end{array} \qquad \begin{array}{c} \text{kinase} \\ \xrightarrow{} \\ \text{C} \\ \text{ATP} \quad \text{ADP} \end{array} \qquad \begin{array}{c} \text{H} \quad \text{O} \\ \diagdown \diagup \\ \text{C} \\ | \\ \text{H}-\text{C}-\text{OH} \\ | \\ \text{H}-\text{C}-\text{O}\sim\text{P} \\ | \\ \text{H} \end{array} \quad \text{energy-rich bond.}$$

α–D–glyceraldehyde   glyceraldehyde-3-phosphate (GALP)

◄ Monosaccharides ►

TRIPLET GENETIC CODE

◄ Genetic code ►

TRIPLOBLASTIC ORGANISATION

Triploblastic organisation is shown by organisms which have three fundamental germ layers in the body: ectoderm, mesoderm and endoderm. The ectoderm is responsible for forming **epidermis** or skin and nervous tissue; the endoderm forms the lining of the gastrointestinal tract, and the mesoderm forms **connective tissues**, including **bone** and muscle. The phylum **Platyhelminthes** has solid mesoderm, consisting of mesenchyme tissue, but in the coelomates, (phylum **Annelida** and above) the mesoderm contains the body cavity or coelom. This gives room for movements of the body organs, allowing **peristalsis**, **heart beat**, **ventilation** movements and so on.

◄ Coelomate organisation ►

TROPHIC LEVELS

Trophic levels are feeding levels within **food chains**. The green

photosynthetic plants occupy trophic level 1, the producer level, since these manufacture their own food by **photosynthesis**. Trophic level 2 contains the **herbivores**, which feed on the green plants, and trophic level 3 contains carnivores, which feed on the herbivores. The ultimate trophic level is that of the **decomposers** in the soil, where **bacteria** and **fungi** cause decay of dead bodies, releasing nutrients back to the soil for recycling via the **producers**. As ascent is made from one trophic level to the next, there tends to be a loss in energy content and a loss in **biomass**.
◄ Pyramid of numbers, biomass and energy ►

TROPISMS

A tropism is a directional **growth response** of part of a plant to a **stimulus** which is unilateral. They are regulated by plant growth substances, such as **auxin**, which stimulates cell elongation. Stems are positively phototrophic, for example, since they grow towards a unilateral light source. This stimulus is perceived by the stem tip, where auxin is synthesised, and auxin diffuses down the stem to the region of cell elongation. Since auxin tends to diffuse away from light, there is more cell elongation on the dark side, so the stem curves towards the light stimulus. Stems are negatively geotropic, growing away from gravity, while roots are positively geotropic and grow towards gravity. Roots are positively hydrotropic since they grow towards water.
◄ Geotropism, Phototropism ►

TRYPSIN

Trypsin is secreted by the **pancreas** into the duodenum as inactive trypsinogen. This is acted on by the **enzyme** enterokinase in the duodenal juice (**succus entericus**), which activates it to trypsin by exposing its active sites. The trypsin will then digest **proteins** and polypeptides to smaller fragments by hydrolysing the peptide links between certain **amino acids** in the protein structure.
◄ Active site, Polypeptide ►

TURBELLARIA

This is a class of organisms in the phylum **Platyhelminthes**. They are free-living flatworms with ciliated outer surfaces, such as Planarian worms (e.g. *Polycelis*).

TURBIDITY

Turbidity means cloudiness in a solution or suspension. In aquatic ecosystems, it is a significant factor determining the distribution of organisms.

Increased turbidity will mean less light penetration and so restrict photosynthetic plants and bacteria.

◄ Aquatic habitats ►

TURGOR, TURGIDITY

Turgor pressure should now be called pressure potential (ψp). It is a positive pressure in a turgid plant cell. If the water potential gradient is such that water flows from outside the cell into the cell sap in the vacuole, then the cell contents will eventually press against the elastic cellulose cell wall, as the contents expand due to water uptake. When no more water can enter the cell due to the restriction of the cell wall, the cell is said to be fully turgid. It is the turgidity of parenchyma cells in plant stems that gives support in herbaceous plants. As turgidity is lost the plant will wilt. Changes in turgor are responsible for some plant movements, such as the opening and closing of stomata by guard cells, and the closing up of Venus flytrap.

◄ Nastic responses, Nasty, Plasmolysis ►

TYMPANIC MEMBRANE

The tympanic membrane is a thin, semitransparent membrane of fibrous connective tissue situated between the external auditory canal and the air-filled middle ear cavity. Its outer surface is concave and covered by skin; the inner convex surface is lined with mucous membrane. The handle of the hammer ear ossicle is attached to the central area of the tympanic membrane, so that when the tympanic membrane vibrates due to sound waves, these vibrations can be passed on via ear ossicles to the inner ear.

TYPHOID

Typhoid is a virulent and serious disease in humans caused by the bacterium *Salmonella typhi*. It is characterised by high fever, slow pulse, enlargement of the lymph nodes, pink-coloured spots on the abdomen and severe diarrhoea. Death occurs in about 15 per cent of untreated cases. Infection is via food containing the bacteria or by drinking water containing sewage contaminated with the bacteria. Control is thus by correct and rigid hygiene, and by proper sewage disposal and treatment. Shellfish which live in estuaries where sewage may be released are likely food sources since the shellfish concentrate the bacteria and plankton from the water when they feed.

Sufferers should be nursed in isolation and their urine and faeces properly disinfected. Chloramphenicol is a suitable antibiotic, though protection is available by vaccination.

ULNA

The ulna is a long bone of the forelimb between the elbow joint and wrist joint. It lies alongside the radius on the lateral or posterior side.
◀ Skeleton, Forelimbs of mammals ▶

ULTRACENTRIFUGATION

Ultracentrifugation is a technique used to sediment cell organelles, protein molecules and nucleic acid molecules, where the rate of sedimentation can be used as a measure of molecular weight. Differential centrifugation can be used to separate organelles from suspensions of smashed-up cells. Nuclei, for example, sediment in ten minutes spinning at 1,000g, whereas mitochondria require thirty minutes at 10,000g (1g = normal gravitational force).
◀ Mitochondrion, Nucleus, Organelle, Proteins ▶

ULTRAFILTRATION

Ultrafiltration is filtration under pressure. The best example is in the formation of glomerular filtrate in the Bowman's capsules of the nephrons. The glomerular capillaries occur between two arterioles rather than between an arteriole and a venule, so the blood hydrostatic pressure here is a lot higher than in other capillaries. Pressure is also increased by the fact that the efferent arteriole that leaves the glomerular capillaries is narrower than the afferent arteriole supplying them, thus creating a damming effect. The blood pressure in the glomerulus is around 60 mms of mercury, compared with other capillaries of the body, where the pressure is around 30 mms of mercury. This high blood pressure forces water and small molecular solutes such as salts, glucose, amino-acids and urea through the very thin podocytic membranes into the capsules.
◀ Kidneys, Nephron, Veins, Venules ▶

ULTRASTRUCTURE

Ultrastructure refers to the fine structure of cells and their organelles as seen using electron microscopy, and it can also be applied to molecular structures. Ultrastructure cannot be seen with light microscopy, since the structures are too small.

◄ Cell, Electronmicroscope, Organelle ►

ULTRA-VIOLET LIGHT

U-V light is of shorter wavelength than visible light, that reaching the Earth's surface being in the range of 290 – 400 nm (visible light is 400 – 700 nm). U-V light, particularly if less than 300 nm is strongly absorbed by proteins and nucleic acids and may cause mutation and cancers. As the **ozone layer** of the atmosphere is progressively destroyed by **CFCs** more U-V light can penetrate to the Earth's surface, increasing the risk of skin cancers. Looking at a U-V light source may cause conjunctivitis.

UMBILICAL CORD

The umbilical cord attaches the **fetus** to the **placenta**. It carries two umbilical **arteries** from fetus to placenta and one umbilical vein from placenta to the fetal liver.

UNDULIPODIA

Undulipodia are the **cilia** and flagella of **eukaryotic cells** – that is, those cilia and flagella having a 9+2 arrangement of **microtubules**. The term should not be used for the simpler cilia and flagella of prokaryotic cells.

◄ Flagellum ►

UNICELLULAR ALGAE

These are single-celled algae, generally belonging to the phylum Chlorophyta, green algae (e.g. Chlamydomonas).

◄ Chlorophyta ►

UNIT MEMBRANE

The **plasma** membrane of the cell and the membranes of such organelles as the **nucleus**, mitochondria and **endoplasmic reticulum** are all unit membranes.

A unit membrane consists basically of two layers of protein between which are two layers of lipid, but this arrangement may be modified (eg. the fluid mosaic structure of the plasma membrane, or the double nuclear envelope with pores).

◄ Cell membranes, Fluid mosaic model of cell membrane structure, Lipids, Proteins ►

URBANISATION

Urbanisation is the spreading of cities, towns and industries into the countryside thus damaging or destroying habitats and biological communities. Apart from the damage caused by land clearance for building, urbanisation often alters the local water tables and land drainage patterns, which will affect the local biotic communities and extra pollutants may also enter the environment. On the other hand, some new urban habitats are created (e.g. walls and demolition sites).

◄ Habitat, Pollution ►

UREA

Urea is the main nitrogenous waste product of mammals. Since it is highly soluble in water, it can be removed in a relatively small volume of urine and thus not cause a water shortage in the land-dwelling mammal. Unwanted (toxic) amino acids are deaminated in the liver, and the amino groups are converted into urea, via the ornithine cycle. The urea is then carried in the blood to the kidneys and released in the urine.

◄ Excretion ►

URETER

A ureter is a tube passing from the renal pelvis of the kidney to the bladder. It is lined with a transitional epithelium and its function is to carry urine to the bladder for temporary storage.

◄ Kidneys, Urinogenital system ►

URETHRA

The urethra is the tube from the bladder to the exterior in mammals. In females it is short and conducts urine to the exterior. In males it extends through the penis and is joined by the vas deferens, so it can transfer either urine or semen out of the body.

◄ Urinogenital system ►

URIC ACID

Uric acid is a nitrogenous excretory waste product that is insoluble in water and can therefore be excreted in solid form. It is excreted by many terrestrial arthropods, and reptiles and **birds**, in order to minimise water loss, and reduce weight for flight. It is essential for birds and reptiles that their young excrete an insoluble nitrogenous end product, or they could otherwise poison themselves in the confines of the egg.

◀ Excretion, Reptilia ▶

URINE

Urine is an aqueous solution produced by the **kidneys** that contains waste products and unwanted ions. It is stored in the bladder until released by urination, and it is used by many mammals to mark their territory. It will contain dissolved salts, hydrogen ions, hydrogencarbonate ions, excretory products such as urea, uric acid and creatinine, but should not normally contain glucose or protein.

URINOGENITAL SYSTEM

The urinary and genital systems are often grouped together since they are so closely associated, both anatomically and during embryological development (see Figs. U.1 and U.2).

◀ Kidneys, Ovary, Testis, Ureter, Urethra, Uterus ▶

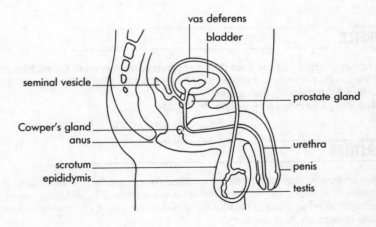

a) median section

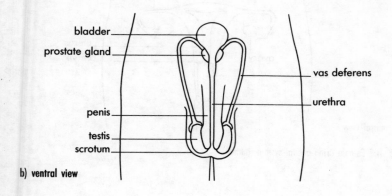

bladder
prostate gland
vas deferens
urethra
penis
testis
scrotum

b) ventral view

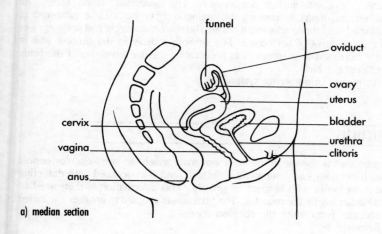

funnel
oviduct
ovary
uterus
cervix
bladder
vagina
urethra
clitoris
anus

a) median section

Fig. U.1 Male urino-genital system (human)

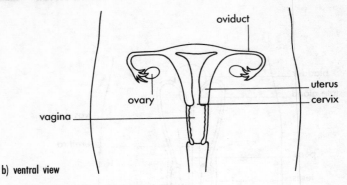

b) ventral view

Fig. U.2 Female urino-genital system (human)

UTERUS

The uterus is commonly known as the womb, and it occurs in marsupial and true mammals. It is the place in the female reproductive tract where the **embryo** develops during **pregnancy**. The glandular inner lining, or endometrium, helps to nourish the young embryo before the **placenta** is established, and its development during the **menstrual cycle** and pregnancy is under the control of hormones. The **smooth muscle** in the uterine wall is greatly increased in pregnancy, in preparation for the expulsion of the **fetus** and placenta at **birth**.
◀ Hormone, Urinogenital system ▶

UTRICULUS

The utriculus is the sac in the inner **ear** from which the **semi-circular canals** arise. It contains endolymph and an otolith, and is concerned with detecting head movements with respect to **gravity**. This information is then used to enable balancing by the muscles. The utriculus is coupled to another sac called the sacculus from which the **cochlea** arises.
◀ Balance ▶

VACCINE

A vaccine is a preparation containing **antigens** that is administered to a patient in order to induce the development of active **immunity**. Vaccinations commonly given to children are to develop immunity to diptheria, pertussis (whooping cough), tetanus, measles, polio and rubella. The antigens present in the vaccine are the pathogenic viruses or **bacteria**, which have either been killed, or have been attenuated, or weakened. The immune system still recognises them as foreign, and develops antibodies against them. Booster doses of vaccine enhance the immune response, so that if the body is challenged by the live organisms, then they are destroyed by **antibody**, before they can establish the disease.

◄ Pathogens, Virus, Viral replication ►

VACUOLE

A sap vacuole occurs in living plant cells and is a sap-filled space surrounded by a membrane known as the **tonoplast**. The sap is isotonic to the **cytoplasm** and contains a solution of salts, sugars, amino acids and organic acids. Such vacuoles are not present in animal cells, though some protoctistans do contain contractile vacuoles for **osmoregulation**, and may form food vacuoles if they feed heterotrophically (e.g. *Amoeba, Paramecium*).

◄ Heterotrophs, Heterotrophic nutrition, Phagocytosis, Protoctista ►

VARIATION

The phenotypic differences between individuals of a **species** are termed variation, and may arise from **genetic variation** or from differences caused by the effects of the environment on the **phenotype** during development. Some variation is discontinuous (e.g. the peas used by Mendel in his experiments were either tall or short, with no overlap between them), while other variation is continuous (e.g. the plot of human stature against frequency in the population would show a continuous 'top hat' curve).

Genetic variation occurs due to **mutation** and to changes during **meiosis**. Environmental influences affect the way many of these genetic variations will be expressed, and the **selection pressure** exerted by the environment will determine which variations survive from generation to generation.

◀ Speciation ▶

VASCULAR BUNDLE

A vascular bundle contains the transport tissue of the plant – that is, the **xylem**, which transports water and salts, and the **phloem**, which transports dissolved organic compounds. In the open vascular bundles of dicotyledons the xylem and phloem are separated by intra-fascicular **cambium** which can initiate **secondary thickening** in woody species. In the closed vascular bundles of monocotyledons there is no intra-fascicular cambium, and these do not develop secondary growth. In **dicotyledon** stems and conifers the vascular bundles are arranged in a ring around the pith, giving mechanical support, but in **monocotyledon** stems the vascular bundles are scattered throughout the stem tissues. The xylem and phloem in each bundle are positioned on the same radius, with the phloem external to the xylem.

◀ Stem structure ▶

VASCULAR CAMBIUM

Vascular cambium is meristematic tissue which develops as a ring around the stem during the **secondary thickening** of a dicotyledonous stem. It is formed by the intra-fascicular **cambium** within each **vascular bundle**, which becomes joined by the development of an inter-fascicular cambium between the bundles. The cambial cells divide mitotically to produce secondary **xylem** to the inside and secondary **phloem** to the outside.

◀ Meristem, Mitosis ▶

VASOCONSTRICTION, VASODILATION

The diameter of the lumen of **arteries** and **arterioles** can be altered by the contraction and relaxation of the **smooth muscle** in the vessel wall. The process is controlled by the autonomic nervous system and is important in **thermoregulation**. Vasoconstriction (Fig. V.1a) reduces blood flow to the skin surface and so conserves heat while vasodilation (Fig. V.1b) increases blood flow and so causes increased heat radiation from the skin. Although there may be precapillary sphincters at the start of a capillary bed which can constrict to curtail flow to the capillaries, the terms vasoconstriction and vasodilation apply to arterioles and *not* to the capillaries themselves, which have no muscle.

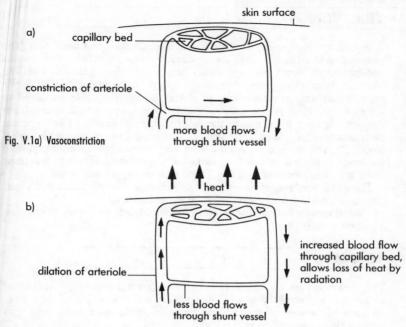

Fig. V.1a) Vasoconstriction

Fig. V.1b) Vasodilation

◄ Autonomic nervous control ►

VECTOR

A vector is a carrier of **disease** or infection. Common vectors include sucking insects, such as **aphids** which spread plant **virus** diseases, and *Anopheles* mosquitoes, which transmit malarial parasites between humans. Vectors are made use of in **genetic engineering** where bacterial **plasmids** or a **bacteriophage** virus is used to 'infect' a bacterium with foreign DNA.

◄ Disease transmission, Malaria ►

VEGETATIVE REPRODUCTION

Vegetative reproduction is a form of **asexual reproduction** in plants, which allows the plant to spread out over new ground away from the parent plant. A part of the plant which includes a shoot apex or bud separates from the parent plant and develops into an independent offspring. The vegetative reproductive structure often contains a food store for **perennation** (in which case it appears swollen). Vegetative reproductive structures in flowering plants include bulbs, corms, rhizomes, runners and suckers.

VEINS, VENULES

A venule is a small vein that results from the branching of a large vein. The direction of blood flow is from the capillary beds to the venules to the veins and then to the **heart**. Veins generally have a wider lumen than **arteries** and have semilunar valves along their length to prevent backflow of blood. Their walls contain only small amounts of elastic tissue and muscle compared to arteries, their blood pressure is lower and they lack a pulse (since the pulse is damped out when blood passes through **capillaries**). Almost all veins return blood from the body to the right side of the heart and so contain deoxygenated blood. The only exceptions are the pulmonary veins which return blood from the lungs to the left side of the heart, and the umbilical vein, which returns blood from the **placenta** to fetus. These contain oxygenated blood.

The word 'vein' may also be used to describe the vascular bundles of a leaf, and the supporting tracheal air tubes in the insect wing.

◄   Blood vessels, Pulmonary blood circulation, Tracheal system, tracheoles, Vascular bundle ►

VENA CAVA

The vena cavae are main **veins** from the body, returning deoxygenated blood to the right atrium of the heart. The posterior vena cava returns blood from the parts of the body posterior to the forelimbs, while the anterior vena cava returns blood from the head, neck and forelimbs.

VENTILATION

Ventilation is an active process involving the aeration of an internal respiratory surface in order to allow oxygen uptake for **respiration** and carbon dioxide removal. In terrestrial animals it is air that is moved during ventilation, while in aquatic animals it is water. In both cases, work must be done by muscles in order to pump the air or water over the exchange surfaces.

◄   Respiratory surfaces and systems, Ventilation mechanisms ►

VENTILATION MECHANISMS

Special mechanisms are required in order to ventilate the alveolar surfaces of **lungs** in **mammals**, the gill filaments in fish and the tracheoles in **insects**. These mechanisms operate by first reducing the pressure at the respiratory surface to less than the environmental pressure, so that air or water rushes over the surface. The pressure at the respiratory surface is then raised above the environmental pressure, so the air or water is forced out. The **respiratory surfaces** and associated tissues and ducts must therefore be capable of withstanding these pressure changes and any dimension changes occuring during ventilation movements. The lungs, **trachea** and bronchi, for example, contain elastic tissue and the trachea contains C-rings of cartilage.

In mammals, there are two pleural membranes, one attached to the inner wall of the thorax cavity and the other to the outside of the lungs. Between the pleural membranes is an airtight cavity which is at a lower pressure than the air in the lungs. This means that the lungs are held expanded against the thorax wall and any changes in thoracic volume will cause corresponding changes in lung volume. The thoracic volume is increased by the contraction of the diaphragm muscle, so that the diaphragm becomes flattened, and by the contraction of the external intercostal muscles to pull the ribs up and out. Increased volume results in a decreased internal pressure, and air rushes in from the atmosphere in order to equilibrate the pressure difference. Expiration is a more passive process. The diaphragm relaxes, returning to its domed resting position, and the external intercostal muscles relax, allowing the rib cage to move downwards and inwards. In this way the lung volume is decreased, pressure increases and air is pushed back to the atmosphere. At the end of expiration the alveoli elastically recoil to cause a surge in the air flow leaving them, and hence more efficient alveolar emptying (Fig. V.2 a),b) and c). There are stretch receptors located in the walls of the bronchi and bronchioles which coordinate the alternation of inspiration with expiration by the inflation reflex. The rate and depth of breathing, meanwhile, is regulated by the respiratory centre in the **brain** stem which responds to the CO_2 level in the blood. If CO_2 rises, then the ventilation rate is increased.

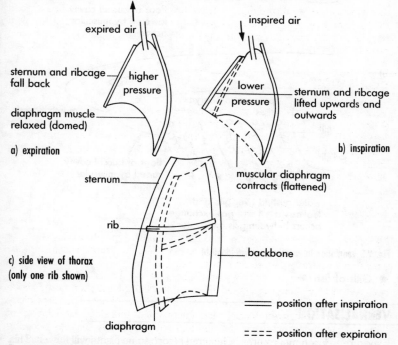

Fig. V.2 Ventilation movements (human):

In fish, water is taken in through the mouth, passed over the gills, where gas exchange occurs, and passed out via the gill slits in cartilaginous fish, or the operculum in bony fish. The floor of the buccal cavity is lowered while the mouth is open and the increased volume causes a decreased pressure so water rushes in. The mouth is then closed and the buccal floor raised, which forces the water between the gills and out through the gill slits or operculum (Fig. V.3).

In insects the movement of air through the **tracheal system** is facilitated by dorso-ventral flattening and expanding of the chitinous body segments due to the muscles attached to the inside of the **exoskeleton**.

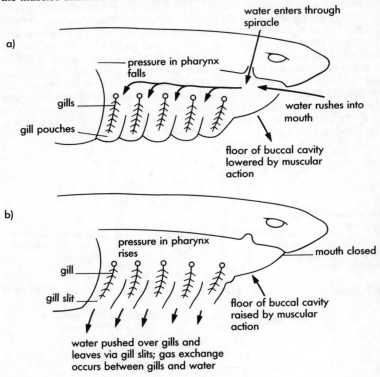

Fig. V.3 Ventilation in *cartilaginous fish* (dogfish)

◀ Gills of fish ▶

VERNALISATION

Exposure to low temperatures is required before some plants will flower. This particularly applies to biennials and perennials, and is called vernalisation. A temperature of around 4°C is usually required, and the duration of the cold period may vary from a few days to several months. The part of a plant that must undergo vernalisation also varies. For some plants, a few days' vernalisation of the seeds speeds up the onset of flowering (e.g. winter cereals), while in other plants it is the main stem apex or perennating organ that must be exposed to cold.

Biennials grow vegetatively during the first year, overwintering as corms, bulbs, etc., and then grow and flower the second year. Flowers, however, are only produced if the perennating organs have been subjected to cold during the winter; if they have been kept warm over winter, vegetative growth continues.

The vernalisation effect can be transmitted between plants by grafting, so it is thought that a **hormone** may be involved. This hormone has been named vernalin, but it is probably a **gibberellin**.

◀ Perennation, Seed ▶

VERTEBRAE, VERTEBRAL COLUMN

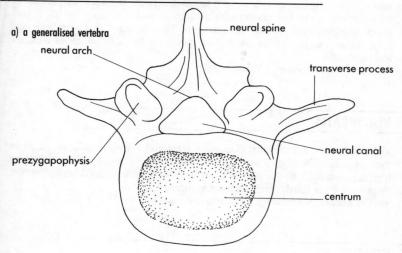

a) a generalised vertebra

neural spine

neural arch

transverse process

neural canal

prezygapophysis

centrum

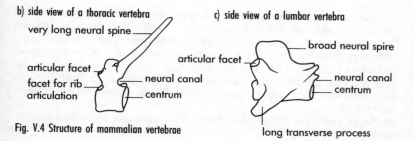

b) side view of a thoracic vertebra

very long neural spine

articular facet
facet for rib articulation

neural canal

centrum

c) side view of a lumbar vertebra

broad neural spire

articular facet

neural canal

centrum

long transverse process

Fig. V.4 Structure of mammalian vertebrae

The vertebral column lies along the dorsal mid-line of a vertebrate animal and is composed of short bones called vertebrae (Fig. V.4a, b and c). The bones form a hollow rod which houses and protects the **spinal cord**, and though joints between individual vertebrae allow only small movement, the bending allowed by the whole vertebral column is considerable.

In fish all the vertebrae from skull to tail are similar, but in tetrapods vertebrae in different areas have become modified and specialised. In the human, for example, the vertebral column consists of thirty-three vertebrae, but since some are fused there are only twenty-six bones. These make up the following regions:

- Cervical region in neck – 7 vertebrae;
- Thoracic region in thorax – 12 vertebrae;
- Lumbar region in small of back – 5 vertebrae;
- Sacral region in pelvis – 5 vertebrae fused to give the sacrum;
- Caudal region below sacrum – 4 vertebrae fused to give the coccyx.

Each vertebra consists of a solid body or centrum, above which is the neural arch, which covers the spinal cord. The neural arch also bears facets for articulation with the vertebrae in front and behind. Between the centra of adjacent vertebrae are resilient fibro-cartilage pads or discs, which act as shock-absorbers and protect the vertebrae from damage. The vertebrae also have transverse processes and dorsal spines for the attachment of muscles and ligaments.

◄ Bone, Fused bones, Skeleton ►

VERTEBRATES

Vertebrates are animals that possess a skull and vertebral column. Most of the phylum Chordata are vertebrates: the classes Chondrichthyes (cartilaginous fish), **Osteichthyes** (bony fish), **Amphibia** (amphibians), **Reptilia** (reptiles), **Aves** (birds) and Mammalia (**mammals**).

◄ Chordates, Vertebrae, Vertebral column ►

VESICLE

Vesicles are small, round cavities in the **cytoplasm** of cells, usually only visible under the **electron microscope**. Golgi vesicles for example, contain secretions from the cisternae, and may become **lysosomes** or fuse with the **plasma** membrane to release their secretion. Phagocytes, such as neutrophils and monocytes, ingest **bacteria** into phagocytic vesicles, while foldings of the plasma membrane may take fluids into cells, forming pinocytic vesicles. In synaptic knobs, the synaptic vesicles contain the neurotransmitter substance, acetylcholine.

◄ Golgi complex, Phagocytes, Pinocytosis, Synapse, Synaptic transmission ►

VESTIGIAL STRUCTURES

Vestigial structures are structures which in ancestral types of animals and plants had some function and were probably well developed, but in modern forms they are simplified and reduced with no apparent function. Boa constrictors are limbless but have vestiges of the girdles and limb bones in their skeleton, while in man the external ear muscles are vestigial, at best producing only feeble movements of the pinnae.

Some vestigial organs may have a role in development by producing organiser or inducer substances. An example, is the pineal body of mammals, which was long thought to be a vestige of the ancient pineal eye. It is now known to secrete a **hormone**, called melatonin, which inhibits reproductive activity by inhibiting gonadotrophins.

VILLUS/VILLI

Villi are finger-shaped projections of the mucosa of the **small intestine**. Each villus is about 1 mm long and they occur in enormous numbers. They are lined by columnar epithelium, which itself has microvilli, so there is a huge surface area for absorption of dietary substances. The walls of the villi contain **smooth muscle** so they can constantly contract and relax and wave around in the digested food. Each villus contains a profuse capillary network whose blood drains to the hepatic portal vein, and a branch of the lymphatic system called a lacteal.

In the **placenta** there are chorionic villi which greatly increase the area of contact and exchange between placental tissues and maternal tissues.
◀ Absorption, Ileum ▶

VINEGAR PRODUCTION

Vinegar (ethanoic acid) is formed by the partial oxidation of ethanol:

$$CH_3CH_2OH + O_2 \rightarrow CH_3COOH + H_2O$$

ethanol   ethanoic
                 acid

This is a natural souring of alcohol carried out by such bacteria as *Acetobacter* and *Acetomonas*. In the Orleans process poor-quality wine is held in partially filled casks and a bacterial starter culture added. The oxidative process carried out by the bacteria is slow, taking several weeks. Eventually vinegar can be tapped off from the bottom of the casks, and fresh wine added to restore the original volume. In Britain much vinegar is produced from cider or malt wort rather than wine.

VIRUS, VIRAL REPLICATION

The largest virions (single virus particles) are 400 – 500 nm diameter, and can just be seen under the best light microscopes which have a resolution limit of 200 nm. A virion has a protein coat or capsid, which encloses DNA or RNA. Some viruses also have an envelope made of **carbohydrates** or lipoprotein, and some viruses also contain enzymes.

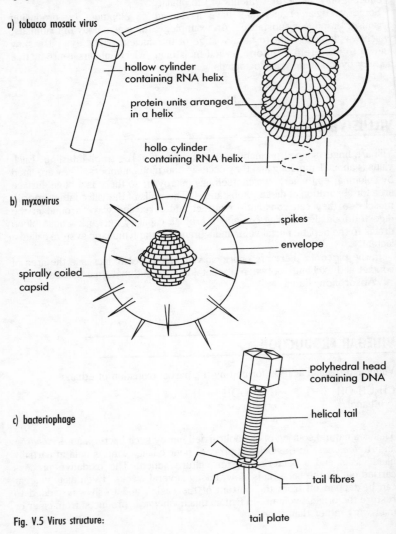

a) tobacco mosaic virus

hollow cylinder containing RNA helix

protein units arranged in a helix

hollo cylinder containing RNA helix

b) myxovirus

spikes

envelope

spirally coiled capsid

c) bacteriophage

polyhedral head containing DNA

helical tail

tail fibres

tail plate

Fig. V.5 Virus structure:

Shape-wise the viruses fit into three groups:

- Helices, such as Tobacco Mosaic Virus (TMV), (Fig V.5 a) where the capsid polypeptides are arranged in a helix like a hollow rod. In the myxoviruses (mumps, measles, influenza, (Fig V.5 b), the helical capsid is enclosed in an envelope.
- Polyhedral forms, where the capsid forms a many-sided shape, such as an icosahedron with twenty equal faces, or naked forms such as Adenoviruses (infect adenoids and tonsils), and enveloped forms such as **Rubella** virus (German measles).
- Complex viruses, such as the bacteriophages (Fig. V. 5 c), which have an icosahedral head containing a single DNA helix, a helical tail and a tail plate from which long filaments project.

Viruses are obligate parasites and can grow and replicate only within living cells. In replication, T_2 coliphage is a **bacteriophage** which infects the bacteria *Escherichia coli*. The T_2 phage attaches itself to a specific recognition site on the surface of *E. coli* and releases lysozyme, which softens and penetrates the bacterial wall. The phage tail contracts and DNA is injected out of the head of the phage into the bacterium. There is then a latent phase, during which there is no apparent activity. During this time, the phage DNA is suppressing the metabolic reactions of the host, and using the host mRNA to synthesise phage proteins and enzymes so that new virions can be assembled. The bacterial wall is then hydrolysed and the phage particles are released to infect new bacteria.

VISUAL CORTEX

The visual cortex is part of the cerebral cortex of the **brain**. There is a primary visual area which receives impulses from the retina, via the optic nerves, and interprets shape and colour. There is also a visual association area, which receives sensory impulses from the thalamus and primary visual area, and relates present visual experiences to past ones, enabling recognition and assessment of what is seen. It is here, for example, that the inverted image formed on the retina is interpreted as an object the same way up as ourselves.

◀ Eye, Focusing, Cerebral hemispheres, Cerebrum ▶

VITAMINS

Vitamins are organic nutrients, needed in small amounts to maintain growth and normal metabolism. They do not serve as building materials or energy providers, but usually act as co-enzymes. Most cannot be synthesised by the body, but are ingested in the diet or synthesised by bacteria in the gut. Vitamins A, D, E and K are fat-soluble, so are absorbed with dietary fat and can be stored in adipose tissue, while vitamins B and C are water-soluble, dissolve in the body fluids and cannot be stored. Lack of a certain vitamin will cause specific deficiency symptoms. Different heterotrophs have different vitamin requirements, but humans require the following:

► FAT-SOLUBLE VITAMINS

Vitamin A

This is present in milk, butter and fish liver oils, and it can also be formed from the provitamin carotene in the intestines, carotene being present in green or yellow vegetables. It keeps the skin healthy, regulates the growth of bones and teeth and is essential for the formation of rhodopsin in the rods and cones of the retina. Deficiency can result in night blindness when rod vision is lost, or full blindness when rod and cone vision is lost. The cornea may become ulcerated (xerophthalmia), and the skin become dry, scaly and prone to infections.

Vitamin D

In sunlight provitamin D_3, a derivative of cholesterol, is converted in the skin to Vitamin D, calciferol. Dietary Vitamin D is present in fish liver oils, egg yolk and milk. It is required for absorption of calcium and phosphorus from the gut, and the use of these ions in bones, teeth and for blood clotting. Deficiency of Vitamin D causes rickets in children and osteomalacia in adults; in both these diseases there is a withdrawal of calcium from bony tissue, with consequential weakening of the bones.

Vitamin E

This is present in green vegetables and wheat germ. Deficiency results in abnormal structure and function of plasma membranes, mitochondria and lysosomes. In red cell formation this may be linked to the development of haemolytic anaemia.

Vitamin K

This is present in green vegetables and liver and is also produced by symbiotic intestinal bacteria. It is a co-enzyme involved in the synthesis of prothrombin and other clotting factors by the liver, and it is known as the antihaemorrhagic vitamin, since delayed clotting and excessive bleeding occur in deficiency.

► WATER SOLUBLE VITAMINS

Vitamin B_1 (Thiamine)

This occurs in eggs, meat and nuts. It is a co-enzyme in glycolysis, and is required for the synthesis of acetylcholine. Deficiency leads to beri-beri.

Vitamin B_2 (Riboflavin)

This also occurs in eggs, meat and nuts, and forms FAD (flavine adenine dinucleotide) which is required for the electron transport system in respiration. Deficiency results in blurred vision, dermatitis and anaemia.

Niacin (Nicotinamide)

This is present in yeast, meat, pulses and nuts and is an important component of the hydrogen-transfering co-enzyme NAD (nicotinamide adenine dinucleotide) and NADP (nicotinamide adenine dinucleotide phosphate). Deficiency results in pellagra.

Vitamins B_6 and B_{12}

Other B-vitamins include Vitamin B_6, a co-enzyme for the decarboxylation of amino acids, and Vitamin B_{12}, which is required for red cell formation. Deficiency results in pernicious anaemia.

Pantothenic acid

This is a component of co-enzyme A, which transfers pyruvic acid into the Krebs cycle after glycolysis.

Folic acid

This is important in red cell formation. Deficiency results in macrocytic anaemia (large red cells).

Biotin

This is an essential co-enzyme for the synthesis of purines and fatty acids. Deficiency causes depression and dermatitis.

Vitamin C (Ascorbic Acid)

This is present in citrus fruits, tomatoes and green vegetables, but is rapidly destroyed by heat or oxidation. It promotes protein metabolism and collagen synthesis, thus helping in wound healing, and it is involved with the detoxification of poisons. Deficiency results in anaemia and scurvy, symptoms of scurvy include poor growth of connective tissue, impaired wound healing, swollen gums, loose teeth and gum bleeding.

◀ Niacin, Riboflavin, Thiamine ▶

VIVIPAROUS

Viviparous means 'live birth' and occurs in the placental **mammals**. Here the embryo develops in the maternal organism, deriving its nutrition via a **placenta** from the maternal blood stream, and thus has to be born, at the end of the **pregnancy** or gestation period.

VOLUNTARY MUSCLE

Voluntary muscle is attached to the skeleton and under the control of the voluntary nervous system.

◄ Striated muscle ►

VOLUNTARY NERVOUS SYSTEM

The voluntary nervous system is under conscious control, or can be controlled by will. This distinguishes it from the autonomic nervous system which cannot be controlled by will.

◄ Autonomic nervous control, Nervous system ►

WALKING UPRIGHT

Humans are bipedal – that is, they walk upright on two legs. Thus the long bones of the hindlimbs, such as the femurs, tibias and fibulas, have become longer than in man's ancestors and 'cousins' (anthropoid apes). The big toe is no longer opposable to the next toe, as it is in the apes, but provides a larger foot surface on the ground. The foot is no longer flat but is developed into an arch-like structure with a well-developed heel. Thus man can stand on tip-toe and has resilience or 'spring' in his walk. Man's stride involves the heel and ball of each foot; in effect, an ape walk would be like trying to walk on one's heels only.

Being bipedal has freed the forelimbs to do other things, and has allowed the development of the hands. It also made the whole face visible and so encouraged the development of communication. Together with the development of the brain, this has led to all man's achievements to date.

WASTE RECYCLING

Earth's resources are finite or limited and are being used up at an ever-increasing rate. For **conservation** purposes and to eke out resources, it is important that things are recycled after use rather than destroyed (e.g. recycling of paper conserves trees from which paper is made, recycling of metals saves fuel required in production of metal and reduces the need for mining). **Organic compounds** are recycled in nature (e.g. the proteins of dead organisms are broken down in decay and recycled via the **nitrogen cycle**).

WASTELAND

Wasteland is land that is not used for cultivation or is not in use for industrial or commercial reasons. In cities and towns it might be land left after clearance of slums or unwanted factories. Such land is usually an important reservoir of wildlife. In the case of **conservation**-minded farmers, who often leave a few corners of their farms uncultivated, such areas may contain the only original natural flora and fauna of the area, so should be protected. In the case of cleared land in towns, a natural **succession** of animals and plants may occur, eventually resulting in scrubland or woodland, if not interfered with. Such reservoirs of wildlife provide areas for study and appreciation of living things. Mown parklands laid out with formal flower beds are all very well, but do not produce the large variety of species that wild habitats do. It is important to conserve the ever-dwindling variety of living things.

Derelict land is land so altered and damaged by man that living communities of animals and plants cannot successfully establish themselves there. Areas may be polluted: for example, near copper mines there are high residues of copper salts in the soil.

◀ Pollution ▶

WASTE SUBSTANCES

Waste substances are excretory compounds-toxic byproducts produced as a result of an organism's metabolism. Since they are toxic they have to be removed (e.g. **urea, uric acid**, creatinine and **ammonia** are toxic nitrogenous end products removed in the **urine**). Alternatively, they have to be stored in an inert form out of harm's way (e.g. calcium oxalate crystals and tannins in the piths and heartwood of plants).

◀ Excretion ▶

WATER

Water is the most abundant chemical in living systems: roughly 70–90 per cent of living material is water. Water is important to life largely because of its excellent properties as a solvent for a wide range of chemicals. It is a good solvent because of the marked polarity of water molecules, and because of their ability to form a **hydrogen bond**, thus ionic and polar compounds dissolve in it. It is the medium in which most cell and biochemical reactions occur, it is an excellent **transport** medium since it flows, carrying dissolved solutes and suspended cells, and it has high surface tension, cohesion and adhesion and is thus held in capillary spaces by capillarity. It holds heat since it has a high specific heat capacity, and thus retains metabolic heat within organisms. It is a metabolite in its own right (e.g. it is raw material of **photosynthesis**), and is involved in the hydrolytic reactions of **digestion** and food mobilisation. It has high latent heat of vaporisation, which helps to cool biological surfaces.

◀ Solvent ▶

WATER CONSERVATION

Water conservation is particularly important in terrestrial animals and in plants which live in habitats with limited water. Land animals have developed many adaptations to reduce water loss (e.g. impermeable body surfaces such as the keratinised outer **epidermis** of **mammals** and the wax-covered chitinous **exoskeleton** of **insects**; the development of long loops of Henle and long collecting ducts for water reabsorption from the urine, and the associated ADH mechanism; and in birds, the use of uric acid as a solid excretory material not requiring water as a solvent). Xerophytic plants living in arid areas have thick cuticles to reduce water loss by evaporation, sunken stomata to reduce transpiration, water storage tissue to collect water when available and retain it, and inverted stomatal rhythms so that stomata are closed during the hottest part of the day.

WATER FLEA

Water fleas are small animals belonging to phylum Arthropoda, superclass Crustacea, living in fresh and sea water. They have laterally compressed bodies and use setae on their legs for filter feeding. Their bodies are transparent, so the pumping action of the heart is clearly visible under the light microscope (e.g. *Daphnia*).
◄ Arthropids ►

WATER POTENTIAL

Water potential is signified by the greek letter psi, ψ. Water movement, particularly in plant physiology, should be regarded in terms of water potential. The water potential of pure water at atmospheric pressure is taken to be zero for all measurements and comparisons. The water potential of a system (e.g. cell sap) is the difference between the chemical potential of the water in the system and the chemical potential of pure water at the same temperature and pressure. This shows as a force acting on water molecules in a solution when separated from pure water by a membrane that is permeable only to water. Water potentials of solutions are negative values since they are lower than pure water. Water tends to move from high water potential (pure water) to lower water potential (solution).

Osmosis should now be defined as 'the movement of water molecules from a region of higher water potential to a region of lower water potential, through a differentially permeable membrane'.
◄ Plasmolysis, Turgor ►

WATERPROOFING

Biological surfaces are often waterproofed, in an attempt to curtail water loss when there is a need for conservation. For example, epidermal cells of the aerial parts of plants are coated on their outer walls with a fatty substance called cutin, often forming a distinct layer called the cuticle. Cutin is impermeable to water, so the cuticle may be particularly thick in xerophytic plants, which live in arid areas. In secondary thickened plants the cells of the phellem, which make up the bark, are coated with suberin, another water-impermeable substance. The outermost layer of the insect exoskeleton also consists of a waxy layer to reduce loss by evaporation. In mammals the outer layer of the **epidermis** consists of nothing but flattened keratin-filled ghosts of cells; this is the cornified layer and is responsible for waterproofing the skin. Similar layers are present in birds.

◀ Terrestrial life, adaptations for, Xerophytes ▶

WATER PURIFICATION

Water in nature is almost always contaminated with micro-organisms. This is particularly so if faecal matter pollutes the water, when *Cholera* vibrios and *Salmonella* species (which cause **Typhoid**) may contaminate the water and be a risk to human health. The common but relatively harmless intestinal bacterium *Escherichia coli*, if present in large numbers in water, indicates contamination with faeces. It is important that water for domestic use and human consumption be purified.

If water is allowed to stand in a reservoir for two to three weeks, there is sedimentation of particles, and as the nutrient level declines, so does the population of micro-organisms. If the water is filtered through fine gravel or sand beds, the bulk of contaminants are removed, and the **bacteria, fungi** and **protozoa** which grow in the slime layer over the filter beds decay the organic matter. The addition of chlorine at a concentration of 0.02–2 parts per million will kill any remaining water-borne disease organisms.

River water requires additional processing before it is suitable for human intake. It is coarse-filtered to remove floating material, aerated to reduce odour and treated to reduce mineral content.

◀ Micro-organism ▶

WATER UPTAKE IN ROOTS

Water is absorbed mainly through the root hair regions in younger roots (Fig. W.1). The **root hairs** have a huge surface area in contact with the soil solution, so osmotic uptake of water is highly efficient. A **water potential** gradient is maintained between the root hair cells and the cells adjacent to the **xylem**, the root hair cells having the higher potential. This gradient is maintained because the xylem sap has a lower water potential than the soil solution, and the water is moving up the xylem, lowering its water potential.

Soil solution is fairly dilute, with a higher water potential than the root hair cell sap, so water enters the root hairs and other piliferous layer cells by **osmosis**. The water is then moved across to the xylem by the **apoplastic pathway, symplastic pathway** and vacuolar pathway. The symplasm is the mass of protoplasts in the plant which are interconnected by **plasmodesmata** (cytoplasmic strands). Once water enters the cytoplasm it can move from cell to cell through the plasmodesmata without passing any membranes and so move all across the cortex to the xylem region. The apoplasm is the collective term for all the **cell walls** which lie adjacent and in contact with each other. Up to 50 per cent of the cellulose wall may be 'free space' which can be occupied by water and so water can pass through it. As water is drawn up the xylem, more water is drawn into the xylem from the root cortex apoplast, a continuous flow being maintained by the cohesion of water molecules together. However, the water cannot flow directly from root apoplast to xylem, due to the presence of the **endodermis**, and its Casparian strips of water-impermeable suberin. Water (and salts) must therefore pass from the apoplast to the cytoplasm and vacuoles of the endodermal cells before being passed to the xylem. This probably enables the plant to control its uptake of water (and salts). Water can also flow osmotically from the vacuole to the vacuole of the cortical parenchyma cells.

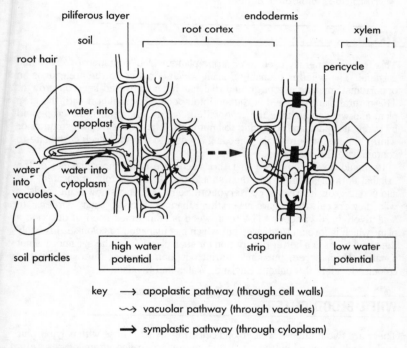

Fig. W.1 Water uptake in roots

WAVE OF DEPOLARISATION

A wave of depolarisation is the reversal of the **resting potential** on an axon or muscle fibre from positive outside to negative outside, over a small area (which passes along the axon) permeable to sodium ions for a few ten-thousandths of a second so that sodium ions rush into the axon along the **diffusion** gradient. The area of potential reversal is propagated along the axon by local currents.

◀ Nerve impulse, transmission ▶

WEED MANAGEMENT

Weed management can be done by chemical control using **herbicides** such as 2−4 dichlorophenoxyacetic acid (2−4−D) and 2−4−5 trichlorophenoxyacetic acid (2−4−5−T). These have many auxin-like properties and are selective − that is, they will kill broad-leaved weeds but not the narrow-leaved grasses of lawns and cereals. Alternatively, **biological control** can be used (e.g. caterpillars of the Cinnabar moth control ragwort, *Senecio jacobea*.
◀ Herbicides, Biological control ▶

WEEDS

This term is generally used to describe plants which 'contaminate' crops and gardens. The weed is probably a plant which is native to the area, or is an opportunist, making use of ground that has been cultivated for crop growth. The natural plant or weed is thus in **interspecific competition** with the crop plant and will contaminate the crop with its seeds, and reduce the crop **yield** by taking up space and removing **soil nutrients**. The weeds may be summer or winter annuals or perennials, shedding seeds into the soil which germinate to contaminate the next crop.

It should be remembered that the weeds are often the remnants of the original flora of an area, and thus should not be completely eradicated, but allowed to grow in areas of **conservation**. Some gardeners now plant seeds of wild flowers in their gardens rather than restricting their gardens to selectively bred varieties. The term weed is sometimes used to describe a plant which is foreign to an area but which has managed to colonise. Probably the word 'alien' is a better description for such plants (e.g. the sycamore is not a native British tree, but since its introduction many centuries ago it has colonised widely throughout England, Wales and Scotland).

WHITE BLOOD CELLS

There are two groups of white blood cells (Fig. W.2). Those with polymorphic nuclei and granules in their cell cytoplasm are called granulocytes (e.g. neutrophils, eosinophils and basophils) while agranulocytes include monocytes and lymphocytes. The total white cell count in humans should be in the range of $5-9 \times 10^9$ cells per litre. Of these 60−70 per cent are neutrophils, 2−4 per cent are eosinophils, 0.5−1 per cent are basophils, 20−25 per cent are lymphocytes and 3−8 per cent are monocytes. The granulocytes and monocytes are formed in the red bone marrow, but the lymphocytes form in the lymphoid tissue. Most white cells (leucocytes) can show diapedesis − that is, they can squeeze through the minute spaces between the cells of the capillary wall, into surrounding tissues, through which they can move by amoeboid action.

Neutrophils and monocytes act as macrophages or phagocytes ingesting any **bacteria** that invade the body, the neutrophil granules contain lysozyme, which is used to digest the ingested bacteria. Eosinophils combat irritants that cause allergies or that are released by parasites. They produce antihistamines and can destroy antigen-antibody complexes. Basophils form the mast cells of the **connective tissue**. When they leave the circulation, they release the anticoagulant heparin, which prevents **blood clotting** in the vessels, and histamine and serotonin, which promote the inflammatory response. Lymphocytes, when activated, produce the immune response of cell and humoral **immunity** (antibodies).

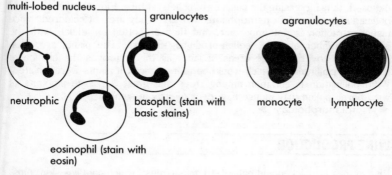

multi-lobed nucleus

granulocytes

agranulocytes

neutrophic

basophic (stain with basic stains)

monocyte

lymphocyte

eosinophil (stain with eosin)

Fig. W.2 White blood cells

◀ Allergy, B-lymphocytes, Blood ▶

WILDLIFE AND COUNTRYSIDE ACT 1981

This is a comprehensive measure for safeguarding species and sites in Britain. SSSIs are **sites of special scientific interest** and the Act requires that each owner of an SSSI knows of its location, why it is of special interest and of operations that could adversely affect it. Owners must give three months' notice, in writing, of their intention to perform such a listed operation. The NCC (Nature Conservancy Council) has been the main body involved in the implementation of the Act.

WIND DISPERSAL

Wind dispersal is a method of dispersing seeds from the parent plant so that they do not have to grow and germinate in competition with the parent plant but can colonise new areas. Orchids produce seeds which are small enough to blow as dust. 'Censer' mechanisms are where small seeds are thrown out of capsules into the wind currents (e.g. poppy). Winged fruits, such as the sycamore and ash, have the pericarp extended into a wing and are blown about in a helicopter-like fashion. Plumed fruits are seen with the hairy pappus of composites, such as dandelion and thistle, and plumed seeds are seen in willows. The plumes act as parachutes to catch the wind.

WIND POLLINATION

Wind pollination occurs when the pollen is transferred from the **anthers** of one flower to the stigmas of another flower of the same species by wind. The pollen produced is very light and dust-like for blowing in the wind, and is produced in copious amounts since there is much wastage. Anthers are large and pendulous, hanging out of the reduced sepals and petals, so as to release the pollen into the wind efficiently. The stigmas are large and feathery and also exposed, thus increasing the chances of pollen capture. Flowers that use wind pollination are termed **anemophilous flowers**. They are not coloured, since insect attraction is not important, and they are often unisexual, with the greatest number of male, pollen-producing flowers. The plants are often gregarious, covering large areas of land, as this improves the chance of successful **pollination**, which would be more difficult if plants were isolated. Wind pollination is common among trees and grasses. Large amounts of wind-borne pollen may induce hay fever **allergy** in some people.

◄ Floral morphology ►

WINE PRODUCTION

Ripe grapes are picked and pulped, to give a 'must' which contains skin, pips, pulp and juice. This must be treated with sulphur dioxide to prevent spoilage by wild yeasts and undesirable bacteria on the fruit skins. **Fermentation** of the 'must' is often begun by adding a 'starter' culture of the **yeast**, *Saccharomyces cerevisiae*. As fermentation continues, the alcohol produced will extract the red pigments from the grape skins, so if a white wine is required, these are removed early on. Complete breakdown of the sugar in the 'must' will produce a dry wine, but if fermentation is stopped before all the sugar is used up, a sweet wine is formed. The yeast is killed at an alcohol content of about 15 per cent. The fermented liquor is stored in vats to allow sedimentation, then it is filtered and bottled.

WOODLAND ENVIRONMENT

The **climax** vegetation over most of southern Britain is deciduous oak wood (*Quercus robur*), while in Scotland and above about 1,000 feet in England the climax vegetation is pinewood (*Pinus sylvestris*). Beechwood is also fairly common in some areas and oakwood may be preceded by birchwood in the natural **succession** to the climax.

In calcium-rich deep clays or loams the usual woodland is of oak, often in association with other trees such as ash (*Fraxinus excelsior*). These trees form the canopy layer since they are tall, and this controls the amount of light which can penetrate to the lower layers. This restricts the other plant species to shade-tolerant plants, although some spring plants can grow before the canopy leaves fully open and adversely shade them. In the shrub layer common plants are hazel (*Corylus avellana*), elder (*Sambucus nigra*) and hawthorn (*Crataegus mongyna*). In the herbaceous level on the forest floor will be found shade-lovers, such as wood sanicle (*Sanicula europea*) and ground ivy (*Glechoma hederacea*). These are rarely found in exposed situations and flower in the reduced light intensity of the summer, when the canopy is in full leaf. In the spring, before light is greatly impeded, other herbs may grow and flower (e.g. primrose, *Primula vulgaris*, dog's mercury *Mercurialis perennis*, and wood anemone, *Amenome nemorosa*).

WORLD CONSERVATION STRATEGY

The World Conservation Strategy is an initiative that was launched on an international level in 1980. It attempts to modernise concepts of **conservation** and to make a positive input into planning and environmental protection. It attempts to balance the needs of conservation against the needs to use the world resources.

WORLDWIDE FUND FOR NATURE (WWF)

The headquarters of the WWF are in Godalming, Surrey, and the Fund aims to raise money to enable **conservation** projects to continue or be started in any area of the world.

XANTHOPYLL

Xanthophylls are yellow photosynthetic pigments chemically similar to, and classed as, carotenes. They have broad absorption spectra (e.g. fucoxanthin), which helps to give brown algae their colour.

X-CHROMOSOME

This is the sex chromosome found paired in the homogametic sex and single in the heterogametic sex. Besides carrying genes regulating sexuality, it carries genes governing colour vision and blood clotting ability.
◀ Sex determination, Sex linkage ▶

XENOPUS TADPOLES

Xenopus is the African clawed toad. Its tadpoles can be used to observe expansion and contraction of melanophore cells in their tail fins according to the darkness of their surroundings, and also used to observe blood flow through the capillaries in their tail fins.

XEROPHYTES

Xerophytes are plants which show a particular ability for growing in places where the water supply would be inadequate for ordinary plants. They have special features in their form and internal anatomy which usually reduce water loss by transpiration (e.g leaves reduced to spines, cacti, gorse, broom – and stems therefore green for photosynthesis; water storage tissue in leaves or stems – cacti, *Sedum sps.*; rolled leaves – maram grass, crowberry, cross-leaved heath; sunken stomata and thick cuticle (marram grass).
◀ Terrestrial life, adaptations for, Water conservation, Waterproofing ▶

X-RAY DIFFRACTION

X-ray diffraction is a technique used to analyse crystal and molecular structures. It has been invaluable in discovering the structure of **proteins** and DNA.

XYLEM

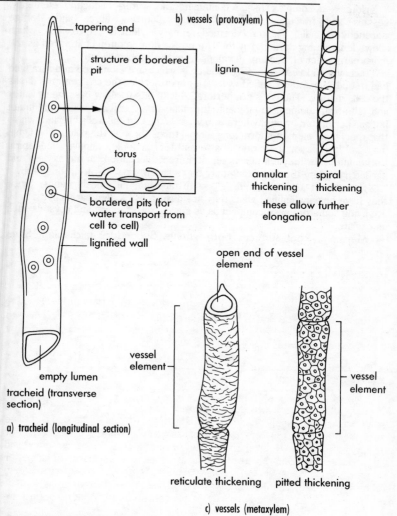

Fig. X.1 Structure of xylem elements

Xylem (Fig. X.1 a, b and c) is the vascular tissue that transports **water** and dissolved mineral salts upwards through the plant body. Primary xylem differentiates during the development of the primary plant body – that is, the plant which develops directly from the embryo, and is formed by the meristematic tissue known as procambium. Secondary xylem develops from the vascular **cambium** during woody or secondary **growth**. The xylem also has a mechanical or supporting role.

Xylem is a complex tissue containing the water-conducting elements, vessels and tracheids, together with supporting fibres and storage **parenchyma** cells. The first formed primary xylem is protoxylem, which allows lengthening during growth. The protoxylem is often obliterated as the more permanent metaxylem develops from the procambium.

Tracheids and vessels are lignified cells which are elongated and arranged end to end. Since the lignified walls are impermeable, the cell contents die as the cells mature. The walls are perforated with pits to allow passage of water and salts from element to element. In tracheids the end cell walls stay intact but are perforated by pits, whereas in vessels the end cell walls break down so that the vessel elements form longitudinal tubes through the plant. The lignin may be laid down in various patterns; for example, annular and spiral thickening in protoxylem allows for stem/root elongation, in metaxylem and secondary xylem the thickening may be reticulate or scalariform or pitted.

Xylem **fibres** are elongated cells with tapering, interlocking ends. Since they have heavily lignified walls they are dead cells. Xylem parenchyma cells are living and store such compounds as starch, oils, tannins and crystals such as oxalate.

◄ Meristem, Root surfaces and systems, Secondary thickening, Stem structure ►

Y–CHROMOSOME

The Y-chromosome is a sex chromosome found only in the heterogametic sex. It usually differs structurally from the X-chromosome, often being shorter and thus not able to pair properly with the X-chromosome during meiosis. It carries few genes.

◄ Gene, Sex determination, Sex linkage ►

YEAST

Yeasts are unicellular saprophytes classed in the Ascomycota phylum of the fungi. They occur on the surface of fruits and multiply asexually by budding. Since they cause alcoholic fermentation, they are of great economical importance, producing alcohol for the brewing industry and generating carbon dioxide which causes the dough to rise in baking. *Saccharomyces cerevisiae* and *S. carlsbergensis* are two commonly used species. Yeasts may also be used commercially as a source of microbial protein and vitamins.

◄ Saprophyte, Saprophytism, Wine production ►

YELLOW ELASTIC TISSUE

Yellow elastic tissue contains fibres made of the protein elastin, which return tissues to their original dimensions when pulling forces are removed. They run in all directions through the loose areolar connective tissue, but in ligaments they form parallel longitudinal bundles, attaching bone to bone along lines of stress.

YIELD

The yield is the net production of a crop or a trophic level in a food chain or web. It can be expressed in terms of energy or biomass.

◄ Productivity, Trophic levels ►

YOGHURT MANUFACTURE

Yoghurt is one of the older fermented products, being a cultered buttermilk, originally prepared from the liquid removed from cream during butter manufacture. Nowadays it is usually made from pasteurised skimmed milk. After heat treatment the milk is innoculated with a 2–3 per cent yoghurt culture containing the **bacteria** *Streptococcus thermophilus* and *Lactobacillus bulgaricus*. These are allowed to ferment the lactose in milk to produce lactic acid, which sours the milk. The fermentation is carried out at 42–45°C, and to develop good odour, flavour and consistency the two organisms should be present in about equal proportions.

◄ Fermentation ►

YOLK

The yolk is the stored food material in eggs, and must be sufficient to support the developing embryo until it can be fed in another way.

ZONE

Zones are regions in an ecological **succession** which are characterised by containing particular biotic communities. As the succession develops zone 1 will develop into zone 2 and so on, as new zone 1s develop, due to **colonisation** by pioneer species. For instance, in a **sand dune system**, zone 1 will be occupied by a sea couch grass community, which, as the foredune develops, will change into a marram grass community, characteristic of zone 2.

ZOOSPORE

A zoospore is a flagellated or ciliated motile naked plant **spore** produced in a sporangium or zoosporangium. They are found in the Chlorophyta (green algae), Phaeophyta (brown algae) and Oomycota (downy mildews, potato blight).
◀ Sporangia ▶

ZYGOTE

A zygote is the **diploid** cell which results from the fusion of two gametes before it undergoes division. In plants which undergo **alternation of generations** it is the first cell of the **sporophyte** generation.
◀ Fertilisation, Gamete ▶

ZYGOSPORE

A zygospore is a thick-walled resting or perennating **spore** which contains a **zygote** since it is the result of **gamete** fusion. It is common in the Zygomycota (e.g. *Mucor*) and in some filamentous greeen algae (e.g. *Spirogyra*) which tend to reproduce sexually when conditions are becoming adverse. The zygospore can withstand the poor conditions and germinates on reaching suitable conditions.

◀ Filamentous algae ▶

ZYMOGEN

A zymogen is an inactive precursor of a digestive enzyme (e.g. pepsinogen and trypsinogen are zymogens).